# LECTURES ON
# THE CALCULUS OF VARIATIONS

# LECTURES ON THE CALCULUS OF VARIATIONS

*BY GILBERT A. BLISS*

THE UNIVERSITY OF CHICAGO PRESS
CHICAGO · ILLINOIS

THE UNIVERSITY OF CHICAGO PRESS, CHICAGO 37
Cambridge University Press, London, N.W. 1, England
The University of Toronto Press, Toronto 5, Canada


*Published 1946. Fourth Impression 1957. Composed and printed by*
THE UNIVERSITY OF CHICAGO PRESS, *Chicago, Illinois, U.S.A.*

# PREFACE

The contents of this book are selected from material which I have presented in numerous courses on the calculus of variations at the University of Chicago. They are a selection of related portions rather than a complete account.

The purposes of the book are two: first, the presentation of the notions and principles underlying modern theories of the calculus of variations in as simple and yet as inclusive a form as possible; and, second, the development, as completely as is now possible, of the theory of one of the most comprehensive problems of the calculus of variations which have so far been formulated. For these purposes the book is divided into two parts—Part I, entitled "Simpler Problems of the Calculus of Variations," and Part II, on "The Problem of Bolza."

Part I consists of six chapters which deal with relatively elementary problems of the calculus of variations. In mimeographed form these have often been used as a text for beginning courses in the subject. In the first three chapters I have studied the fundamental problem of the calculus of variations in three-dimensional space, the problem with fixed end-points. I have chosen to begin with the problem in three dimensions because its results are extensible, with little more than the formal notational changes shown in Chapters IV and V, to the corresponding problems in the plane and in higher dimensional spaces and to problems in parametric form. Such extensions cannot be made so conveniently if one starts with the simplest problem in the plane and tries to generalize from there. Chapter VI is an introduction to the theory of problems with variable end-points—problems which in the past have received much less attention than those for which the end-points are fixed.

When the book is used as a text for a course, illustrative examples will always be found valuable. I have listed very few in the text, and there are not many whose details have been worked out with any completeness in the light of modern theory. As references, one could consult Bliss, *Calculus of Variations*, where several problems in the plane have been discussed in more than usual detail, and Bolza, *Vorlesungen über Variationsrechnung*, which has a rich list. In Bolza's book the problems are collectively enumerated in the Index, but for a particular problem the complete discussion is usually scattered, in parts, through the text. Older books, such as Jellet, *An Elementary Treatise on the Calculus of Variations*, list many problems, but usually with few details. It would be a great service to students of the calculus of variations to have a list of the problems of the calculus of variations which have been exhaustively studied in the light of modern theories and to have such extensions of the list as might be made by an experienced student.

Oskar Bolza was professor of mathematics at the University of Chicago for nearly eighteen years. Most of his research during that period was in the calculus of variations. In 1913 he formulated a very general problem in the subject which has frequently been referred to as "the problem of Bolza." It includes as special cases all but a very few of the hitherto formulated problems of the calculus of variations involving only so-called "simple" integrals, as contrasted with multiple integrals. Little was done toward the systematic study of the problem of Bolza until about 1930. Since that time it has been the subject of many memoirs, whose results have made it possible to present here, for the first time in book form, a relatively complete treatment. With the results of the study here made, the theory of the most general problems having variable end-points is brought to a stage of advancement comparable to that achieved up to this time for problems whose end-points are fixed. The Bibliography, at the end of the book, is evidence of the great interest which the problem of Bolza has aroused among mathematicians in the past and which it will doubtless continue to arouse in the future.

Throughout the theory of the calculus of variations applications of the existence theorems for implicit functions and differential equations are frequent and fundamental. These theorems are now well known, but in the literature they are scattered and not in convenient form. I have therefore added an Appendix at the end of the book, in which I have endeavored to simplify proofs and record their results in theorems, which, it is hoped, will be especially convenient and useful for students of the calculus of variations.

The Bibliography of the Problem of Bolza (pp. 287–91) includes the names of numerous mathematicians who in recent years have been interested in the theory. I am indebted to many of them for details presented in this book, but especially to H. H. Goldstine, L. M. Graves, M. R. Hestenes, E. J. McShane, Marston Morse, and W. T. Reid. Both Hestenes and Goldstine, during periods in which they were my research assistants, contributed most valuable assistance in the development of the theory and in the preparation of the manuscript of this book.

GILBERT A. BLISS

UNIVERSITY OF CHICAGO
April 1945

# TABLE OF CONTENTS

## PART I. SIMPLER PROBLEMS OF THE CALCULUS OF VARIATIONS

## PART II. THE PROBLEM OF BOLZA

APPENDIX



BIBLIOGRAPHY



INDEX

# PART I

# SIMPLER PROBLEMS OF THE CALCULUS OF VARIATIONS

# CHAPTER I

## THE CALCULUS OF VARIATIONS IN THREE-SPACE

**1. The nature of problems of the calculus of variations.** A fundamental problem of the differential calculus is that of finding in the range of values of an independent variable $x$ one for which a given function $f(x)$ is a maximum or a minimum. The calculus of variations is also a theory of maxima and minima, but for variables and functions which are more complicated than those of the differential calculus. A relatively simple illustration is afforded by the problem of finding, in a class of arcs joining two given points in $xyz$-space, one which has the shortest length. The independent variable in this case may be designated by the symbol $C$, and its range is the class of arcs joining the two given points. The function to be minimized is the function $I(C)$, whose value for each arc $C$ is the length of that arc.

For the present it will be supposed that the arcs of the class in which a minimum is sought are all in $xyz$-space and defined by functions of the form

$$y(x), \quad z(x) \qquad (x_1 \leqq x \leqq x_2) \tag{1·1}$$

which have continuous derivatives. For the problem of the last paragraph the function to be minimized is then the length integral

$$I(C) = \int_{x_1}^{x_2} [1 + y'^2 + z'^2]^{1/2} dx ,$$

whose value is determined when the derivatives $y'(x)$, $z'(x)$ of the functions $y(x)$, $z(x)$ defining $C$ are substituted in its integrand. Analytically the problem is that of finding, in a class of pairs of functions $y(x)$, $z(x)$ having given values

$$y_1 = y(x_1), \qquad z_1 = z(x_1),$$

$$y_2 = y(x_2), \qquad z_2 = z(x_2)$$

at $x_1$ and $x_2$, one which gives the integral $I(C)$ its minimum value.

A second example from the calculus of variations, which may also be cited here as an illustration, is the so-called "brachistochrone problem," originally discussed by Galileo.[1] If an initial velocity $v_1$ and two fixed points, *1* and *2*, in space are given, then the time of descent of a heavy particle starting at *1* with the velocity $v_1$ and falling, under the action of gravity alone, along an arc $C$ to the point *2* is uniquely determined by the form of the arc $C$. The problem in question is that of finding, in a class of arcs $C$ joining the points *1* and *2*, one

[1] See Galileo, *Dialog über die beiden hauptsächlichsten Weltsysteme* (1630), trans. Strauss, pp. 471–72; and his *Dialogues concerning Two New Sciences* (1638), trans. Crew and De Salvio, p. 239.

down which the particle will fall in the shortest time. The solutions of this famous old problem by the Swiss mathematicians John and James Bernoulli[2] gave rise to the first systematic theory of the calculus of variations. The name of the problem is derived from the Greek words *βραχιστος*, meaning "shortest," and *χρονος*, meaning "time."

An analytic expression for the time of descent can readily be found when a system of axes is taken as shown in Figure 1·1. Let $m$ be the mass of the falling particle $P$, and let $s$ be the length of the arc $C$ from *1* to the position of $P$ at the

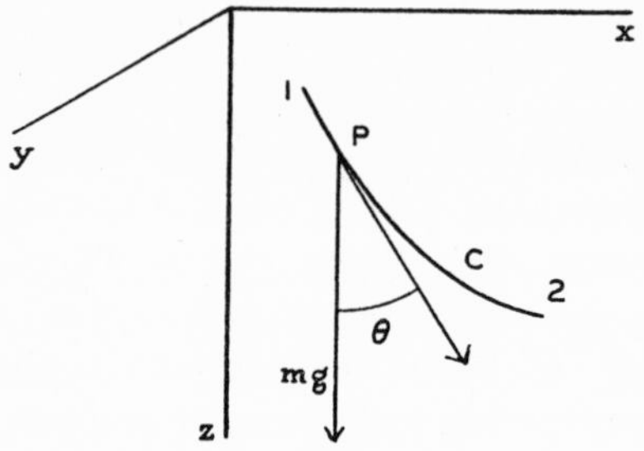


FIG. 1·1

time $t$. Then the force on $P$ in the direction of the tangent to $C$ has the expressions

$$m\left(\frac{d^2 s}{dt^2}\right) = m g \cos \theta = m g \left(\frac{dz}{ds}\right), \tag{1·2}$$

where $g$ is the well-known gravitational constant. When this equation is multiplied by $2ds/dt$ and integrated, it is found that

$$\left(\frac{ds}{dt}\right)^2 = 2gz + c = 2g(z - \alpha) \tag{1·3}$$

where $\alpha = -c/2g$ and, in terms of the initial coordinate $z_1$ and initial velocity $v_1$ at the point *1*, the constant $\alpha$ has the value

$$\alpha = z_1 - \frac{v_1^2}{2g},$$

found by setting $t = t_1$ in equation (1·3). By integrating equation (1·3) again, the time of descent is found to be $1/(2g)^{1/2}$ times the value of the integral

$$I = \int_{s_1}^{s_2} (z - \alpha)^{-1/2} ds = \int_{x_1}^{x_2} \left[\frac{1 + y'^2 + z'^2}{z - \alpha}\right]^{1/2} dx. \tag{1·4}$$

If $I(C)$ represents the value of the integral in the last expression taken along the arc $C$, the problem can be stated as that of finding, in a suitably specified class

[2] For these solutions see Ostwald, *Klassiker der exakten Wissenschaften*, No. 46.

of arcs $C$ joining the points *1* and *2*, one which minimizes the integral $I(C)$. This is a problem similar to that of finding the shortest arc, but with a different integral function $I(C)$ to be minimized.

The two problems which have been formulated above are special cases of the more general problem of finding, in a class of arcs

$$y(x), \quad z(x) \qquad (x_1 \leqq x \leqq x_2) \tag{1·5}$$

joining two fixed points *1* and *2* in $xyz$-space, one which minimizes an integral of the form

$$I(C) = \int_{x_1}^{x_2} f(x, y, z, y', z')\, dx . \tag{1·6}$$

The value of the integral along an arc $C$ is to be found by substituting $y(x)$, $z(x)$ and their derivatives $y'(x)$, $z'(x)$ in place of the variables $y$, $z$, $y'$, $z'$ so that the integrand becomes a function of $x$ alone. This is the problem which will be studied in the present chapter. For the special case of determining the shortest arc joining two points the integrand function $f$ has the value $f = [1 + y'^2 + z'^2]^{1/2}$; and for the brachistochrone problem, $f = [(1 + y'^2+z'^2)/(z - \alpha)]^{1/2}$. There are, of course, many other special cases of interest included in the general problem formulated above.

It should be remarked here that there are other theories of the calculus of variations which apply to problems of many types that are different from those just described. For example, one may restrict the class of arcs in which a minimum for the brachistochrone problem is sought to be those which join two given points and have a given length. Analytically the problem is that of finding, in the class of arcs (1·5) joining two given points *1* and *2* and giving the length integral

$$J = \int_{x_1}^{x_2} [1 + y'^2 + z'^2]^{1/2} dx$$

a fixed value, one which minimizes the integral $I$ of equation (1·4). Such problems, in which one integral $I$ is to be minimized in a class of arcs on which a second integral $J$ has a fixed value, are called "isoperimetric problems." Other problems involve multiple integrals. If one seeks a surface of minimum area in a class of surfaces bounded by a fixed simply closed curve $C$ in $xyz$-space, the integral to be minimized may be taken in the form

$$I = \iint \left[1 + \left(\frac{\partial z}{\partial x}\right)^2 + \left(\frac{\partial z}{\partial y}\right)^2\right]^{1/2} dx\, dy ;$$

and the surfaces over which it is to be evaluated, in the form $z = z(x, y)$. Some of these problems will be considered in more detail in later chapters.

The problem in three-space associated with the integral (1·6) has been selected for preliminary study because its theory illustrates well the methods which are applicable in more complicated cases and because many of the important theorems for the problems which will be studied in later chapters can be deduced with very little effort when the theory of the problem in three-space has been mastered.

**2. The origin of the name "calculus of variations."** The name of the theory which is to be studied here, the "calculus of variations," was adopted as a result of notations which were introduced by Lagrange about the year 1760. In order to compare the value of an integral $I(C)$ along an arc $C$ with its value along a neighboring arc, he altered the functions $y(x)$, $z(x)$ defining $C$, by the addition of increments $\delta y(x)$, $\delta z(x)$ which are also functions of $x$ and which are called *variations* of the functions $y(x)$, $z(x)$. If these increment functions vanish at $x_1$ and $x_2$, the curve defined by the functions

$$y(x)+\delta y(x)\,, \qquad z(x)+\delta z(x) \qquad\qquad (x_1 \leqq x \leqq x_2)$$

will still pass through the end-points of $C$. For convenience, this new curve may be denoted by the symbol $C+\delta C$. The problem to be solved is, then, that of finding, in a given class of arcs joining the end-points of $C$, one such that the inequality

$$\Delta I = I(C+\delta C) - I(C) \geqq 0$$

holds for every pair of variations $\delta y$, $\delta z$ defining an arc $C+\delta C$ also in the class. In attacking this problem writers on the calculus of variations have often used an expansion of the difference

$$\Delta I = \int_{x_1}^{x_2} \{ f(x,\, y+\delta y,\, z+\delta z,\, y'+\delta y',\, z'+\delta z') - f(x,\, y,\, z,\, y',\, z') \}\, dx$$

in the form

$$\Delta I = \delta I + \frac{1}{2!}\,\delta^2 I + \frac{1}{3!}\,\delta^3 I + \dots .$$

Here $\delta I$, $\delta^2 I$, . . . represent integrals of homogeneous polynomials of the first, second, and higher orders in $\delta y$, $\delta z$ and their derivatives $\delta y'$, $\delta z'$ with respect to $x$, found by expanding the integrand of $I$ into a Taylor series. The expressions $\delta I$, $\delta^2 I$, . . . are called the first, second, and higher variations of the integral $I$. These are the notations of Lagrange from which the theory of maxima and minima of functions such as $I(C)$ came to be called the "calculus of variations." At the present time many of the results of the theory can be obtained more readily without extensive use of the $\delta$ notations.

There are analogies between the variations $\delta y$, $\delta z$ of the functions $y(x)$, $z(x)$ and the differential $dx$ of an independent variable $x$ of the differential calculus, and between the variations $\delta I$, $\delta^2 I$, . . . and the differentials $df$, $d^2 f$, . . . of a function $f(x)$. In the years between 1800 and 1850 these analogies were much studied,[3] and the literature of that period indicates a strong desire to unify

[3] See, e.g., Strauch, *Theorie und Anwendung des sogenannten Variationscalcul's*, Vols. I and II (1854), and many other writers.

the methods of the differential calculus and the calculus of variations. Analysis of the type elaborately developed at that time seems, however, to have been relatively unproductive of important results. Recently new and much more significant attempts have been made to identify the theories of maxima and minima in the calculus and the calculus of variations as special instances in more inclusive theories of general analysis or functional calculus, but these developments are still in many respects in a formative stage.[4]

**3. Analytic formulation of the problem.** Suppose that a totality of arcs $C$ has been specified along each of which the integral $I(C)$ of equation $(1\cdot 6)$ has a well-determined value. The arcs of this totality will be called *admissible arcs.* A problem of the calculus of variations associated with such admissible arcs and such an integral is then that of finding, in the class of admissible arcs joining two fixed points, one which gives the integral $I(C)$ its smallest value. The problem so formulated is said to have fixed end-points. It may be modified by specifying the class of arcs in which a minimum is sought to be the class of admissible arcs joining a fixed point and a fixed curve, or a fixed curve and a fixed surface; and other possible modifications of a similar sort are evident. In these latter cases the problem is said to have variable end-points.

The totality of admissible arcs may be defined in many ways when an integral $I$ is given, and to each of these different ways there corresponds a different problem of the calculus of variations. For present purposes it will be supposed, first of all, that there is a region $R$ of sets of real values $(x, y, z, y', z')$ in which the integrand function $f(x, y, z, y', z')$ has continuous derivatives up to and including those of the fourth order. It may have derivatives of higher orders, but the ones just specified are all that are needed for the theory which is to follow.[5] A set $(x, y, z, y', z')$ *interior* to the region $R$ is called an *admissible set.* An arc $C$ is customarily called *regular* if the functions $y(x)$, $z(x)$ defining it are single-valued and have continuous derivatives on the interval $x_1x_2$. The totality of *admissible arcs* to be considered here is then the totality of continuous arcs each of which consists of a finite number of regular sub-arcs whose elements

[4] There is an extensive literature on "functions of lines" by Volterra. In addition, one should note especially the following papers, some of which contain references to other important papers in this field: Hahn, "Ueber die Lagrangeschen Multiplikatorenmethode," *Wiener Berichte,* XIII (1922), 531–50; Sanger, "Functions of Lines and the Calculus of Variations" (diss., University of Chicago), *Contributions to the Calculus of Variations 1931–1932, Department of Mathematics of the University of Chicago,* pp. 191–293 (this title will hereafter be designated as *Contributions*); Goldstine, "Conditions for a Minimum of a Functional" (diss., University of Chicago), *Contributions 1933–1937,* pp. 315–57; Menger, "Metric Methods in the Calculus of Variations," *Proceedings of the National Academy of Sciences,* XXIII (1937), 244–50; Goldstine, "A Multiplier Rule in Abstract Spaces," *Bulletin of the American Mathematical Society,* XLIV (1938), 388–94.

[5] Third derivatives of $f$ are, in fact, sufficient for most of the theory if the imbedding theorems of Section 7 are established by means of the canonical equations of the extremals as in Section 27

$(x, y, z, y', z')$ are all admissible. Such an admissible arc may have a finite number of corners, as indicated in Figure 3·1, at which the integrand function $f[x, y(x), z(x), y'(x), z'(x)]$ will be discontinous, but the integral of this function over the interval $x_1x_2$ is, nevertheless, well defined.

As modifications of the definition of admissible arcs just given, one might require them to be regular, or analytic, or perhaps only rectifiable. The definition given above, however, seems to lead to the simplest introductory theory, and in many geometrical and mechanical problems it is the natural one.

The specification of the region $R$ of sets $(x, y, z, y', z')$ is not an artificial one for purposes of analysis only. Each special problem has a largest region of this sort naturally associated with its integrand function $f(x, y, z, y', z')$. For the shortest-distance problem with the integrand function $(1 + y'^2 + z'^2)^{1/2}$ the largest region $R$ consists of all sets $(x, y, z, y', z')$ with real finite values for the

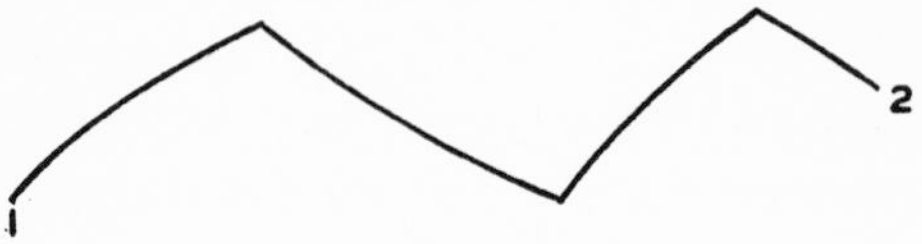


FIG. 3·1

the five coordinates; but for the brachistochrone problem only those sets are admissible for which $z > \alpha$, as is evident from the form of the integrand in the expression (1·4). This does not affect the generality of the theory of the brachistochrone problem; for equation (1·3) shows that, if a particle $P$ starts at the point *1* of an arc $C$ with the velocity $v_1$, its velocity will be zero when it reaches the altitude of the plane $z = \alpha$ on the curve, if the curve reaches that altitude, and that it can never rise above that plane. It is only necessary, therefore, to consider arcs which are below the plane $z = \alpha$, or, as an exceptional case, those which go up to this plane but not above it. Similarly the integrand of the problem of the calculus of variations which corresponds to the special relativity theory in the $xy$-plane is

$$\left[c^2 - \left(\frac{dx}{dt}\right)^2 - \left(\frac{dy}{dt}\right)^2\right]^{1/2}.$$

Analytically this problem is set in the $txy$-space; and the admissible elements $(t, x, y, x', y')$ are those for which the variables $t$, $x$, $y$ have arbitrary finite values but for which $x'$ and $y'$ are restricted by the inequality $c^2 > x'^2 + y'^2$, where it is understood that $x' = dx/dt$, $y' = dy/dt$.

For the examples just cited the region $R$ described in each case was the largest in which the integrand function $f(x, y, z, y', z')$ for the particular problem in question had the continuity properties required for the theory. There is no reason, however, why $R$ should not be selected as a subregion of the largest one possible. This is frequently done when the minimizing properties of a particular arc $E$ with respect to neighboring arcs are to be studied. The region $R$ in that case may be selected as a certain neighborhood of the values $(x, y, z, y', z')$ belonging to $E$, and an arc $E$ which furnishes a maximim or minimum in such a neighborhood is said to furnish a *relative* maximum or minimum. In the following pages theorems concerning such relative extremes are deduced; but, unless otherwise specified, it is always understood that the region $R$ is an arbitrarily selected region in which the integrand $f$ has the desired continuity properties.

**4. The first and second variations.** Consider, now, a particular admissible arc $E$, joining the points *1* and *2* and defined by functions

$$y(x) \quad , z(x) \qquad (x_1 \leqq x \leqq x_2)$$

whose minimizing properties are to be tested. If $a$ is an arbitrary constant, and if $\eta(x)$, $\zeta(x)$ are two functions vanishing at $x_1$ and $x_2$ and having continuity properties similar to those of $y(x)$, $z(x)$, then every arc of the one-parameter family

$$y(x) + a\eta(x), \qquad z(x) + a\zeta(x) \qquad (x_1 \leqq x \leqq x_2) \tag{4·1}$$

passes through the end-points *1* and *2* of $E$, and the family contains $E$ for the particular parameter value $a = 0$. Furthermore, the arcs of the family, for sufficiently small values of $a$, are all admissible, since the elements $(x, y, z, y', z')$ of $E$ are all interior to the region $R$; and the corresponding elements of the arc (4·1) will therefore also be interior to $R$ when $a$ is small. In the notation of Lagrange the equations of the arcs of the family (4·1) are obtained from those of $E$ by adding variations of the special forms $\delta y = a\eta(x)$, $\delta z = a\zeta(x)$ to the functions $y(x)$, $z(x)$ defining $E$.

When the functions (4·1) are substituted in the integrand of the integral $I$, a function of the parameter $a$ of the form

$$I(a) = \int_{x_1}^{x_2} f(x,\ y + a\eta,\ z + a\zeta,\ y' + a\eta',\ z' + a\zeta')\, dx$$

is obtained. It is understood that in the integrand $y + a\eta$ stands for $y(x) + a\eta(x)$, and similarly for the other arguments. If the arc $E$ furnishes a minimum value for the integral $I$, then evidently $I(a)$ must have a minimum at $a = 0$, and the conditions $I'(0) = 0$, $I''(0) \geqq 0$ must be satisfied. The values of these derivatives are readily calculated to be

$$I'(0) = \int_{x_1}^{x_2} \{ f_y\eta + f_z\zeta + f_{y'}\eta' + f_{z'}\zeta' \}\, dx\,,$$

$$I''(0) = \int_{x_1}^{x_2} 2\omega(x,\ \eta,\ \zeta,\ \eta'\ \ \zeta')\, dx\,,$$

where $2\omega$ is the quadratic form in $\eta, \zeta, \eta', \zeta'$ whose matrix of coefficients is

$$\begin{matrix} f_{yy} & f_{yz} & f_{yy'} & f_{yz'} \\ f_{zy} & f_{zz} & f_{zy'} & f_{zz'} \\ f_{y'y} & f_{y'z} & f_{y'y'} & f_{y'z'} \\ f_{z'y} & f_{z'z} & f_{z'y'} & f_{z'z'} \end{matrix}$$

In these expressions the subscripts of $f$ indicate partial derivatives, and the arguments of these derivatives are $x$ and the functions $y(x)$, $z(x)$, $y'(x)$, $z'(x)$ belonging to the arc $E$.

The expressions $I'(0)$, $I''(0)$ are called the *first and second variations of the integral* I *along the arc* E. This nomenclature is not quite in agreement with that described in a preceding paragraph, but it is somewhat more convenient. The first and second variations, according to the earlier definition, would be $aI'(0)$ and $a^2I''(0)$. Similarly, $\eta(x)$, $\zeta(x)$ will be called variations of $y(x)$, $z(x)$ instead of $\delta y = a\eta$, $\delta z = a\zeta$; and they will be designated as *admissible variations* when they have the continuity properties of $y(x)$ and $z(x)$. When it is desired to indicate the dependence of the two variations of $I$ upon the functions $\eta, \zeta$, they will be denoted by $I_1(\eta, \zeta)$, $I_2(\eta, \zeta)$, respectively.

*A first necessary condition that* I(E) *be a minimum is, then, that the first and second variations of* I *along* E *shall satisfy the conditions*

$$I_1(\eta, \zeta) = 0\,, \qquad I_2(\eta, \zeta) \geqq 0$$

*for all admissible variations* $\eta(x)$, $\zeta(x)$ *vanishing at* $x_1$ *and* $x_2$. *For a maximum the last inequality is to be changed in sense.*

**5. The fundamental lemma.** In order to evaluate further the condition $I_1(\eta, \zeta) = 0$, which has just been deduced, the following auxiliary theorem will be of service:

FUNDAMENTAL LEMMA. *Let* M(x) *be a bounded function on the interval* $x_1x_2$, *single-valued and continuous except possibly at a finite number of points at which it is, however, supposed to have unique right- and left-hand limits. Then a necessary and sufficient condition that the integral*

$$\int_{x_1}^{x_2} M(x)\,\eta'(x)\,dx$$

*shall have the value zero for every admissible variation* $\eta(x)$ *vanishing at* $x_1$ *and* $x_2$ *is that* M(x) *be a constant.*

The sufficiency of the condition can be easily verified. To prove the necessity, consider the particular admissible variation

$$\eta(x) = \int_{x_1}^{x} M(x)\,dx - c\,(x - x_1) \tag{5·1}$$

for which the constant $c$ has been so determined that $\eta(x_2) = 0$. One readily sees that the integral

$$(5\cdot 2) \qquad \int_{x_1}^{x_2} [M(x) - c]\, \eta'(x)\, dx$$

must also have the value zero for every admissible variation $\eta(x)$ vanishing at $x_1$ and $x_2$, if the integral of the theorem has this property. But the last integral has the value

$$\int_{x_1}^{x_2} [M(x) - c]^2 dx$$

for the particular variation $(5\cdot 1)$, and this value can vanish only if $M(x) = c$ at every point at which $M(x)$ is defined.

**6. Necessary conditions from the first variation.** For the particular case when $\zeta(x) = 0$, the first variation $I_1(\eta, \zeta)$ has the form

$$I_1(\eta, 0) = \int_{x_1}^{x_2} \{ f_y \eta + f_{y'} \eta' \}\, dx\,;$$

and since $\eta(x)$ vanishes at $x_1$ and $x_2$ and

$$\frac{d}{dx}\, \eta \int_{x_1}^{x} f_y dx = \eta f_y + \eta' \int_{x_1}^{x} f_y dx\,,$$

except at corners of $E$ or $\eta(x)$, it follows by an integration by parts that

$$I_1(\eta, 0) = \int_{x_1}^{x_2} \left[ f_{y'} - \int_{x_1}^{x} f_y dx \right] \eta'(x)\, dx\,.$$

But $I_1(\eta, 0)$ must have the value zero for every admissible variation $\eta(x)$ vanishing at $x_1$ and $x_2$, and hence the lemma of the preceding section shows that the expression in the square bracket must be constant. A similar argument applied to $I_1(0, \zeta)$ justifies the following theorem:

I. THE FIRST NECESSARY CONDITION. *An admissible arc* E *is said to satisfy the condition I if there exist two constants* c *and* d *such that the equations*

$$(6\cdot 1) \qquad f_{y'} = \int_{x_1}^{x} f_y dx + c\,, \qquad f_{z'} = \int_{x_1}^{x} f_z dx + d$$

*are identities along* E. *Every admissible arc* E *which gives the integral* I *a minimum or maximum value must satisfy the condition I.*

It is understood, of course, that in equations $(6\cdot 1)$ the arguments of the derivatives of $f$ are the functions $x$, $y(x)$, $z(x)$, $y'(x)$, $z'(x)$ belonging to $E$.

The equations of the theorem have three important consequences, the first of which is the pair of differential equations (first discovered by Euler[6] in 1744) which are described in the following corollary:

COROLLARY 6·1. EULER'S EQUATIONS. *On every sub-arc between corners of an admissible arc* E *which satisfies the condition I the functions* $f_{y'}$, $f_{z'}$ *have derivatives and the equations*

$$\frac{d}{dx} f_{y'} = f_y, \qquad \frac{d}{dx} f_{z'} = f_z$$

*are satisfied.*

This is evident because the second member of the first equation (6·1), for example, has the derivative $f_y$ except at corners. At a corner it has forward and backward derivatives which are the values of $f_y$ calculated for the coordinates $x$, $y$, $z$ at the corner, and for the derivatives $y'$, $z'$ belonging to the sub-arcs of $E$ beginning and ending at the corner, respectively.

The expressions in the second members of equations (6·1) are continuous functions of $x$, and these equations therefore show further that at a corner of $E$ the two values of $f_{y'}$ calculated for the sub-arcs of $E$ meeting at the corner must be the same. This gives a very simple justification of the following corner condition on a minimizing arc which was discovered independently by Weierstrass and Erdmann.[7]

COROLLARY 6·2. THE WEIERSTRASS-ERDMANN CORNER CONDITION. *At each value* x *defining a corner of an admissible arc* E *that satisfies the condition I, the right and left limits of the functions* $f_{y'}$ *and* $f_{z'}$ *are equal. This property is sometimes expressed by the equations*

$$(6\cdot 2) \qquad \begin{aligned} &f_{y'}[x, y, z, y'(x-0), z'(x-0)] \\ &\qquad = f_{y'}[x, y, z, y'(x+0), z'(x+0)], \\ &f_{z'}[x, y, z, y'(x-0), z'(x-0)] \\ &\qquad = f_{z'}[x, y, z, y'(x+0), z'(x+0)] \end{aligned}$$

*in which* $y'(x+0)$, *for example, is a symbol for the right-hand limit of* $y'(x)$ *at the value* x.

It happens for many problems that this condition forbids the possession of corners by a minimizing arc. This is true for the brachistochrone and shortest-distance problems mentioned above and for all problems with integrands of the form

$$f = \varphi(x, y, z)\,[1 + y'^2 + z'^2]^{1/2}$$

with $\varphi \neq 0$, as one readily verifies. Cases are well known, however, for which minimizing arcs do have corners.

Hitherto, no assumptions concerning continuity properties of the arc $E$ have been made except that it is continuous and consists of a finite number of

[6] For a translation of Euler's memoir see Ostwald, *op. cit.*, esp. p. 54.

[7] See, e.g., Bolza, *Vorlesungen über Variationsrechnung*, p. 366; also Weierstrass, *Werke*, VII (1927), 110.

regular sub-arcs. Hilbert, however, has shown that under certain circumstances these sub-arcs must have continuous derivatives of orders higher than the first, as indicated in the following corollary:

COROLLARY 6·3. HILBERT'S DIFFERENTIABILITY CONDITION.[8] *Let* E *be an admissible arc satisfying the condition I. Then near every element* (x, y, z, y′, z′) *of* E *which is not at a corner, and at which the determinant*

$$(6\cdot 3)\qquad \begin{vmatrix} f_{y'y'} & f_{y'z'} \\ f_{z'y'} & f_{z'z'} \end{vmatrix}$$

*is different from zero, the functions* y(x), z(x) *defining* E *have continuous* n*th derivatives when the integrand function* f *has all partial derivatives of orders* ≦ n *continuous near* (x, y, z, y′, z′).

The proof of this statement can be made quite simply by means of well-established properties of implicit functions. The equations

$$f_{y'}\,[x,\, y\,(x)\,,\, z\,(x)\,,\, u,\, v] \\ -\int_{x_1}^{x} f_y\,[x,\, y\,(x)\,,\, z\,(x)\,,\, y'\,(x)\,,\, z'\,(x)\,]\,dx - c = 0\,,$$

$$f_{z'}\,[x,\, y\,(x)\,,\, z\,(x)\,,\, u,\, v] \\ -\int_{x_1}^{x} f_z\,[x,\, y\,(x)\,,\, z\,(x)\,,\, y'\,(x)\,,\, z'\,(x)\,]\,dx - d = 0$$

in the variables $x$, $u$, $v$, formed for the functions $y(x)$, $z(x)$ defining $E$, are a pair of equations which may be represented by the notations

$$F\,(x,\, u,\, v) = 0\;, \qquad G\,(x,\, u,\, v) = 0\;,$$

and to which the theorems concerning implicit functions are applicable.[9] These theorems indicate that, near a particular solution $x, u, v$ of these equations at which the functional determinant $F_uG_v - F_vG_u$ is different from zero, the solutions of the equations form two functions $u(x)$, $v(x)$, which have continuous derivatives with respect to $x$ of as many orders as are possessed by the functions $F$ and $G$ themselves with respect to the variables $x$, $u$, $v$. But the equations above have the solution $u(x) = y'(x)$, $v(x) = z'(x)$, as is evident from the fact that $E$ satisfies the condition I; and the functional determinant $F_uG_v - F_vG_u$ of the equations is the determinant (6·3) of Corollary 6·3. Furthermore, the functions $F$ and $G$ have continuous first derivatives in $x$, $u$, $v$ near each solution $(x, u, v) = [x, y'(x), z'(x)]$ not corresponding to a corner of $E$, when the function $f$ has continuous second derivatives and $y(x)$, $z(x)$ have continuous first derivatives. Hence, near a point of $E$ at which the determinant (6·3) is differ-

[8] See, e.g., Bolza, *op. cit.*, p. 30.

[9] See, e.g., Bliss, "Fundamental Existence Theorems," *Princeton Colloquium Lectures on Mathematics* (New York, 1913), pp. 7–12, and "A New Proof of the Existence Theorem for Implicit Functions," *Bulletin of the American Mathematical Society*, XVIII (1912), 175–79. See also the Appendix of this book.

ent from zero the solution $u(x) = y'(x)$, $v(x) = z'(x)$ has at least continuous first derivatives, and the functions $y(x)$, $z(x)$ have at least continuous second derivatives. One can prove more than this by making use of the third derivatives of $f$. For, if the functions $y(x)$, $z(x)$ are known to have continuous second derivatives, the first members of the equations above will also have continuous second derivatives, when $f$ has continuous third derivatives, and hence the solution $u(x) = y'(x)$, $v(x) = z'(x)$ will have continuous second derivatives. By successive steps one can prove in this manner that, when $f$ has continuous $n$th derivatives, the functions $y(x)$, $z(x)$ defining a minimizing arc must also have continuous $n$th derivatives near every point, not a corner, at which the determinant (6·3) is different from zero.

The proofs of the two preceding paragraphs do not apply at a corner of $E$. If the determinant (6·3) is different from zero at the values $x$, $y$, $z$, $y'(x+0)$, $z'(x+0)$ belonging to a corner, it will be different from zero on a sufficiently short arc following the corner. On that arc the functions $y'(x)$, $z'(x)$ belonging to $E$ will have continuous derivatives $y''$, $z''$ satisfying the equations

$$f_{y'x} + f_{y'y}y' + f_{y'z}z' + f_{y'y'}y'' + f_{y'z'}z'' = f_y ,$$

$$f_{z'x} + f_{z'y}y' + f_{z'z}z' + f_{z'y'}y'' + f_{z'z'}z'' = f_z ,$$

found by differentiating the equations (6·1) with respect to $x$. These equations, solved for $y''$ and $z''$, show that $y''$ and $z''$ approach unique limits at the corner, since $y$, $z$, $y'$, $z'$ have that property. But the well-known equation

$$\frac{g(x) - g(a)}{x - a} = g'[a + \theta(x - a)] \qquad (0 < \theta < 1)$$

shows that a function $g(x)$ having a derivative $g'(x)$ on an interval $a < x \leqq a + h$ will also have a forward derivative at $x = a$ if $g'(x)$ has a unique limit at $x = a$. Hence $y'(x)$ and $z'(x)$ have right-hand derivatives $y''$ and $z''$ at the corner. Similar arguments can be made for arcs with second end-points at a corner and for the higher derivatives considered in the last paragraph.

There is a third equation similar to equations (6·1), and deducible by similar methods, which is at times useful and yet not often seen in the literature. If we write the equations of the minimizing arc in the parametric form

$$(6{\cdot}4) \qquad x = t , \qquad y = y(t) , \qquad z = z(t) \qquad (x_1 \leqq t \leqq x_2) ,$$

then this arc must minimize the integral $I$ in the class of all parametric arcs

$$x = \xi(t) , \qquad y = \eta(t) , \qquad z = \zeta(t) \qquad (t_1 \leqq t \leqq t_2)$$

with suitable continuity properties, joining the points *1* and *2* and having $\xi'(t) > 0$ on the interval $t_1t_2$. Every such arc is, in fact, representable in the form (1·1) originally specified. For such an arc the integral $I$ has the value

$$I = \int_{t_1}^{t_2} f\left(\xi, \eta, \zeta, \frac{\eta'}{\xi'}, \frac{\zeta'}{\xi'}\right) \xi' \, dt ,$$

where the primes on $\xi$, $\eta$, $\zeta$ denote derivatives with respect to $t$. This is an integral similar to our original one but containing the variables $t$, $\xi$, $\eta$, $\zeta$ instead of $x$, $y$, $z$. By reasoning quite similar to that used above we infer that three equations similar to equations (6·1) must now be satisfied along the minimizing arc. Only the first one gives new results, as one readily verifies, and it has the form

$$f - \frac{\eta'}{\xi'} f_{y'} - \frac{\zeta'}{\xi'} f_{z'} = \int_{t_1}^{t} f_x \xi' dt + e \,.$$

Along the minimizing arc (6·4) this takes the form indicated in the following theorem:

THEOREM 6·1. *For every admissible arc* E *which gives the integral* I *a maximum or a minimum there must exist a constant* b *such that the equation*

$$f - y' f_{y'} - z' f_{z'} = \int_{x_1}^{x} f_x dx + b \tag{6·5}$$

*is an identity along* E. *On every sub-arc of* E *between corners the equation*

$$\frac{d}{dx}(f - y' f_{y'} - z' f_{z'}) = f_x \tag{6·6}$$

*is satisfied, and at each corner of* E *the expression* $f - y'f_{y'} - z'f_{z'}$ *has right and left limits which are equal.*

In equations (6·5) and (6·6) the primes indicate derivatives with respect to $x$ as before. Equation (6·6) and the last statement of the theorem are easily deducible from equation (6·5). Equation (6·6) is also deducible directly from Euler's equations of Corollary 6·1 when the arc $E$ has second derivatives $y''$, $z''$ on its sub-arcs between corners.

**7. Families of extremals.** The differentiability property of an admissible arc $E$ satisfying the condition I, proved in Corollary 6·3 of the last section, is important because it shows that the Euler differential equations differentiated out in the form

$$\begin{aligned} &f_{y'x} + f_{y'y} y' + f_{y'z} z' + f_{y'y'} y'' + f_{y'z'} z'' - f_y = 0 \,, \\ &f_{z'x} + f_{z'y} y' + f_{z'z} z' + f_{z'y'} y'' + f_{z'z'} z'' - f_z = 0 \end{aligned} \tag{7·1}$$

are satisfied by every sub-arc of $E$ along which the determinant (6·3) $f_{y'y'}f_{z'z'} - (f_{y'z'})^2$ is different from zero. An arc on which this determinant is different from zero will be called a *non-singular* sub-arc of $E$. The application of the corollary lies in the fact that the derivatives $df_{y'}/dx$ and $df_{z'}/dx$ along $E$, occurring in Euler's equations, can be expressed in the expanded form given for them in the last equations when it is known that the functions $y(x)$, $z(x)$ defining $E$ have second derivatives.

An admissible arc defined by functions $y(x)$, $z(x)$ having continuous first and second derivatives, and satisfying the equations (7·1), is called an *extremal.* From the results just stated it is evident that every non-singular sub-arc, without corners, of a minimizing arc $E$, is necessarily an extremal.

The differential equations (7·1) are of the second order; and the totality of their solutions will, therefore, in general, form a four-parameter family of curves defined by functions of the form

$$y(x, a, b, c, d), \qquad z(x, a, b, c, d). \tag{7·2}$$

For a particular case the family (7·2) is to be found by any available method of integrating equations (7·1). It is frequently helpful to know that, when one of the variables $x$, $y$, $z$ is not present explicitly in the integrand function $f$, a first integral of Euler's equations can be written down at once. If $x$ is not present, equation (6·5) or the readily provable relation

$$\frac{d}{dx}(f - y'f_{y'} - z'f_{z'}) = y'\left(f_y - \frac{d}{dx}f_{y'}\right) + z'\left(f_z - \frac{d}{dx}f_{z'}\right)$$

shows that a first integral is

$$f - y'f_{y'} - z'f_{z'} = \text{constant}.$$

If $y$ is not present, a first integral is $f_{y'}$ = constant, and a similar remark holds for $z$.

Near a non-singular extremal arc $E$, equations (7·1), linear in $y''$ and $z''$, have solutions for $y''$, $z''$ of the form

$$y'' = A(x, y, z, y', z'), \qquad z'' = B(x, y, z, y', z'); \tag{7·3}$$

and the functions $A$, $B$ have continuous partial derivatives of at least the order $m - 2$ when the integrand function $f$ has continuous derivatives of the $m$th order. The existence theorems for differential equations[10] tell us that these equations have one and but one solution through each initial element $(x, y, z, y', z') = (\xi, \eta, \zeta, \eta', \zeta')$ in a sufficiently small neighborhood of those on the arc $E$. The functions defining these extremals have the form

$$\varphi(x, \xi, \eta, \zeta, \eta', \zeta'), \qquad \psi(x, \xi, \eta, \zeta, \eta', \zeta'), \tag{7·4}$$

and the functions $\varphi$, $\psi$, $\varphi_x$, $\psi_x$ have continuous partial derivatives of at least as high orders as those possessed by $A$ and $B$ in a neighborhood of the sets $(x, \xi, \eta, \zeta, \eta', \zeta')$ belonging to $E$. We can now prove the following theorem:

THEOREM 7·1. THE IMBEDDING THEOREM. *Every non-singular extremal arc* E *is imbedded for values* $x_1 \leqq x \leqq x_2$, $a_0$, $b_0$, $c_0$, $d_0$ *in a four-parameter family of extremals*

$$y(x, a, b, c, d), \qquad z(x, a, b, c, d) \tag{7·5}$$

[10] See, e.g., Bliss, *Princeton Colloquium Lectures on Mathematics* (1913), p. 86; Goursat-Hedrick, *A Course in Analysis*, Vol. II, Part II, chap. ii; or, preferably, the Appendix, pp. 269–83 of the present volume. The theorems in the last reference are designed especially for use in the theory of the calculus of variations.

*whose functions* y, z, $y_x$, $z_x$ *have continuous partial derivatives of at least the second order*[11] *in a neighborhood of the sets* (x, a, b, c, d) *belonging to* E. *Furthermore, the determinant*

$$(7\cdot 6)\qquad \begin{vmatrix} y_a & y_b & y_c & y_d \\ z_a & z_b & z_c & z_d \\ y_{ax} & y_{bx} & y_{cx} & y_{dx} \\ z_{ax} & z_{bx} & z_{cx} & z_{dx} \end{vmatrix}$$

*is different from zero along* E.

The first part of the theorem is evident if we substitute for $\xi$ in equations (7·4) a fixed value $x_0$ on the interval $x_1x_2$ and change the notations $\eta, \zeta, \eta', \zeta'$ to $a, b, c, d$.

It remains only to show that the determinant (7·6) is different from zero. The fact that the solution (7·4) passes through the initial element $(\xi, \eta, \zeta, \eta', \zeta')$ is expressed by the equations

$$\eta = \varphi(\xi, \xi, \eta, \zeta, \eta', \zeta'), \qquad \zeta = \psi(\xi, \xi, \eta, \zeta, \eta', \zeta'),$$

$$\eta' = \varphi_x(\xi, \xi, \eta, \zeta, \eta', \zeta'), \qquad \zeta' = \psi_x(\xi, \xi, \eta, \zeta, \eta', \zeta'),$$

which are identities in these variables. By differentiating them successively with respect to $\eta, \zeta, \eta', \zeta'$ and remembering that $\xi, \eta, \zeta, \eta', \zeta'$ are now to be replaced by $x_0, a, b, c, d$, it is seen that the determinant (7·6) has at $x = x_0$ the value unity. We shall see in Section 27 that, if for a family of the form (7·5) this determinant is different from zero at one value of $x$, it remains different from zero everywhere on the arc $E$.

THEOREM 7·2. *Through an arbitrarily selected point* 0 *of a non-singular extremal arc* E *there passes a two-parameter family of extremals*

$$(7\cdot 7)\qquad y(x, \alpha, \beta), \qquad z(x, \alpha, \beta)$$

*containing* E *for values* $x_1 \leqq x \leqq x_2$, $\alpha_0$, $\beta_0$ *and such that the functions* y, z, $y_x$, $z_x$ *belonging to the family have continuous partial derivatives of at least the second order in a neighborhood of the values* (x, α, β) *belonging to* E. *Furthermore, the family can be so chosen that the matrix*

$$(7\cdot 8)\qquad \begin{matrix} y_\alpha & z_\alpha & y_{\alpha x} & z_{\alpha x} \\ y_\beta & z_\beta & y_{\beta x} & z_{\beta x} \end{matrix}$$

*has rank two at every point of* E.

The extremals of the family (7·5) which pass through the arbitrarily selected point $(x_0, y_0, z_0)$ on $E$ form such a family. The equations of the family can be found by substituting $x_0, y_0, z_0$ for $\xi, \eta, \zeta$ in equations (7·4) and denoting $\eta', \zeta'$ by $\alpha, \beta$. The rank of the matrix (7·8) is then evidently two, since the matrix

[11] We can replace "second order" by "order $m - 2$" if the integrand $f$ is assumed to have continuous partial derivatives of order $m$ with $m > 2$.

consists of the last two columns of the determinant (7·6), which is different from zero along $E$. The theorem can also be established by starting with any family (7·5) with the properties described in Theorem 7·1 and solving the equations

$$y_0 = y(x_0, a, b, c, d), \qquad z_0 = z(x_0, a, b, c, d)$$

for two of the parameters $a, b, c, d$ in terms of the others.

If the functions (7·5) or (7·7) are substituted in equations (7·3), it is evident that the second derivatives $y_{xx}, z_{xx}$ also have continuous partial derivatives of the second order. Furthermore, if the integrand function $f$ has continuous $m$th derivatives in the region $R$ of Section 3, then the functions $A, B$ in equations (7·3) have continuous partial derivatives of order $m - 2$, and the same is true of the six functions $y, z, y_x, z_x, y_{xx}, z_{xx}$ belonging to the families (7·5) and (7·7).

**8. Auxiliary theorems.** In a number of situations to be encountered later it will be necessary to consider the variation of the value of the integral $I$ taken along a variable arc $E$ whose end-points *3* and *4* describe two fixed curves $C$ and $D$, as shown in Figure 8·1. The functions defining $E$ may be taken in the

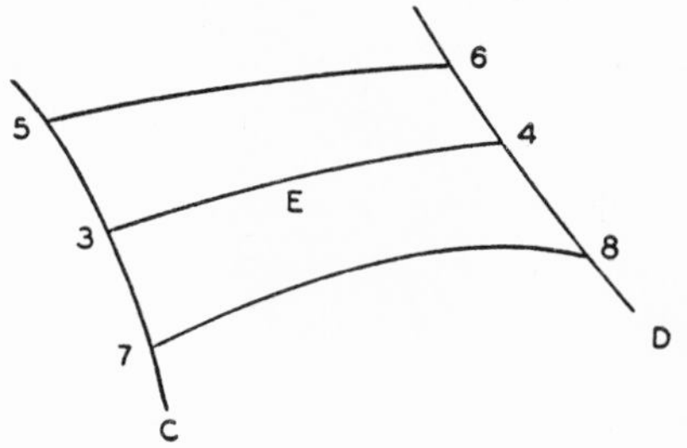


FIG. 8·1

form $y(x, a), z(x, a)$, the displacement of $E$ being caused by variation of the value of the parameter $a$. If $t$ is a parameter defining the position of the point *3* on $C$, then the coordinate $x_3$ of the point *3* and the value of $a$ defining the arc $E$ through *3* are functions of $t$, and the functions defining $C$ may be written in the parametric form

$$(8·1) \qquad x_3(t), \qquad y[x_3(t), a(t)] = y_3(t), \qquad z[x_3(t), a(t)] = z_3(t).$$

Since the point *4* on $D$ is also determined when $t$ is given, and by the same value of $a$ as that corresponding to *3*, it follows that $D$ will be defined by functions of the same form as those for $C$ but with the subscript 3 replaced by 4 wherever it occurs.

In order to carry through the analysis of the following paragraphs, it is assumed that the functions $x_3(t), x_4(t), a(t)$, defining the arcs $C$ and $D$ described above, have continuous derivatives on an interval $t' \leqq t \leqq t''$. Furthermore, for the values $(x, a)$ specified by the conditions

$$x_3(t) \leqq x \leqq x_4(t), \qquad a = a(t) \qquad\qquad (t' \leqq t \leqq t'')$$

the functions $y(x, a)$, $z(x, a)$ define admissible arcs without corners, and in a neighborhood of these values $(x, a)$ they and their derivatives $y_x(x, a)$, $z_x(x, a)$ have continuous first partial derivatives with respect to $a$.

The value of the integral $I$ taken along the arc $E$ is a function $I(t)$ defined by the equation

$$I(t) = \int_{x_3}^{x_4} f[x, y(x, a), z(x, a), y'(x, a), z'(x, a)]\,dx,$$

in which $x_3$, $x_4$, $a$ are the functions of $t$ just described. The derivative of this function is

$$(8\cdot 2)\quad I'(t) = \left[f\frac{dx}{dt}\right]_3^4 + \frac{da}{dt}\int_{x_3}^{x_4}\{f_y y_a + f_z z_a + f_{y'} y_a' + f_{z'} z_a'\}\,dx,$$

where the arguments of $f$ and its derivatives are those shown in the integrand of $I(t)$ and where the first term on the right indicates, as is customary, the value of the bracket at the point *4* minus the value at the point *3*. If an arc $E$ of the family happens to satisfy the Euler equations

$$\frac{d}{dx} f_{y'} - f_y = 0, \qquad \frac{d}{dx} f_{z'} - f_z = 0,$$

so that along it

$$f_y y_a + f_{y'} y_a' = \frac{d}{dx}\left(f_{y'} y_a\right), \qquad f_z z_a + f_{z'} z_a' = \frac{d}{dx}\left(f_{z'} z_a\right),$$

then for that particular arc $E$ the derivative $(8\cdot 2)$ has the value

$$I'(t) = \left[\frac{f dx}{dt} + \frac{da}{dt}(f_{y'} y_a + f_{z'} z_a)\right]_3^4.$$

From equations $(8\cdot 1)$ it follows that along $C$

$$(8\cdot 3)\qquad dy_3 = y' dx_3 + y_a da, \qquad dz_3 = z' dx_3 + z_a da,$$

and similar equations with subscripts 4 hold along $D$. Hence, when the values of $y_a da/dt$, $z_a da/dt$ are substituted from these equations, the following theorem is justified:

THEOREM 8·1. *The value of the integral* I, *taken along a variable arc* E *with the continuity properties described above and whose end-points* 3 *and* 4 *describe two fixed curves* C *and* D, *has the differential*

$$(8\cdot 4)\qquad dI = [f dx + (dy - y' dx) f_{y'} + (dz - z' dx) f_{z'}]_3^4$$

*at each position of the variable arc at which that arc satisfies Euler's differential equations. In the expression for* dI *the values* x, y, z, y′, z′ *occurring in* f *and elsewhere are those belonging to* E *at the points* 3 *and* 4, *and* dx, dy, dz *are differentials belonging to* C *or* D.

It is evident that the differential of $I$ can be easily calculated, from the expression (8·2), for a position of the variable arc which is not an extremal. The case signalized in the theorem is, however, the important one.

As a special case one should note that if the arc $C$ or $D$ degenerates into a point the formula of the theorem is still valid, the differentials $dx$, $dy$, $dz$ along the degenerate arc being all zero.

When the arc $E$ satisfies Euler's differential equations in every one of its positions, the formula of the theorem justifies a further interesting result. The functions $y(x, a)$, $z(x, a)$ in the second member of the formula and their derivatives $y'(x, a)$, $z'(x, a)$ with respect to $x$ are all functions of $t$ calculable with the help of equations (8·1). The differentials $dx$, $dy$, $dz$ are, furthermore, functions of $t$ multiplied by $dt$, defined by equations (8·3). Hence the expressions on the two sides of formula (8·4) are functions of $t$ multiplied by $dt$ and can be integrated with respect to $t$ from a value $t'$ defining the position $E_{56}$ of the arc $E$ to a value $t''$ defining $E_{78}$, as shown in Figure 8·1. If the notation $I^*$ is used for the integral

$$(8\cdot5) \qquad I^* = \int [f dx + (dy - y'dx) f_{y'} + (dz - z'dx) f_{z'}] ,$$

the result of the integration can be expressed as in the following corollary:

Corollary 8·1. *If the ends of a variable extremal arc* E *describe two curves* C *and* D, *the difference between the values of* I *at two positions* $E_{56}$ *and* $E_{78}$ *of* E, *shown in Figure 8·1, is given by the formula*

$$(8\cdot6) \qquad I(E_{78}) - I(E_{56}) = I^*(D_{68}) - I^*(C_{57}) ,$$

*where* I* *is a notation for the integral* (8·5).

The integral $I^*$, which occurs frequently in the theory of the calculus of variations, was introduced by Hilbert and is usually designated by his name. In calculating its value along the arc $C_{57}$ in the formula of the corollary it should be remembered that the element $(x, y, z, y', z')$ occurring in its integrand is that of the moving extremal at its intersection with $C_{57}$. The coordinates of this element are therefore functions of $t$. The differentials $dx$, $dy$, $dz$, on the other hand, are those of $C_{35}$ itself. Similar remarks hold for the integral $I^*(D_{68})$.

**9. The necessary conditions of Weierstrass and Legendre.** The necessary conditions on a minimizing arc found in Section 6 were deduced by means of special variations $\delta y = a\eta(x)$, $\delta z = a\zeta(x)$, whose derivatives with respect to $x$ evidently approach zero with the variations themselves when the parameter $a$ approaches zero. Weierstrass[12] noticed that not all variations have this prop-

[12] *Op. cit.*, pp. 210 ff.

erty; and by constructing a family of arcs containing the minimizing arc $E$, but whose directions do not everywhere approach those of $E$, he was able to prove the necessary condition which is to be deduced in this section.

Let *3* be an arbitrarily selected point of the arc $E$, and let *4* be a second point on $E$ at the right of *3* but so near to *3* that there is no corner of $E$ between

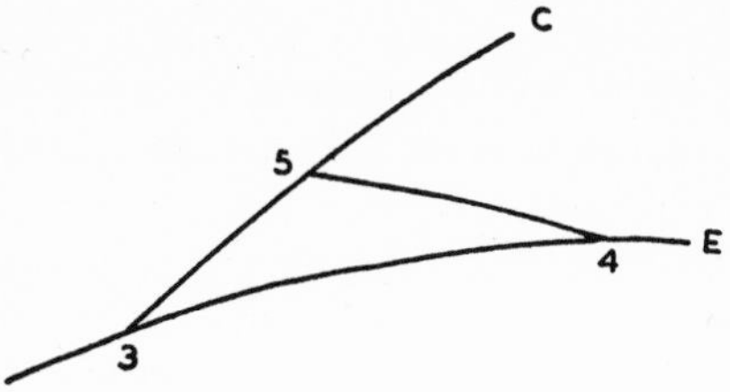


FIG. 9·1

them. Through the point *3* an arbitrary admissible arc $C$ may be chosen, defined by functions of the form

$$Y(x), \qquad Z(x) \qquad\qquad (x_3 \leqq x \leqq x + \epsilon).$$

It is then possible to join the point *5* of $C$ to the fixed point *4* by a one-parameter family of arcs $E_{54}$, one of which is the segment $E_{34}$ joining *3* with *4*. The family of arcs

$$y(x) + \left[\frac{Y(a) - y(a)}{x_4 - a}\right](x_4 - x), \qquad z(x) + \left[\frac{Z(a) - z(a)}{x_4 - a}\right](x_4 - x),$$

in which $a = x_5$ is the parameter, is an example of such a family. If the original arc $E_{12}$ joining the points *1* and *2* is a minimizing arc, then the sum

$$(9\cdot1) \qquad I(C_{35} + E_{54}) = \int_{x_3}^{x_5} f(x, Y, Z, Y', Z')\,dx + I(E_{54})$$

is a function of the coordinate $x_5$, and this function must not decrease as the point *5* moves away from *3* on the arc $C$. Its differential with respect to $x_5$ must, therefore, not be negative when *5* is at *3*. But since the arc $E_{34}$ satisfies Euler's differential equations, it is possible to calculate the differential of $I(E_{54})$ when *5* is at *3* by means of the auxiliary theorem of the last section. The differential of the whole sum above is then readily found to be the value at *3* of the expression

$$\begin{aligned} f(x, y, z, Y', Z')\,dx - f(x, y, z, y', z')\,dx \\ - (dy - y'dx)\,f_{y'}(x, y, z, y', z') \\ - (dz - z'dx)\,f_{z'}(x, y, z, y', z'), \end{aligned}$$

where $x, y, z, y', z'$ belong to $E$ and where the differentials $dx, dy, dz$ are those of $C$. The first term of this expression is the differential of the first integral in the second member of equation (9·1), since $Y = y$ and $Z = z$ at the point *3;* and the other terms are the differential of $I(E_{54})$ at the point *3*, as given by Theorem 8·1. With the help of the notation

$$(9\cdot 2)\quad \begin{aligned} E(x, y, z, y', z', Y', Z') &= f(x, y, z, Y', Z') - f(x, y, z, y', z') \\ &- (Y' - y') f_{y'}(x, y, z, y', z') - (Z' - z') f_{z'}(x, y, z, y', z') \end{aligned}$$

the differential of $I(C_{35} + E_{54})$ when *5* is at *3* can now be expressed in the form

$$E(x, y, z, y', z', Y', Z')\, dx\,|^3 .$$

and the following theorem is proved:

II. THE NECESSARY CONDITION OF WEIERSTRASS. *An admissible arc* E *is said to satisfy the condition II of Weierstrass if at every element* (x, y, z, y′, z′) *of* E *the condition*

$$E(x, y, z, y', z', Y', Z') \geqq 0$$

*is satisfied for every admissible element* (x, y, z, Y′, Z′) *with* (Y′, Z′) ≠ (y′, z′). *Every arc* E *which minimizes the integral* I *must satisfy the condition II.*

The function (9·2) is called the *E*-function of Weierstrass. It evidently vanishes when the pair $(Y', Z')$ coincides with $(y', z')$. The exclusion from the theorem of the case when these two pairs are equal is made because in later paragraphs it will be desirable to strengthen the condition $E \geqq 0$ by excluding the equality, and this can be done only for pairs $(Y', Z')$ which are different from $(y', z')$.

The proof of the necessary condition of Weierstrass given above applies to all elements $(x, y, z, y', z')$ of a minimizing arc not belonging to a backward tangent at a corner. But if the condition holds at all elements preceding a corner, it must hold also, by continuity, at the element belonging to the backward tangent.

There is a further important necessary condition on a minimizing arc, due to Legendre,[13] which is an easy consequence of that of Weierstrass. It was originally proved in a very different manner and is much older than the condition II. By means of Taylor's formula with a remainder term the *E*-function is expressible by the equation

$$(9\cdot 3)\quad \begin{aligned} 2E(x, y, z, y', z', Y', Z') &= (Y' - y')^2 f_{y'y'} \\ &+ 2(Y' - y')(Z' - z') f_{y'z'} + (Z' - z')^2 f_{z'z'} , \end{aligned}$$

where the second derivatives of $f$ have arguments of the form

$$(9\cdot 4)\quad x, y, z, y' + \theta(Y' - y'), z' + \theta(Z' - z') \qquad (0 < \theta < 1) .$$

If $Y'$ and $Z'$ are replaced by the values

$$Y' = y' + \epsilon\eta , \qquad Z' = z' + \epsilon\zeta ,$$

[13] See Ostwald, *op. cit.*, No. 47, pp. 56 ff.

where $\eta$ and $\zeta$ are arbitrary real constants, and if $\epsilon$ is then made to approach zero, one finds at once the following further condition:

III. Legendre's Necessary Condition. *An admissible arc* E *is said to satisfy the condition III of Legendre if at each element* (x, y, z, y′, z′) *of* E *the condition*

$$\eta^2 f_{y'y'} + 2\eta\zeta f_{y'z'} + \zeta^2 f_{z'z'} \geqq 0 \tag{9·5}$$

*is satisfied for every pair of real values* $\eta$, $\zeta$ *such that* $\eta^2 + \zeta^2 = 1$, *the arguments of the derivatives of* f *being the coordinates* (x, y, z, y′, z′) *of the element of* E. *Every arc* E *which minimizes the integral* I *must satisfy the condition III.*

The restriction $\eta^2 + \zeta^2 = 1$ is imposed because it will be desirable later to use a stronger condition derived from III by excluding the equality sign in (9·5). If the condition in the theorem holds for $\eta^2 + \zeta^2 = 1$, it will hold for all real values $\eta$, $\zeta$, as one readily verifies.

The conditions deduced from the first variation in preceding sections are valid for both minimizing and maximizing arcs, but this is not true for the conditions of Weierstrass and Legendre. The inequalities in the statements of these latter conditions, as given above, must be changed in sense for a maximizing arc, as one easily sees by examining the proofs. The situation is quite analogous to that in the calculus when maxima and minima of a function $f(x)$ are being studied. The condition $f'(a) = 0$ must hold at a value $x = a$ defining either a maximum or a minimum; but at a minimum the second derivative condition is $f''(a) \geqq 0$, and for a maximum this inequality must be changed in sense.

From the proof of Legendre's condition III given above it is evident that III is a consequence of the condition II of Weierstrass, but the converse is not always true. The consequence of III in the following corollary is not the same as II, but it will be useful in the proof of one of the sufficiency theorems which will be given in a later section.

Corollary 9·1. *If the condition*

$$\eta^2 f_{y'y'} + 2\eta\zeta f_{y'z'} + \zeta^2 f_{z'z'} > 0 \tag{9·6}$$

*is valid at every element* (x, y, z, y′, z′) *of an arc* $E_{12}$ *for all values* $\eta$, $\zeta$ *such that* $\eta^2 + \zeta^2 = 1$, *then the inequality*

$$E(x,\ y,\ z,\ y',\ z',\ Y',\ Z') > 0$$

*will be satisfied at least for all elements* (x, y, z, y′, z′) *and* (x, y, z, Y′, Z′) *lying in a sufficiently small neighborhood* N *of those on* $E_{12}$ *and having* (Y′, Z′) ≠ (y′, z′).

The proof is simple, since, if the inequality (9·6) holds at every one of the closed set of elements $(x, y, z, y', z', \eta, \zeta)$ for which $\eta^2 + \zeta^2 = 1$ and $(x, y, z, y', z')$ belongs to $E_{12}$, it will also hold when the arguments of the derivatives of $f$ are replaced by the set (9·4), provided that $(x, y, z, y', z')$ and $(x, y, z, Y', Z')$ remain in a sufficiently small neighborhood of the set of elements of this type on $E_{12}$. The formula (9·3) then establishes the desired result.

**10. Envelope theorems and Jacobi's necessary condition.** Besides the three necessary conditions on a minimizing arc which have been proved in preceding sections, there is a fourth condition, the necessary condition of Jacobi, which remains to be discussed.[14] Historically the order of discovery of these necessary conditions was the Euler condition in 1744, Legendre's condition in 1786, Jacobi's condition in 1837, and the condition of Weierstrass about 1879. The proofs of the conditions given here are quite different from those of the original discoverers, except in the case of the necessary condition of Weierstrass, and it is for this reason that the order of presentation chosen is not that of discovery. The proof of Jacobi's necessary condition to be given in this section depends upon a so-called "envelope theorem," which seems to be the contribution of Darboux (1894) for the case of geodesic lines on a surface and of Zermelo (1894) and Kneser (1898) for more general problems of the calculus of variations.[15] It is one of the most interesting and most beautiful theorems in the domain of geometrical analysis.

A proof of the envelope theorem can readily be made with the help of Corollary 8·1. A variable extremal arc was there considered whose end-points described two curves, $C$ and $D$. For two positions, $E_{34}$ and $E_{56}$, of the variable arc the values of the integral $I$ were found to be related by the formula

$$I(E_{56}) - I(E_{34}) = I^*(D_{46}) - I^*(C_{35}) , \tag{10·1}$$

where $I^*$ represents the Hilbert integral (8·5). In the special case when the curve $C$ is a fixed point *1* and the variable extremal arc $E$ is in every position

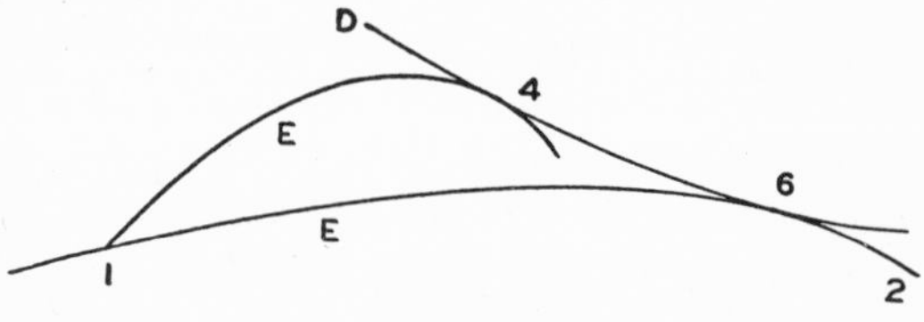


FIG. 10·1

tangent to the curve $D$, as shown in Figure 10·1, the last formula justifies the conclusion that

$$I(E_{16}) - I(E_{14}) = I(D_{46}) ,$$

since the term $I^*(C_{35})$ in formula (10·1) must in this case be replaced by zero and since the term $I^*(D_{46})$ is seen to be equal to $I(D_{46})$ because the direction $dx:dy:dz$ of the curve $D$ coincides with the direction $1:y':z'$ of the variable ex-

[14] See Ostwald, *op. cit.*, No. 47, pp. 87 ff.

[15] Darboux, *Théorie des surfaces*, III (1894), 88; Zermelo, "Untersuchungen zur Variationsrechnung" (diss., Göttingen, 1894), p. 96; Kneser, *Mathematische Annalen*, L (1898), 27, and his *Lehrbuch der Variationsrechnung*, 1st ed. (1900), p. 93, 2d ed. (1925), p. 116.

tremal arc $E$ at their intersection. Thus the following remarkable theorem is justified:

THEOREM 10·1. THE ENVELOPE THEOREM. *If a one-parameter family of extremal arcs* E *has an envelope* D, *as shown in Figure 10·1, then the equation*

$$I(E_{16}) = I(E_{14}) + I(D_{46}) \tag{10·2}$$

*holds for every position of the point* 4 *preceding the point* 6 *on* D.

The envelope theorem is analogous to the well-known string property of the evolute of a curve. An evolute $D$ of a curve $C$, shown in the first diagram in Figure 10·2, has the property that the end *3* of a string $E$ will describe an arc $C$

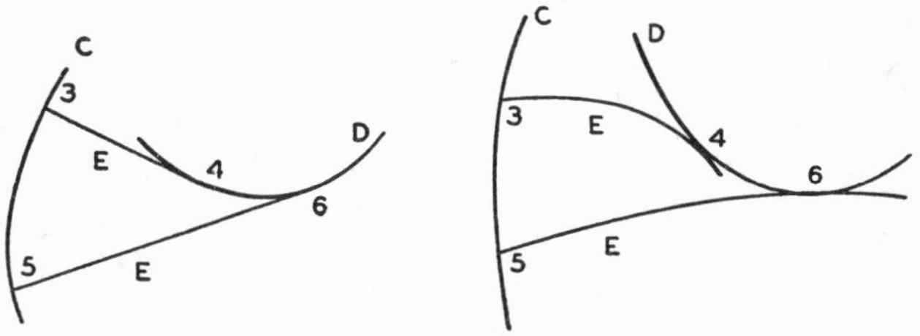


FIG. 10·2

orthogonal to $E$ when its other end *6* is fixed on $D$ and the string is caused to wrap itself around $D$. In other words, the length of the composite arc $E_{34} + D_{46}$ is equal to that of $E_{56}$ for every position of the point *4* on $D$ at the left of *6*. There is an envelope theorem slightly different from that in Theorem 10·1, which has a still closer analogy with this so-called "string property." A direction $dx:dy:dz$ is said to be *transversal* to the direction $1:y':z'$ at a point $(x, y, z)$ if it makes the integrand

$$\begin{aligned} f(x, y, z, y', z')\,dx + (dy - y'dx)\,f_{y'}(x, y, z, y', z') \\ + (dz - z'dx)\,f_{z'}(x, y, z, y', z') \end{aligned} \tag{10·3}$$

of Hilbert's integral vanish. With this definition, and by a slight modification of the proof of the last theorem, the following result can now be established:

THEOREM 10·2. *If each arc* E *of a one-parameter family of extremals is cut transversally by a curve* C *and if the family has further an envelope* D, *as shown in the second diagram of Figure 10·2, then the equation*

$$I(E_{56}) = I(E_{34}) + I(D_{46})$$

*holds for every position of the point* 4 *preceding the point* 6 *on* D.

The modification in the proof of Theorem 10·1 in order to establish Theorem 10·2 is simply that the term $I^*(C_{35})$ in equation (10·1) vanishes for the latter theorem because $C$ cuts the arcs $E$ transversally, and not because $C$ reduces to a point. For the length integral in space for which $f = (1 + y'^2 + z'^2)^{1/2}$ it is easily proved that transversality is orthogonality and that the extremals are straight lines. Hence the string property of the evolute is, in fact, a special case of Theorem 10·2.

A contact point *6* of an extremal arc $E_{12}$ with an envelope $D$, such as is shown in Figure 10·1, is said to be a point *conjugate* to *1* on the arc $E_{12}$. In the next section a second definition of a conjugate point is given, and in Section 13 it is shown that the conjugate points *6* just described are included in this latter definition. In terms of the notion of a conjugate point the necessary condition of Jacobi can now be stated as follows:

IV. Jacobi's Necessary Condition. *A non-singular extremal arc* $E_{12}$ *is said to satisfy the condition IV of Jacobi if it has on it between* 1 *and* 2 *no point* 6 *conjugate to* 1. *Every non-singular minimizing arc* $E_{12}$ *without corners is an extremal arc satisfying this condition.*

The proof of the theorem is simple. In the first place it should be noted that the minimizing or maximizing arc $E_{12}$ is non-singular and therefore an extremal arc, as stated in the second paragraph of Section 7, and it is the only extremal arc through one of its elements $(x, y, z, y', z') = (\xi, \eta, \zeta, \eta', \zeta')$. If there is a conjugate point *6* on $E_{12}$ of the kind shown in Figure 10·1, then formula (10·2) shows that the composite arcs $E_{14} + D_{46} + E_{62}$ all give to the integral $I$ the same value as $E_{12}$, whatever the position of the point *4* preceding *6* on the envelope $D$. If $I(E_{12})$ were a minimum or maximum, these composite arcs near $E_{12}$ would therefore also be minimizing or maximizing arcs, non-singular near the point *6*, since $E_{12}$ is so. In that case $D_{46}$ would have to be an extremal arc, which is impossible, since the only extremal through the common element $(x, y, z, y', z')$ of $D_{46}$ and $E_{16}$ at the point *6* is $E_{12}$ itself.

The proof of Jacobi's condition in the preceding paragraph applies only to conjugate points *6* which are contact points of an envelope $D$ with a branch projecting backward toward the point *1*. It would fail, for example, in the not uncommon case[16] when the envelope has a cusp at *6* with both branches receding from *1*. In the next section a more inclusive definition of conjugate points will be given, for which Jacobi's condition, as stated above, can also be proved. For the conjugate points considered here the following stronger conclusion can be deduced:

Theorem 10·3. *On a non-singular minimizing arc* $E_{12}$ *without corners there cannot be a conjugate point* 6 *of the type shown in Figure 10·1, with a branch of the envelope* D *projecting backward from* 6 *toward the point* 1, *either between* 1 *and* 2 *or at* 2.

An examination of the proof given above justifies this statement at once. It is easy to see that the condition IV and Theorem 10·3 apply to maximizing, as well as to minimizing, arcs.

[16] For a discussion of the possible cases in the plane see Bolza, *op. cit.*, pp. 358 ff.

**11. A second proof of Jacobi's condition.** Let $E_{12}$ be a non-singular minimizing arc without corners for the integral $I$, so that, by definition, the determinant $f_{y'y'}f_{z'z'} - (f_{y'z'})^2$ is different from zero along it. According to the differentiability condition of Hilbert in Corollary 6·3, such an arc must have continuous second derivatives and be an extremal. It is only to such non-singular extremals that the Jacobi condition, deduced in the last section and here, applies.

The proof of Jacobi's condition which will be made in this section[17] depends upon the fact that the second variation

$$I_2(\eta, \zeta) = \int_{x_1}^{x_2} 2\omega(x, \eta, \zeta, \eta', \zeta')\,dx$$

of Section 4, formed for a minimizing arc $E_{12}$, must be greater than or equal to zero for all admissible variations $\eta$, $\zeta$ vanishing at $x_1$ and $x_2$. A pair $\eta$, $\zeta$ making $I_2(\eta, \zeta)$ zero must therefore define an arc which minimizes this second variation in the class of admissible arcs in $x\eta\zeta$-space which join the points $(x_1, 0, 0)$ and $(x_2, 0, 0)$. A minimum problem for $I_2$ is thus suggested which is similar in type to that originally proposed for the integral $I$, but in $x\eta\zeta$-space instead of $xyz$-space. It is called the *accessory minimum problem*, and the word "accessory" will frequently be used to denote its extremals and other concepts connected with it.

The extremals of this new problem are the solutions $\eta$, $\zeta$ of the differential equations

$$(11\cdot 1) \qquad \frac{d}{dx}\omega_{\eta'} - \omega_\eta = 0\,, \qquad \frac{d}{dx}\omega_{\zeta'} - \omega_\zeta = 0\,.$$

Since $2\omega$ is the quadratic form in $\eta, \zeta, \eta', \zeta'$ whose coefficients are displayed in Section 4, it is readily seen that these equations are linear and homogeneous in the variables $\eta, \zeta, \eta', \zeta', \eta'', \zeta''$. Furthermore, the determinant of coefficients of the terms in $\eta''$, $\zeta''$ is $f_{y'y'}f_{z'z'} - (f_{y'z'})^2 \neq 0$. Hence the equations are solvable for $\eta''$, $\zeta''$; and it follows, as stated for Euler's equations in Section 7, that they have one and but one solution through each initial element $(x_0, \eta_0, \zeta_0, \eta_0', \zeta_0')$. In particular, the unique solution through $(x_0, \eta_0, \zeta_0, \eta_0', \zeta_0') = (x_0, 0, 0, 0, 0)$ is $\eta \equiv 0$, $\zeta \equiv 0$, as one readily verifies by substituting these functions in the equations.

The equations (11·1) are sometimes called "Jacobi's differential equations," since for analogous problems their solutions were first utilized by him;[18] but in the following pages they will be designated as the *accessory* system of differential equations in accord with the nomenclature described above, and also with one introduced by von Escherich[19] in his studies of more complicated problems.

[17] First given in Bliss, "Jacobi's Condition for Problems of the Calculus of Variations in Parametric Form," *Transactions of the American Mathematical Society*, XVII (1916), 195.

[18] See Ostwald's *Klassiker*, No. 47, pp. 88 ff.; or Jacobi's original publication, "Zur Theorie der Variationsrechnung und der Differentialgleichungen," *Journal für die angewandte Mathematik*, XVII (1837), 68. For further references see Bolza, *op. cit.*, p. 60.

[19] "Die zweite Variation der einfachen Integrale," *Wiener Berichte*, CVII (1898), 1236.

DEFINITION OF A CONJUGATE POINT. *A point* 6 *is said to be* CONJUGATE *to the point* 1 *on an extremal arc* $E_{12}$ *if there exists a solution* $(\eta, \zeta) = (u, v)$ *of the accessory equations with elements* u, v *vanishing at* $x_1$ *and* $x_6$ *but not both identically zero between* $x_1$ *and* $x_6$.

This is a somewhat artificial definition whose significance will appear later. In particular, it will be shown that the contact points *6* of envelopes *D* described in the last section are conjugate to *1* in the sense defined here.

To prove Jacobi's condition IV for the new type of conjugate points, let *6* be such a conjugate to *1* between *1* and *2* on $E_{12}$, having a pair of functions $u$, $v$ as described in the definition above. An admissible arc in $x\eta\zeta$-space with a corner at $x_6$ can then be defined by the equations

$$(11\cdot2)\qquad \begin{aligned} (\eta,\ \zeta) &\equiv (u,\ v) \qquad \text{for} \qquad x_1 \leqq x \leqq x_6\,, \\ (\eta,\ \zeta) &\equiv (0,\ 0) \qquad \text{for} \qquad x_6 \leqq x \leqq x_2\,. \end{aligned}$$

With the help of equations (11·1) and the well-known and readily verifiable homogeneity property of Euler for the homogeneous quadratic form $2\omega$,

$$(11\cdot3)\qquad 2\omega = \eta\omega_\eta + \zeta\omega_\zeta + \eta'\omega_{\eta'} + \zeta'\omega_{\zeta'}\,,$$

it is clear that the variations $\eta$, $\zeta$ defined above give to the second variation the value

$$\begin{aligned} I_2(\eta.\ \zeta) &= \int_{x_1}^{x_6} [\eta\omega_\eta + \zeta\omega_\zeta + \eta'\omega_{\eta'} + \zeta'\omega_{\zeta'}]\, dx \\ &= [\eta\omega_{\eta'} + \zeta\omega_{\zeta'}]_1^6\,; \end{aligned}$$

and this is zero, since the functions $(\eta, \zeta) = (u, v)$ vanish at $x_1$ and $x_6$. The arc (11·2) in $x\eta\zeta$-space would therefore minimize the second variation $I_2(\eta, \zeta)$, when $E_{12}$ is a minimizing arc for the original problem in $xyz$-space, and would have to satisfy the Weierstrass-Erdmann corner condition of Corollary 6·2 for the second variation at the point *6*. Since $\omega_{\eta'}$ and $\omega_{\zeta'}$ vanish at the right of $x_6$ and have the values

$$\omega_{\eta'} = [f_{y'y'}u' + f_{y'z'}v']^6\,, \qquad \omega_{\zeta'} = [f_{z'y'}u' + f_{z'z'}v']^6$$

at $x_6 - 0$, this implies that $u'$ and $v'$ would vanish with $u$ and $v$ at $x_6$ and hence that $u$ and $v$ would vanish identically, which is contrary to the definition of a conjugate point. Hence, when the arc $E_{12}$ minimizes $I$, there can be no point *6* conjugate to *1* between *1* and *2* on $E_{12}$.

The proof of Jacobi's condition, which has just been given, has the advantage that it applies to all conjugate points irrespective of the character or existence of an enveloping curve *D* through them. It does not, however, give any information about the case when the point *2* itself is conjugate to *1*, even when there is an envelope *D* through *2* with a branch extending toward *1*, as described in Section 10. The methods of this and the preceding section are evidently supplementary in that each gives some information which the other fails to justify.

**12. The determination of conjugate points.**[20] Four solutions $(u_i, v_i)$ $(i = 1, \ldots, 4)$ of the accessory differential equations $(11 \cdot 1)$ of an arc $E_{12}$ have a determinant

$$d(x) = \begin{vmatrix} u_1 & u_2 & u_3 & u_4 \\ v_1 & v_2 & v_3 & v_4 \\ u_1' & u_2' & u_3' & u_4' \\ v_1' & v_2' & v_3' & v_4' \end{vmatrix},$$

which is either identically zero or else everywhere different from zero. For, when this determinant vanishes at one value of $x$, say at $x_0$, the constant coefficients in the linear expressions

$$(12 \cdot 1) \qquad \begin{aligned} u &= c_1 u_1 + c_2 u_2 + c_3 u_3 + c_4 u_4 , \\ v &= c_1 v_1 + c_2 v_2 + c_3 v_3 + c_4 v_4 \end{aligned}$$

can be determined so that not all of them are zero, and, furthermore, so that $u$, $v$ and their first derivatives all vanish at $x_0$. But the pair $(u, v)$ is also a solution of the accessory equations, since these equations are linear; and hence $u$ and $v$ must vanish identically in $x$, as explained in the preceding section. The determinant above is then evidently identically zero if it vanishes at a single point, and the solutions $(u_i, v_i)$ are linearly dependent.

A set of four solutions $(u_i, v_i)$ with determinant $d(x)$ different from zero is called a "fundamental system of solutions of the accessory equations." Every other solution $(u, v)$ is expressible in terms of them in the form $(12 \cdot 1)$. This follows since for a solution $(u, v)$ selected arbitrarily the equations $(12 \cdot 1)$ and their derivatives with respect to $x$ can be solved at a fixed value $x_0$ for the constants $c_i$. The solution

$$\begin{aligned} u &- c_1 u_1 - c_2 u_2 - c_3 u_3 - c_4 u_4 , \\ v &- c_1 v_1 - c_2 v_2 - c_3 v_3 - c_4 v_4 \end{aligned}$$

of the accessory equations then vanishes with its derivatives at $x_0$ and hence is identically zero.

THEOREM $12 \cdot 1$. *If for four solutions* $(u_i, v_i)$ *of the accessory equations of a non-singular extremal arc* $E_{12}$ *the determinant*

$$D(x, x_1) = \begin{vmatrix} u_1(x) & u_2(x) & u_3(x) & u_4(x) \\ v_1(x) & v_2(x) & v_3(x) & v_4(x) \\ u_1(x_1) & u_2(x_1) & u_3(x_1) & u_4(x_1) \\ v_1(x_1) & v_2(x_1) & v_3(x_1) & v_4(x_1) \end{vmatrix}$$

[20] For the properties of solutions of linear differential equations deduced in Section 12 one may consult also the references in the footnote of p. 68, below.

*is not identically zero, then the points* 6 *conjugate to* 1 *on* $E_{12}$ *are determined by the zeros* $x_6$ *of* $D(x, x_1)$.

To prove this, let *6* be a point conjugate to *1* on $E_{12}$. The solutions $(u_i, v_i)$ in the determinant $D(x, x_1)$ are necessarily linearly independent and form a fundamental system, since otherwise the determinant $D$ would surely vanish identically. Hence a particular solution $(u, v)$ characterizing the conjugate point *6*, as in the definition of a conjugate point in Section 11, would be expressible in terms of the solutions $(u_i, v_i)$ in the form (12·1). But since the elements $u, v$ of such a solution must vanish at $x_6$, it follows that $D(x_6, x_1) = 0$.

Conversely, suppose that $x_6$ is a zero of the determinant $D(x, x_1)$. Then the constants $c_i$ in the expressions (12·1) can be determined so that $u$ and $v$ vanish at both $x_1$ and $x_6$. The functions $u, v$ so determined cannot vanish identically, since the solutions $u_i, v_i$ are linearly independent; and hence $x_6$ defines a point *6* conjugate to *1* on the extremal arc $E_{12}$.

The determinants $D(x, x_1)$ not identically zero are those for which the solutions $u_i, v_i$ of the accessory equations are linearly independent. For, if the $u_i, v_i$ are linearly dependent, the determinant evidently vanishes identically; if they are linearly independent, then $D(x, x_1)$ is not identically zero, since it has the form $D(x, x_1) = (x-x_1)^2 A(x, x_1)$ with $A(x_1, x_1) = d(x_1) \neq 0$, as indicated in the proof of Theorem 12·2 below.

The following theorem is an easy consequence of the preceding paragraphs and is useful in the proofs of the sufficiency theorems of Chapter II.

THEOREM 12·2. *If a non-singular extremal arc* $E_{12}$ *has on it no point conjugate to* 1, *then the points* 0 *sufficiently near to* 1, *on the extension of* $E_{12}$ *to the left of* 1, *have also no conjugates on* $E_{12}$.

To prove the theorem one may first subtract the third from the first row in the determinant $D(x, x_0)$ of Theorem 12·1 and apply Taylor's formula with integral form of the remainder. The differences in the first row of $D(x, x_0)$ then have the values

$$u_i(x) - u_i(x_0) = (x - x_0) \int_0^1 u_i'[x_0 + \theta(x - x_0)]\, d\theta \qquad (i = 1, \ldots, 4).$$

After a similar process has been applied to the second and fourth rows, it is clear that $D(x, x_0)$ is expressible in the form

$$D(x, x_0) = (x - x_0)^2 A(x, x_0),$$

where $A(x_1, x_1) = d(x_1)$. The function $A(x, x_1)$ is different from zero at $x = x_1$, since $d(x_1) \neq 0$; and it is different from zero on the rest of the interval $x_1 \leqq x \leqq x_2$ since *1* has no point conjugate to it on $E_{12}$. It follows readily by continuity considerations that $A(x, x_0)$ will be different from zero on $x_1 \leqq x \leqq x_2$ if $x_0 < x_1$ is sufficiently near to $x_1$. Furthermore, $D(x, x_0)$ will also have this property, and the theorem is proved.

Besides the method of determining conjugate points in Theorem 12·1, there is a second one, which may be described as follows:

THEOREM 12·3. *If the columns of a determinant*

$$\Delta(x) = \begin{vmatrix} u_1 & u_2 \\ v_1 & v_2 \end{vmatrix}$$

*are two solutions of the accessory equations of a non-singular extremal arc* $E_{12}$, *with all elements* $u_i$, $v_i$ $(i = 1, 2)$ *vanishing at* $x_1$, *and if the determinant itself is not identically zero, then the points* 6 *conjugate to* 1 *on* $E_{12}$ *are determined by the zeros* $x_6$ *of* $\Delta(x)$.

The proof is much like that of the criterion of Theorem 12·1 and need not be given in detail. It is necessary to know, however, that every solution $(u, v)$ of the accessory equations, with elements $u$, $v$ both vanishing at $x_1$, is linearly expressible in terms of the solutions $(u_i, v_i)$ of the determinant $\Delta(x)$ of Theorem 12·3 in the form

$$u = c_1 u_1 + c_2 u_2, \qquad v = c_1 v_1 + c_2 v_2. \tag{12·2}$$

A first remark, in order to prove this, is that the determinant

$$\begin{vmatrix} u_1' & u_2' \\ v_1' & v_2' \end{vmatrix} \tag{12·3}$$

is surely different from zero at $x_1$. Otherwise, constants $c_1$ and $c_2$ could be determined so that the functions $u$, $v$ in equations (12·2) would have derivatives zero at $x_1$; and since these functions themselves vanish there, it follows that they would be identically zero. This is, however, impossible, since $\Delta(x)$ is, by hypothesis, not identically zero.

Suppose, then, that $(u, v)$ is an arbitrarily selected solution of the accessory equations with elements vanishing at $x_1$. Since the determinant (12·3) does not vanish at $x_1$, constants $c_1$ and $c_2$ can be determined so that the derivatives of the solutions

$$u - c_1 u_1 - c_2 u_2, \qquad v - c_1 v_1 - c_2 v_2$$

both vanish at $x_1$. But these solutions themselves are zero at $x_1$ and hence vanish identically. The remainder of the proof of Theorem 12·3 is like that of Theorem 12·1.

One of the very striking contributions which Jacobi made to the theory of the calculus of variations was his use of the fact that when a family

$$y(x, a, b, c, d), \qquad z(x, a, b, c, d) \tag{12·4}$$

of extremals is known, such as was described in Theorem 7·1, solutions of the accessory equations along every member of the family can be found by simple differentiations. To simplify the proof, only the parameter $a$ will be exhibited for the moment. The first of the Euler equations

$$\frac{d}{dx} f_{y'}[x,\ y(x\ \ a),\ z(x,\ a),\ y'(x,\ a),\ z'(x,\ a)] \\ - f_y[x,\ y(x,\ a),\ z(x,\ a),\ y'(x,\ a),\ z'(x,\ a)] = 0$$

is an identity in $x$ and $a$. When differentiated with respect to $a$, it gives

$$\frac{d}{dx}[f_{y'y}y_a + f_{y'z}z_a + f_{y'y'}y'_a + f_{y'z'}z'_a] \\ - [f_{yy}y_a + f_{yz}z_a + f_{yy'}y'_a + f_{yz'}z'_a] = 0$$

which is precisely the first of the accessory equations (11·1) with $\eta$, $\zeta$ replaced by $y_a$, $z_a$. A similar argument shows that the pair $(y_a, z_a)$ satisfies the second of the accessory equations as well as the first. Furthermore, three other solutions of the accessory equations are furnished by the derivatives of the family (12·4) with respect to $b$, $c$, $d$; and the following corollary is evident:

COROLLARY 12·1. *On a member* E *of a four-parameter family of extremals*

$$(12\cdot 5) \qquad y(x,\ a,\ b,\ c,\ d), \qquad z(x,\ a,\ b,\ c,\ d)$$

*the points* 6 *conjugate to a point* 1 *are determined by the zeros* $x_6$ *of the determinant*

$$D(x,\ x_1,\ a,\ b,\ c,\ d) = \begin{vmatrix} y_a(x) & y_b(x) & y_c(x) & y_d(x) \\ z_a(x) & z_b(x) & z_c(x) & z_d(x) \\ y_a(x_1) & y_b(x_1) & y_c(x_1) & y_d(x_1) \\ z_a(x_1) & z_b(x_1) & z_c(x_1) & z_d(x_1) \end{vmatrix},$$

*provided that this determinant is not identically zero along* E.

It is understood that in the elements of the determinant $D$ the parameters $a$, $b$, $c$, $d$ have been suppressed for the sake of simplicity in notation.

From the first paragraph of this section it is now evident that, if the determinant

$$d(x) = \begin{vmatrix} y_a & y_b & y_c & y_d \\ z_a & z_b & z_c & z_d \\ y_{ax} & y_{bx} & y_{cx} & y_{dx} \\ z_{ax} & z_{bx} & z_{cx} & z_{dx} \end{vmatrix}$$

is different from zero at one point of an extremal arc $E_{12}$ of a family (12·5), it will be different from zero everywhere on $E_{12}$, as was stated in the proof of Theorem 7·1. The proof of Theorem 12·2 shows, therefore, that on an arc $E_{12}$ of such a family the determinant $D$ of the corollary is not identically zero, since it has the form $D = (x - x_1)^2 A(x, x_1)$ with $A(x_1, x_1) = d(x_1) \neq 0$.

As a final corollary, the following is readily provable:

COROLLARY 12·2. *On a member* E *of a two-parameter family of extremals*

$$y(x, \alpha, \beta), \qquad z(x, \alpha, \beta) \tag{12·6}$$

*each of which passes through a fixed point* 1, *the points* 6 *conjugate to* 1 *are determined by the zeros* $x_6$ *of the determinant*

$$\Delta(x, \alpha, \beta) = \begin{vmatrix} y_\alpha(x) & y_\beta(x) \\ z_\alpha(x) & z_\beta(x) \end{vmatrix},$$

*provided that this determinant is not identically zero along* E.

The columns of $\Delta(x, \alpha, \beta)$ are solutions of the accessory equations, as has been seen above, and their elements all vanish at $x_1$. This follows because the extremals (12·6) all pass through the point *1*, and the equations

$$y_1 = y(x_1, \alpha, \beta), \qquad z_1 = z(x_1, \alpha, \beta)$$

are therefore identities in $\alpha$, $\beta$. Differentiation of these equations with respect to $\alpha$ and $\beta$ shows that the derivatives $y_\alpha$, $z_\alpha$, $y_\beta$, $z_\beta$ all vanish at $x_1$.

It happens for some special problems that the extremals can be found in a parametric form not easily reducible to the non-parametric one. Under such circumstances it is important to have a criterion for the determination of conjugate points expressed in terms of the parametric equations defining the extremals. Let these equations be

$$\begin{aligned} x &= X(u, a, b, c, d), \\ y &= Y(u, a, b, c, d), \\ z &= Z(u, a, b, c, d). \end{aligned} \tag{12·7}$$

The non-parametric equations would then be found by solving the first equation (12·7) for $u$ as a function

$$u = U(x, a, b, c, d) \tag{12·8}$$

and substituting in the last two equations. The determinant $D(x, x_1, a, b, c, d)$ for the non-parametric family so determined is readily seen to be equal to the determinant

$$\begin{vmatrix} X_a(u) & X_b(u) & X_c(u) & X_d(u) & X_u(u) & 0 \\ Y_a(u) & Y_b(u) & Y_c(u) & Y_d(u) & Y_u(u) & 0 \\ Z_a(u) & Z_b(u) & Z_c(u) & Z_d(u) & Z_u(u) & 0 \\ X_a(u_1) & X_b(u_1) & X_c(u_1) & X_d(u_1) & 0 & X_u(u_1) \\ Y_a(u_1) & Y_b(u_1) & Y_c(u_1) & Y_d(u_1) & 0 & Y_u(u_1) \\ Z_a(u_1) & Z_b(u_1) & Z_c(u_1) & Z_d(u_1) & 0 & Z_u(u_1) \end{vmatrix}, \tag{12·9}$$

except for a factor $X_u(u)X_u(u_1)$, which is different from zero since $X_uU_x \equiv 1$. The value $u_1$ corresponds to $x_1$ by means of the equation (12·8); and if we denote the determinant (12·9) by $D(u, u_1, a, b, c, d)$, the conjugate points to *1* on an extremal (12·7) will be defined by the zeros $u \neq u_1$ of this determinant.

**13. The geometric interpretation of conjugate points.** In this section it is to be proved that if a non-singular extremal arc $E_{12}$ has on it a contact point *6* with the envelope of a one-parameter family of extremals through the point *1*, then *6* is a conjugate to *1* in the sense of the analytic definition of a conjugate point in Section 11. Conversely, with the help of an additional hypothesis, it turns out that every conjugate point according to the analytic definition is a contact point of an envelope.

Let the functions defining a one-parameter family of extremals through the point *1* with an envelope $D$ be

$$y(x, t), \qquad z(x, t) \qquad [x_1 \leqq x \leqq x(t), \ t' \leqq t \leqq t_0]. \tag{13·1}$$

The family is supposed to contain the non-singular extremal arc $E_{12}$ for $t = t_0$; and each extremal of the family touches the envelope $D$, as shown in Figure 10·1, at the point determined by $x = x(t)$, so that the functions defining $D$ are

$$x(t), \qquad y[x(t), t] = Y(t), \qquad z[x(t), t] = Z(t). \tag{13·2}$$

The functions $x(t)$ and (13·1) and the derivatives $y_x$, $z_x$ are supposed to have continuous partial derivatives of at least the first order in a neighborhood of the values $(x, t)$ belonging to the arc $E_{12}$, and it is furthermore assumed that $y_t$, $z_t$ do not vanish identically along $E_{12}$. The fact that $D$ is tangent at each of its points to one of the extremals (13·1) is expressed by the equations

$$x'(t) = \lambda, \qquad y_x x' + y_t = \lambda y_x, \qquad z_x x' + z_t = \lambda z_x, \tag{13·3}$$

where $\lambda$ is a factor of proportionality and where the arguments of the derivatives of $y$ and $z$ are $x(t)$, $t$. But these equations and the identities in $t$,

$$y_1 = y(x_1, t), \qquad z_1 = z(x_1, t),$$

imply that the elements of the solution $y_t$, $z_t$ of the accessory equations vanish at both $x_1$ and $x(t_0) = x_6$ on the arc $E_{12}$. Since $y_t(x, t_0)$, $z_t(x, t_0)$ do not both vanish identically on the interval $x_1x_6$, the point *6* must be conjugate to *1*, according to the analytic definition of a conjugate point; and we have the following theorem:

THEOREM 13·1. *Let* $E_{12}$ *be a particular extremal arc contained in a one-parameter family of extremals (13·1). If the family has an envelope* D, *as shown in Figure 10·1, and satisfies the hypotheses of the preceding paragraphs, then the contact point* 6 *of* $E_{12}$ *with* D *is a point conjugate to* 1 *on* $E_{12}$, *according to the analytic definition of a conjugate point in Section 11.*

In order to prove the converse of this result, let the extremal $E_{12}$ be contained in the two-parameter family of extremals

$$(13\cdot4)\qquad y(x, \alpha, \beta), \qquad z(x, \alpha, \beta)$$

of Theorem 7·2 for parameter values $\alpha_0$, $\beta_0$. All the extremals of this family pass through the point *1*. Furthermore, let *6* be a point conjugate to *1* on $E_{12}$ defined by a zero $x_6$ of the determinant $\Delta(x, \alpha_0, \beta_0)$. In order to carry through the analysis, the additional assumption is made that the derivative $\Delta_x(x_6, \alpha_0, \beta_0)$ is different from zero. From the value of the derivative $\Delta_x$ as a sum of determinants it follows that $y_\alpha$, $y_\beta$, $z_\alpha$, $z_\beta$ do not all vanish at $(x_6, \alpha_0, \beta_0)$. If $y_\alpha$ is different from zero, for example, the first two of the differential equations

$$(13\cdot5)\qquad \begin{aligned} \Delta_x dx + \Delta_\alpha d\alpha + \Delta_\beta d\beta &= 0\,, \\ y_\alpha d\alpha + y_\beta d\beta &= 0\,, \\ z_\alpha d\alpha + z_\beta d\beta &= 0 \end{aligned}$$

can be solved for $dx/d\beta$, $d\alpha/d\beta$; and they determine uniquely a solution $x(\beta)$, $\alpha(\beta)$ through the initial point $(x_6, \alpha_0, \beta_0)$. The determinant $\Delta$ vanishes identically on this solution, since it vanishes at the initial point $(x_6, \alpha_0, \beta_0)$ and has its total derivative with respect to $\beta$ identically zero because of the first equation (13·5). Hence the last equation (13·5) is also satisfied identically by $x(\beta)$, $\alpha(\beta)$. A similar argument can be made if $y_\alpha$ vanishes, since one of the three derivatives $y_\beta$, $z_\alpha$, $z_\beta$ must then be different from zero at $(x_C, \alpha_0, \beta_0)$.

In every case three functions, $x(t)$, $\alpha(t)$, and $\beta(t)$, are determined, $t$ being $\alpha$ or $\beta$, which take the initial values $x_6$, $\alpha_0$, $\beta_0$ for a value $t = t_0$. On the one-parameter family of extremals

$$(13\cdot6)\qquad \begin{aligned} v[x, \alpha(t), \beta(t)] &= y(x, t)\,, \\ z[x, \alpha(t), \beta(t)] &= z(x, t) \end{aligned}$$

the curve $D$ defined as in (13·2) by the function $x(t)$ satisfies equations (13·3), since the last two equations (13·5) show that the derivatives $y_t$, $z_t$ vanish identically along it. It follows readily that the family (13·6) is a one-parameter family of extremals with an envelope $D$ touching the extremal arc $E_{12}$ at the conjugate point *6*.

THEOREM 13·2. *If a point* 6 *on an extremal arc* $E_{12}$ *is conjugate to the initial point* 1, *according to the analytic definition of a conjugate point in Section 11, and if the further hypotheses of the preceding two paragraphs are satisfied, then* 6 *is a contact point of* $E_{12}$ *with the envelope* D *of a one-parameter family of extremals through the point* 1. *If this envelope has a branch projecting from* 6 *toward the point* 1, *then* 6 *is also a conjugate point to* 1 *of the kind discussed in Section 10.*

It should be noted that the envelope $D$ of the theorem may have a singular point at the point *6* with no branch projecting backward from *6* toward the point *1;* or, in particular, it may degenerate into the point *6* itself. In these cases the necessary condition of Jacobi cannot be proved, as in Section 10, by means of the envelope theorem.

It will perhaps be interesting to consider further the geometric properties of conjugate points by means of somewhat more intuitive arguments. If the values of $x$ which make the determinant $\Delta(x, \alpha, \beta)$ vanish on the extremals (13·4) are determined by a function $x = X(\alpha, \beta)$, then the functions

$$X(\alpha, \beta), \quad y[X, \alpha, \beta], \quad z[X, \alpha, \beta]$$

determine a surface $S$. The normal to this surface at each point $(\alpha, \beta)$ is readily seen to be orthogonal to the corresponding extremal of the family (13·4), and

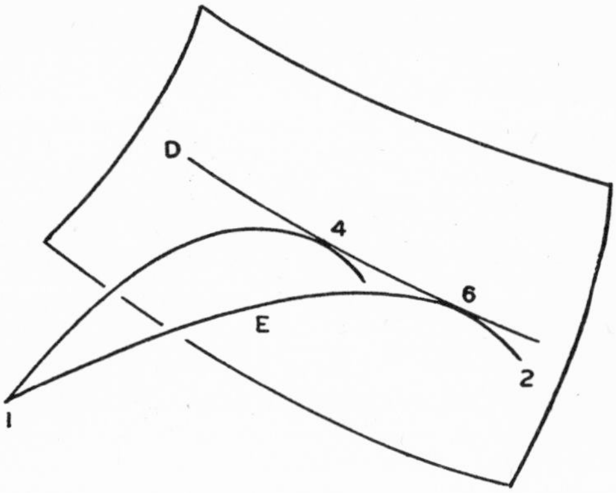


FIG. 13·1

hence the surface is an enveloping surface for the family. One can also verify, without difficulty, the fact that $S$ has no singular point near the point *6* if the matrix

$$\begin{matrix} \Delta_\alpha & y_\alpha & z_\alpha \\ \Delta_\beta & y_\beta & z_\beta \end{matrix}$$

is of rank two at *6*. At each point of $S$ the extremal of the family (13·4) tangent to $S$ defines a direction, and these directions form a slope field on $S$ similar to that defined by a differential equation of the first order in a plane. Hence, through each point of $S$ there passes one and but one curve tangent to the slope field. The particular curve $D$ of this sort, through the point of contact *6* of $E_{12}$ with $S$, is an envelope of a one-parameter family of extremals through the point *1* of the type discussed frequently in preceding pages.

## CHAPTER II

## SUFFICIENT CONDITIONS FOR A MINIMUM

**14. Introduction.** Before the time of Weierstrass, writers on the calculus of variations did not recognize the fact that when a number of properties of a minimizing arc have been discovered there still may be a doubt as to whether these properties are sufficient actually to insure the presence of a minimum. The necessary conditions of Euler, Legendre, and Jacobi were published in 1744, 1786, and 1837, respectively, but apparently without inspiring any attempt to prove that an arc satisfying them would surely give the integral $I$ a minimum value. Weierstrass,[1] however, after adding a fourth necessary condition in 1879, proceeded to prove by a very ingenious and beautiful method that the four necessary conditions known to him, when suitably strengthened, will actually guarantee the minimizing property.

The sufficiency proofs given in the following two sections are essentially those of Weierstrass in their structure, though different from his in some of their details. A fundamental notion for his method of proof is the so-called "field of extremals." The fields which he used are for problems in the plane and are special in character because all of their extremals pass through a fixed point. In Section 18, below, a definition of a more general field is given, applicable either in the plane or in higher spaces, and a sufficiency theorem is proved which in its interpretations for special problems is sometimes much more powerful than the theorems of Weierstrass. It will be noted that the notion of a field in a space of more than two dimensions is not merely a notational extension of the corresponding notion for the plane. New characteristics are involved which were first studied by A. Mayer.[2] In Sections 20 and 22, below, and in Chapter III, the properties of Mayer fields are developed in more detail.

The second variation of an integral of the calculus of variations has been the subject of extensive study, and an elaborate transformation theory has been devised in order to deduce from it the necessary conditions of Legendre and Jacobi. These conditions can now be proved by the simpler methods explained in Chapter I, but there remains a voluminous literature for the understanding of which a thorough knowledge of the second variation is required. In Section 23 the essential results of the transformation theory of the second variation are

[1] *Werke*, VII, 210–17 and 218–29. For a comprehensive study see Duren, "The Development of Sufficient Conditions in the Calculus of Variations" (diss., University of Chicago), *Contributions 1930*, p. 245.

[2] "Über den Hilbertschen Unabhängigkeitssatz in der Theorie des Maximums und Minimums der einfachen Integrale," *Sächsischer Berichte*, LVII (1905), 49, and *Mathematische Annalen*, LXII (1906), 325. See also Duren, *op. cit.*

obtained quite simply by an application of the results of Section 19. Finally, in Section 24, a sufficiency proof for a weak relative minimum is given which depends upon the theory of the second variation but which, when properly phrased, does not depend upon the notion of a field. The first proof of this sort was also given by Weierstrass.[3]

**15. Auxiliary theorems.** In order to develop the sufficiency theorems of Weierstrass, it is necessary first to study some auxiliary properties of two-parameter families of extremals. Let

$$y = y(x, \alpha, \beta), \qquad z = z(x, \alpha, \beta) \tag{15·1}$$

be such a family, containing a particular extremal arc $E_{12}$ for values $x_1 \leqq x \leqq x_2$, $\alpha_0$, $\beta_0$ and having the properties described in Theorem 7·2. Such a family is said to simply cover a region $F$ of $xyz$-space for values $(x, \alpha, \beta)$ satisfying conditions of the form

$$x_1 - \epsilon \leqq x \leqq x_2 + \epsilon, \qquad |\alpha - \alpha_0| \leqq \epsilon, \qquad |\beta - \beta_0| \leqq \epsilon \tag{15·2}$$

if through each point $(x, y, z)$ of $F$ there passes one and but one of the extremals; or, in other words, if for each point $(x, y, z)$ in $F$ the equations (15·1) have one and only one solution $(x, y, z, \alpha, \beta)$ satisfying (15·2). The values $\alpha$, $\beta$ belonging to these solutions define two single-valued functions $\alpha(x, y, z)$, $\beta(x, y, z)$ in the region $F$. The functions

$$\begin{aligned} p(x, y, z) &= y_x[x, \alpha(x, y, z), \beta(x, y, z)], \\ q(x, y, z) &= z_x[x, \alpha(x, y, z), \beta(x, y, z)] \end{aligned} \tag{15·3}$$

are called the *slope functions* of the family in $F$. If the determinant

$$\Delta(x, \alpha, \beta) = y_\alpha z_\beta - y_\beta z_\alpha$$

of the family (15·1) is different from zero in the neighborhood (15·2) of the values $(x, \alpha, \beta)$ on $E_{12}$, then well-known theorems concerning implicit functions[4] tell us that the functions $\alpha(x, y, z)$, $\beta(x, y, z)$ have continuous partial derivatives of at least the second order, since the second members of equations (15·1) have this property. It follows at once that the slope functions $p$, $q$ also have such derivatives.

LEMMA 15·1. *If for a family of extremals (15·1) containing a particular arc* $E_{12}$ *the determinant* $\Delta(x, \alpha, \beta)$ *is different from zero along* $E_{12}$, *then there is a region (15·2) of points* $(x, \alpha, \beta)$ *and a neighborhood* $F$ *of* $E_{12}$ *in* $xyz$*-space such that* $F$ *is simply covered by the extremals (15·1) for values* $(x, \alpha, \beta)$ *in (15·2) in the manner described above and, further, such that in* $F$ *the slope functions* $p(x, y, z)$, $q(x, y, z)$ *of the family, as well as the functions* $\alpha(x, y, z)$ *and* $\beta(x, y, z)$, *have continuous partial derivatives of the second order.*

To justify the lemma, we shall first show that there exists a region (15·2)

[3] Werke, Vol. VII, chap. xviii.

[4] See the references in Sec. 7, above.

such that no point $(x, y, z)$ belongs to two distinct solutions $(x, y, z, \alpha, \beta)$ and $(x, y, z, \alpha', \beta')$ of equations (15·1) with $(x, \alpha, \beta)$ and $(x, \alpha', \beta')$ satisfying (15·2). With the help of Taylor's formula with integral form of remainder term we see that

$$(15\cdot 4)\qquad \begin{aligned} y(x, \alpha, \beta) - y(x, \alpha', \beta') &= (\alpha - \alpha') A_1 + (\beta - \beta') A_2, \\ z(x, \alpha, \beta) - z(x, \alpha', \beta') &= (\alpha - \alpha') B_1 + (\beta - \beta') B_2 \end{aligned}$$

where

$$A_1 = \int_0^1 y_\alpha [x, \alpha' + \theta(\alpha - \alpha'), \beta' + \theta(\beta - \beta')]\, d\theta$$

and $A_2$, $B_1$, $B_2$ have similar expressions. Since the determinant

$$D(x, \alpha, \beta, \alpha', \beta') = A_1 B_2 - A_2 B_1$$

reduces to $\Delta(x, \alpha, \beta)$ when $(\alpha', \beta') = (\alpha, \beta)$, it is different from zero along $E_{12}$ and hence is different from zero in the region (15·2) when $\epsilon$ is sufficiently small. It follows at once from equations (15·4) that no two distinct solutions of equations (15·1) satisfying (15·2) have the same projection $(x, y, z)$.

The second step in the proof of the lemma is to show that there exists a neighborhood $F$ of the arc $E_{12}$ in $xyz$-space such that every point $(x, y, z)$ in $F$ belongs to a solution $(x, y, z, \alpha, \beta)$ of equations (15·1) satisfying (15·2). If this were not so, there would exist a sequence of neighborhoods $F_n$ $(n = 1, 2, \ldots)$ condensing on the arc $E_{12}$, each containing a point $(x, y, z)_n$ belonging to no solution. The points $(x, y, z)_n$ would have an accumulation point $(\xi, \eta, \zeta)$ necessarily on $E_{12}$. But from the usual existence theorems concerning implicit functions, applied at the initial solution $(\xi, \eta, \zeta, \alpha_0, \beta_0)$ of equations (15·1), it would follow that to every point $(x, y, z)$ in a sufficiently small neighborhood of $(\xi, \eta, \zeta)$ there would correspond a solution satisfying (15·2). This is a contradiction.

The solutions $(x, y, z, \alpha, \beta)$ of equations (15·1) satisfying (15·2) and corresponding to points $(x, y, z)$ in $F$ define two functions $\alpha(x, y, z)$, $\beta(x, y, z)$ which have continuous partial derivatives of the second order in $F$. This can be seen by applying the implicit function theorem at each such solution $(x, y, z, \alpha, \beta)$, since the second members of equations (15·1) have continuous second derivatives. It is easy to see, then, that the slope functions $p(x, y, z)$, $q(x, y, z)$ of the family (15·1) also have such derivatives in $F$, as stated in the lemma.

LEMMA 15·2. *If a non-singular extremal arc* $E_{12}$ *has on it no point conjugate to its initial point* 1, *then on the extension of* $E_{12}$ *there is a point* 0 *in the order* 012 *such that the extremals through* 0 *form a two-parameter family (15·1) with determinant* $\Delta(x, \alpha, \beta)$ *different from zero along* $E_{12}$.

This is an immediate consequence of Theorems 12·2 and 7·2 and Corollary 12·2.

**16. The sufficiency theorems of Weierstrass.** In the preceding pages the Roman numerals I, II, III, and IV designate the necessary conditions for a minimum deduced in Sections 6, 9, 10, and 12 of the preceding chapter. The statements of the sufficiency theorems in this and later sections are greatly simplified by the introduction of further notations due to Bolza. The symbols II′ and III′ are used to denote the necessary conditions of Weierstrass and Legendre with the equality signs excluded in the statements of II and III in Section 9. Similarly, IV′ is Jacobi's condition IV of Section 10 strengthened to exclude points *6* conjugate to *1* from the end-point *2* of an extremal arc $E_{12}$ as well as from the interior of the arc. It is understood that $C_{12}$ is an arc with the points *1* and *2* as end-points and that $I(C_{12})$ is the value of the integral $I$ taken along this arc.

If an arc $E_{12}$ gives $I$ a minimum value relative to the class of admissible arcs $C_{12}$ in a sufficiently small neighborhood of the elements $(x, y, z, y', z')$ on $E_{12}$, then $I\ (E_{12})$ is said to be a *weak relative minimum*. A minimum provided by $E_{12}$ relative to the class of admissible arcs $C_{12}$, restricted only to have their points $(x, y, z)$ in a sufficiently small neighborhood $F$ of $E_{12}$ in $xyz$-space, is

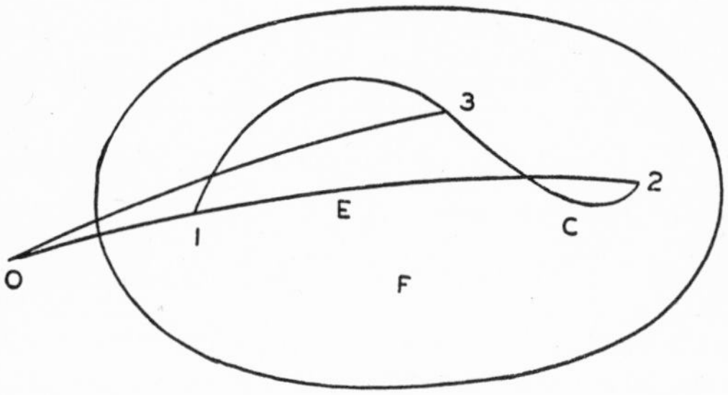


FIG. 16·1

called a *strong relative minimum*. The first theorem to be proved is, then, the following one:

THEOREM 16·1. SUFFICIENT CONDITIONS FOR A WEAK RELATIVE MINIMUM. *If an admissible arc* $E_{12}$ *without corners satisfies the conditions I, III′, IV′, then there exists a neighborhood* $R_1$ *of the values* $(x, y, z, y', z')$ *belonging to* $E_{12}$ *such that the inequality* $I(C_{12}) > I(E_{12})$ *holds for every admissible arc* $C_{12}$ *in* $R_1$ *and not identical with* $E_{12}$.

To prove the theorem, one should first note that the condition III′ implies that the determinant $f_{y'y'}f_{z'z'} - (f_{y'z'})^2$ is different from zero along $E_{12}$. Otherwise the quadratic form (9·5) could not be positive definite at each element of $E_{12}$, as III′ requires. Since $E_{12}$ satisfies condition I, it follows from the proof of Hilbert's differentiability condition in Corollary 6·3 that $E_{12}$ has continuous second derivatives $y''$, $z''$ and satisfies the Euler equations differentiated out in the form (7·1). Hence $E_{12}$ is a non-singular extremal arc.

Lemmas 15·2 and 15·1 now tell us that there is a point *0* on the extension of $E_{12}$ to the left of *1* such that the two-parameter family (15·1) of extremals through *0* simply covers a neighborhood $F$ of $E_{12}$ in $xyz$-space, as shown in Figure 16·1. For every admissible arc $C_{12}$ in $F$ the one-parameter family of extremals through the point *0* and a movable point *3* on $C_{12}$ is a family to which Corollary 8·1 applies. The equation analogous to (8·6) for this family gives

$$I(E_{12}) = I(E_{02}) - I(E_{01}) = I^*(C_{12});$$

and, consequently,

$$I(C_{12}) - I(E_{12}) = I(C_{12}) - I^*(C_{12})$$

$$(16\cdot 1) \qquad = \int_{x_1}^{x_2} E[x, y, z, p(x, y, z), q(x, y, z), y', z']\, dx,$$

where the variables $y$, $z$ in the integrand function $E$ are to be replaced by the functions $y(x)$, $z(x)$ defining the arc $C_{12}$ and where $p(x, y, z)$, $q(x, y, z)$ are the slope functions of the family of extremals simply covering $F$.

The conclusion of Theorem 16·1 now follows without difficulty when the neighborhood $R_1$ is chosen so small that all of its elements $(x, y, z, y', z')$ and the associated elements

$$[x, y, z, p(x, y, z), q(x, y, z)]$$

are in the neighborhood $N$ of Corollary 9·1. For then the integrand function $E$ in equation (16·1) is positive unless

$$(16\cdot 2) \qquad y' = p(x, y, z), \qquad z' = q(x, y, z),$$

and the difference $I(C_{12}) - I(E_{12})$ is positive unless these equations are satisfied at every point of $C_{12}$. The differential equations (16·2), however, have one and only one solution through the point *1*, and that solution is $E_{12}$.

The following sufficiency theorem for a strong relative minimum involves a still further extension of the condition II of Weierstrass. An arc $E_{12}$ is said to satisfy the condition $\mathrm{II}_N$ if there is a neighborhood $N$ of the elements $(x, y, z, y', z')$ on $E_{12}$ such that the condition

$$(16\cdot 3) \qquad E(x, y, z, y', z', Y', Z') \geqq 0$$

holds for all sets $(x, y, z, y', z', Y', Z')$ with $(x, y, z, y', z')$ admissible and in $N$ and with $(x, y, z, Y', Z')$ admissible and having $(Y', Z') \neq (y', z')$. The condition $\mathrm{II}'_N$ is this condition with the equality excluded in (16·3).

LEMMA 16·1. *If an admissible arc* E *is non-singular and satisfies the condition* $II_N$ *of Weierstrass, then it also satisfies the strengthened condition* $II'_N$ *if* N *is properly restricted.*[5]

To prove that the condition $\mathrm{II}'_N$ holds, suppose that there were a set $(x, y, z, y', z', Y', Z')$ with $(x, y, z, y', z')$ in $N$ and with $(x, y, z, Y', Z') \neq (x, y, z, y', z')$ admissible and such that the equality in (16·3) holds. Then the

[5] This lemma is due to Hestenes for non-parametric problems and to Hestenes and Reid for problems with differential equations as side conditions. See Hestenes and Reid, "A Note on the Weierstrass Condition in the Calculus of Variations," *Bulletin of the American Mathematical Society*, XLV (1939), 471–73.

$E$-function with fixed $x, y, z, Y', Z'$ would have a minimum at $(y', z')$, and at this point its derivatives

$$(y' - Y')\, f_{y'y'} + (z' - Z')\, f_{z'y'}\,, \qquad (y' - Y')\, f_{y'z'} + (z' - Z')\, f_{z'z'}$$

with respect to $y', z'$ would have to vanish. This is evidently impossible if $N$ is chosen so small that the determinant (6·3) remains different from zero in it.

With the help of the lemma we can now prove the following theorem:

THEOREM 16·2. SUFFICIENT CONDITIONS FOR A STRONG RELATIVE MINIMUM. *If an admissible arc* $E_{12}$ *without corners is non-singular and satisfies the conditions* $I, II_N, IV'$, *then there is a neighborhood* F *of* $E_{12}$ *in* xyz*-space such that the relation* $I(C_{12}) > I(E_{12})$ *holds for every admissible arc* $C_{12}$ *in* F *not identical with* $E_{12}$.

The proof of this theorem is like that of the preceding theorem down to the last paragraph. The neighborhood $F$ of $E_{12}$ can be taken so small that all of the sets

$$[x,\ y,\ z,\ p(x,\ y,\ z),\ q(x,\ y,\ z)]$$

belonging to $F$ are in the neighborhood $N$ for which the condition $II_N$ holds. The difference $I(C_{12}) - I(E_{12})$ in formula (16·1) is then evidently positive or zero. Since by the last lemma the condition $II'_N$ also holds when $N$ is sufficiently small, this difference is surely positive unless the differential equations (16·2) hold along $C_{12}$, in which case $C_{12}$ is identical with $E_{12}$, as before.

Evidently the conditions I, $II'_N$, III$'$, IV$'$ also insure a strong relative minimum, since III$'$ implies the non-singularity of $E_{12}$ and since the remaining hypotheses of Theorem 16·2 are immediate consequences of I, $II'_N$, IV$'$. These are the conditions which have heretofore usually been given.

In special cases the region $R$ may have the property that when two elements $(x, y, z, y'_1, z'_1)$, $(x, y, z, y'_2, z'_2)$ belong to it so do all the elements $(x, y, z, y', z')$ with $y'_1 \leqq y' \leqq y'_2$, $z'_1 \leqq z' \leqq z'_2$. In this case the region is said to be convex in the variables $y'$ and $z'$, and the following corollary to the last theorem often provides the simplest criterion for a minimum. The notation $III_F$ designates the property that the inequality

$$f_{y'y'}\eta^2 + 2 f_{y'z'}\eta\zeta + f_{z'z'}\zeta^2 \geqq 0 \tag{16·4}$$

holds for all admissible elements $(x, y, z, y', z')$ with projections $(x, y, z)$ in a neighborhood $F$ of the arc $E_{12}$ and for all pairs $\eta, \zeta$ such that $\eta^2 + \zeta^2 = 1$. The notation $III'_F$ is used for this property with the equality sign in (16·4) excluded.

COROLLARY 16·1. *If the region* R *has the convexity property just described, then an admissible arc* $E_{12}$ *without corners and satisfying the conditions* $I, III'_F, IV'$, *will make* $I(E_{12})$ *a strong relative minimum, as described in the last theorem.*

It is evident, with the help of the relation (9·3), that the condition $II'_N$ is a consequence of $III'_F$, and hence the truth of the corollary follows at once from Theorem 16·2. The additional property of the region $R$ is presupposed for the corollary in order that the relation (9·3) may be applicable to all pairs of elements $(x, y, z, y', z')$, $(x, y, z, Y', Z')$ belonging to points $(x, y, z)$ sufficiently near to $E_{12}$.

**17. A comparison of necessary with sufficient conditions.** With the help of the notations introduced in the last section it is possible to construct a table of necessary and of sufficient conditions which indicates clearly the gaps between the two which remain to be closed. The table applies to admissible arcs without corners.

TABLE OF NECESSARY AND OF SUFFICIENT CONDITIONS

| Type of Minimum | Necessary Conditions | Sufficient Conditions |
|---|---|---|
| Weak relative | I, III, IV | I, III′, IV′ |
| Strong relative | I, II, III, IV | I, $\text{II}_N$, IV′, $E$ non-singular |
| Strong relative | ............ | I, $\text{II}'_N$, III′, IV′ |
| Strong relative | ............ | I, $\text{III}'_F$, IV′ |

If corners are permitted, the condition IV of Jacobi must be modified. Such a modification was originally deduced for parametric problems in the plane by Carathéodory and was later studied by Bolza and Dresden for parametric problems in the plane.[6] The minimizing properties of broken extremals in higher spaces have been discussed by Graves, Reid, and Smiley.[7] For many special problems, however, the Weierstrass-Erdmann corner conditions cannot be satisfied, so that minimizing arcs with corners are impossible. The table above is then applicable to all minimizing admissible arcs.

According to its definition, an admissible arc has all of its elements $(x, y, z, y', z')$ *interior* to the region $R$. It is possible that there may be minimizing arcs some of whose elements are on the boundary of $R$. The theory of such minimizing arcs has been studied for some special types of problems, and the methods used can be applied to problems in three-space of the type under consideration here.[8]

**18. The definition and first properties of a field.** In the proofs of the sufficiency theorems of Weierstrass in Section 16 the region $F$ and its slope functions $p(x, y, z)$, $q(x, y, z)$ played an important role. It can readily be seen that the Hilbert integral

$$(18\cdot1)\qquad I^* = \int [f dx + (dy - y'dx) f_{y'} + (dz - z'dx) f_{z'}] ,$$

[6] Carathéodory, "Über die diskontinuirlichen Lösungen in der Variationsrechnung" (diss., Göttingen, 1904), and *Mathematische Annalen*, LXII (1906), 474; Bolza, *Vorlesungen über Variationsrechnung*, chap. viii; Dresden, "The Second Derivatives of the Extremal Integral," *Transactions of the American Mathematical Society*, IX (1908), 480.

[7] Graves, "Discontinuous Solutions in Space Problems of the Calculus of Variations," *American Journal of Mathematics*, LII (1930), 1–28; Reid, "Discontinuous Solutions in the Non-parametric Problem of Mayer in the Calculus of Variations," *American Journal of Mathematics*, LVII (1935), 69–93; Smiley, "Discontinuous Solutions for the Problem of Bolza in Parametric Form" (diss., University of Chicago), *Contributions 1933–1937*, pp. 527–66.

[8] See Bolza, *op. cit.*, pp. 392 ff., where references are given to Weierstrass, Bolza, Bliss, and others. See also Bliss and Underhill, "The Minimum of a Definite Integral for Unilateral Variations in Space," *Transactions of the American Mathematical Society*, XV (1914), 291–310.

with the arguments $y'$ and $z'$ replaced by the slope functions $p$ and $q$, has the same value on all arcs $D_{34}$ in $F$ having suitable continuity properties and the same end-points *3* and *4*. The family of extremals joining the point *0* to a movable point on such an arc is, in fact, a family to which Corollary 8·1 is applicable. For this family, equation (8·6) takes the form

$$I\,(E_{04}) - I\,(E_{03}) = I^*\,(D_{34})\,;$$

and since the first member is completely determined when the end-points *3* and *4* are specified, the integral $I^*(D_{34})$ must have the same property. This result shows that the region $F$ is a field in accordance with the following more general definition:

Definition of a Field. A field is a region $F$ of $xyz$-space with a pair of slope functions $p(x, y, z)$, $q(x, y, z)$ having the following properties:

*a*) They are single valued and have continuous first partial derivatives in $F$;

*b*) The elements

$$[x,\ y,\ z,\ p\,(x,\ y,\ z),\ q\,(x,\ y,\ z)] \tag{18·2}$$

defined by points $(x, y, z)$ in $F$ are all admissible;

*c*) The Hilbert integral (18·1) is independent of the path in $F$ in the sense described above.

The integral $I^*$ has the form

$$I^* = \int (A\,dx + B\,dy + C\,dz)\,, \tag{18·3}$$

where $A$, $B$, $C$ are functions of $x$, $y$, $z$ with the values

$$A = f - p\,f_{y'} - q\,f_{z'}\,,\qquad B = f_{y'}\,,\qquad C = f_{z'} \tag{18·4}$$

in which the arguments of $f$ and its derivatives are those of the set (18·2). A simple computation shows that

$$\begin{aligned} B_x - A_y &= \frac{\partial f_{y'}}{\partial x} + \frac{p\,\partial f_{y'}}{\partial y} + \frac{q\,\partial f_{y'}}{\partial z} - f_y - q\,(B_z - C_y)\,, \\ C_x - A_z &= \frac{\partial f_{z'}}{\partial x} + \frac{p\,\partial f_{z'}}{\partial y} + \frac{q\,\partial f_{z'}}{\partial z} - f_z + p\,(B_z - C_y)\,, \end{aligned} \tag{18·5}$$

where the partial derivatives indicated are to be taken with respect to the variables $x$, $y$, $z$ occurring explicitly in $f$ and its derivatives as well as in the slope functions $p(x, y, z)$, $q(x, y, z)$.

It is well known that the equations

$$B_z - C_y = 0\,,\qquad C_x - A_z = 0\,,\qquad A_y - B_x = 0 \tag{18·6}$$

are necessary conditions for the integral $I^*$ to be independent of the path. These conditions can be deduced readily here, however, by noticing that every arc in the field must be a minimizing arc for $I^*$ when $I^*$ is independent of the path. The Euler equations for the integrand $f = A + By' + Cz'$ of $I^*$ must therefore be identities in $x, y, z, y', z'$; and the equations (18·6) are equivalent to these identities, as is readily provable.

The solutions of the differential equations

$$\frac{dy}{dx} = p(x, y, z), \qquad \frac{dz}{dx} = q(x, y, z) \tag{18·7}$$

in the field $F$ are all extremals, since along such a solution

$$\begin{aligned} \frac{df_{y'}}{dx} - f_y &= \frac{\partial f_{y'}}{\partial x} + \frac{p\,\partial f_{y'}}{\partial y} + \frac{q\,\partial f_{y'}}{\partial z} - f_y, \\ \frac{df_{z'}}{dx} - f_z &= \frac{\partial f_{z'}}{\partial x} + \frac{p\,\partial f_{z'}}{\partial y} + \frac{q\,\partial f_{z'}}{\partial z} - f_z, \end{aligned} \tag{18·8}$$

where the partial derivatives are like those in equations (18·5). The expressions (18·8) evidently vanish as a consequence of equations (18·5) and (18·6).

The equations (18·7) are called the *differential equations of the field*, and their solutions are the *extremals of the field*. Through every point of $F$ there passes one and but one such extremal, so that the totality of extremals of the field $F$, each determined by its intersection with a fixed surface in $F$, can be regarded as a two-parameter family.

An important property of an extremal arc $E_{12}$ of a field is that the values $I^*(E_{12})$ and $I(E_{12})$ are the same, since the integrand of $I^*$ in equation (18·1) reduces to $f$ along $E_{12}$ as a consequence of the equations (18·7).

**19. A fundamental sufficiency theorem.** The Hilbert integral associated with a field has the two following fundamental properties, described in the preceding paragraphs: (1) it is independent of the path in the field, and (2) it has the same value as the original integral $I$ on an extremal arc $E_{12}$ of the field. These properties enable one to prove the following theorem:

THEOREM 19·1. THE INTEGRAL FORMULA OF WEIERSTRASS. *If* $E_{12}$ *is an extremal arc of a field* F *with the slope functions* p(x, y, z), q(x, y, z), *then for every admissible arc* $C_{12}$ *in the field joining the end-points* 1 *and* 2 *of* $E_{12}$ *the formula*

$$I(C_{12}) - I(E_{12}) = \int_{x_1}^{x_2} E(x, y, z, p, q, y', z')\,dx \tag{19·1}$$

*holds, where the variables* y, z *occurring in the integrand function are to be replaced by the functions* y(x), z(x) *belonging to* $C_{12}$.

The proof is simple, since, on account of the properties of the integral $I^*$,

$$I(E_{12}) = I^*(E_{12}) = I^*(C_{12})\cdot$$

and consequently

$$I(C_{12}) - I(E_{12}) = I(C_{12}) - I^*(C_{12})\,.$$

This becomes the formula (19·1) of the theorem when the symbols $I(C_{12})$, $I^*(C_{12})$ are replaced by the integrals which they represent.

The formula (19·1) is sometimes called the "integral formula of Weierstrass." It was proved in Section 16 for the special field whose extremals all pass through a fixed point *0*, and it is now seen to hold also for the more general fields defined in Section 18. With its help the following important theorem can be proved:

THEOREM 19·2. THE FUNDAMENTAL SUFFICIENCY THEOREM. *If* $E_{12}$ *is an extremal arc of a field* F *and if at each point of the field the condition*

$$E[x, y, z, p(x, y, z), q(x, y, z), y', z'] \geqq 0 \tag{19·2}$$

*holds for every admissible set* (x, y, z, y′, z′) *with* (y′, z′) ≠ (p, q), *then the relation* $I(C_{12}) \geqq I(E_{12})$ *is true for every admissible arc* $C_{12}$ *in the field which joins the end-points* 1 *and* 2 *of* $E_{12}$. *If the condition (19·2) holds without the equality sign, then* $I(C_{12}) > I(E_{12})$ *unless* $C_{12}$ *is identical with* $E_{12}$.

The conclusion of the theorem is evident with the help of the formula (19·1) of Weierstrass. If the condition (19·2) holds without the equality sign, then $I(C_{12}) > I(E_{12})$ except when the equations $y' = p$, $z' = q$ are satisfied at every point of $C_{12}$. But in that case the arc $C_{12}$ would have to coincide with $E_{12}$, since the equations $y' = p$, $z' = q$ have one and only one solution through the point *1*, and that solution is $E_{12}$ itself.

The sufficiency theorem which has just been proved is frequently a very useful one in the study of special problems. If an extremal arc $E_{12}$ can be imbedded in a field in which the *E*-function has the property presupposed in the theorem, then its minimizing properties are assured—at least within the field—and no further tests need be applied. In the following section several methods for the construction of such fields are described.

**20. Methods of constructing fields.** It has been seen in Section 18 that every field *F* is simply covered by extremals which may be regarded as forming a two-parameter family. It is the purpose of this section to determine the conditions under which a region *F*, simply covered by a two-parameter family of extremals, will form a field with the slope functions $p(x, y, z)$, $q(x, y, z)$ of the family.

The family of extremals to be considered is supposed to be defined by functions of the form

$$y(x, \alpha, \beta), \qquad z(x, \alpha, \beta), \tag{20·1}$$

which with their derivatives $y_x$, $z_x$ have continuous partial derivatives of at least the second order for all sets $(x, \alpha, \beta)$ satisfying conditions of the form

$$(\alpha, \beta) \text{ interior to } A, \qquad x_1(\alpha, \beta) < x < x_2(\alpha, \beta). \tag{20·2}$$

In these conditions $A$ is a region in the $\alpha\beta$-plane and $x_1(\alpha, \beta)$, $x_2(\alpha, \beta)$ are supposed to be single valued, continuous, and distinct functions in that region. Such a family simply covers a region $F$ of $xyz$-space if, with the region (20·2) in place of (15·2), it satisfies the conditions described in Section 15 for the family (15·1) and the region (15·2).

If a function $\xi(\alpha, \beta)$ is single valued, continuous, and has continuous partial derivatives of at least the first order in the region $A$, then the functions

$$\xi(\alpha, \beta), \quad \eta(\alpha, \beta) = y[\xi(\alpha, \beta), \alpha, \beta], \quad \zeta(\alpha, \beta) = z[\xi(\alpha, \beta), \alpha, \beta] \tag{20·3}$$

define a surface $S$. Such a surface intersects each of the extremals (20·1) in the point defined by $x = \xi$. The following theorem now gives a first characterization of the two-parameter families which simply cover fields:

THEOREM 20·1. *If a two-parameter family of extremals (20·1) is cut by a surface* S *of the form (20·3) and if on* S *the integral* I*, *formed with the slope functions* $y_x(\xi, \alpha, \beta)$, $z_x(\xi, \alpha, \beta)$ *of the intersecting extremals, is independent of the path, then every region* F *of* xyz-*space which is simply covered by the extremals is a field with the slope functions of the family, provided that the determinant* $\Delta(x, \alpha, \beta)$ *of the family is different from zero at each set of values* x, α, β *corresponding to a point in* F.

The proof of this theorem is simple with the help of Corollary 8·1. Every arc $D_{46}$ in the region $F$ determines a one-parameter family of the extremals (20·1) intersecting the surface $S$ in an arc $C_{35}$. The formula (8·6) of Corollary 8·1 applied to this one-parameter family gives the equation

$$I(E_{56}) - I(E_{34}) = I^*(D_{46}) - I^*(C_{35}), \tag{20·4}$$

where the first Hilbert integral $I^*(D_{46})$ is formed with the slope functions of the extremals in the region $F$ and the second $I^*(C_{35})$ is formed with the slope functions of the extremals of the family at their intersections with the surface $S$. Since the integral $I^*(C_{35})$ so formed is, by hypothesis, independent of the path on $S$, it follows that the values of the first, second, and last terms in the equation (20·4) are uniquely determined when the end-points *4* and *6* of the arc $D_{46}$ are given; and $I^*(D_{46})$ must therefore itself be independent of the form of the path $D_{46}$ in $F$. Under these circumstances the region $F$ is a field with the slope functions of the family (20·1), as required by the definition of a field in Section 18.

The property of invariance for $I^*$ on $S$, required in the theorem for a two-parameter family of extremals covering a field, is a natural one, since the Hilbert integral is independent of the path in every field and therefore also on every surface $S$ which cuts across the extremals of the field. It is not necessary for the truth of the theorem, however, that the surface $S$ shall lie within the region $F$ simply covered by the extremals. In special cases it may degenerate into a fixed point or a fixed curve.

Theorem 20·1 provides a method of constructing two-parameter families of extremals which will form fields in every region which they simply cover. Let $S$ be a surface defined by functions of the form

$$\xi(\alpha, \beta), \quad \eta(\alpha, \beta), \quad \zeta(\alpha, \beta) \qquad [(\alpha, \beta) \text{ in } A], \tag{20·5}$$

and let $\eta'(\alpha, \beta)$, $\zeta'(\alpha, \beta)$ be two functions such that the elements

$$(20\cdot 6)\quad [\xi(\alpha, \beta),\ \eta(\alpha, \beta),\ \zeta(\alpha, \beta),\ \eta'(\alpha, \beta),\ \zeta'(\alpha, \beta)]$$

are all admissible. It is presupposed that all of the five functions within the brackets have continuous partial derivatives of the third order in the region $A$. The Hilbert integral (18·1) with the slope functions $\eta'(\alpha, \beta)$, $\zeta'(\alpha, \beta)$, taken along arcs on $S$, has the form

$$\int (P\,d\alpha + Q\,d\beta),$$

where

$$P = f\xi_\alpha + (\eta_\alpha - \eta'\xi_\alpha) f_{y'} + (\zeta_\alpha - \zeta'\xi_\alpha) f_{z'},$$

$$Q = f\xi_\beta + (\eta_\beta - \eta'\xi_\beta) f_{y'} + (\zeta_\beta - \zeta'\xi_\beta) f_{z'},$$

and the arguments of $f$ and its derivatives are the functions (20·6). If there is a function $W(\alpha, \beta)$ with continuous partial derivatives of the third order in $A$, and such that $P = W_\alpha$, $Q = W_\beta$, then it is evident that the Hilbert integral just constructed is the integral of $dW$ and is independent of the path on $S$. According to Theorem 20·1, the two-parameter family of extremals with the initial elements (20·6) will then form a field in every region $F$ which it simply covers.

If the surface (20·5) and the function $W(\alpha, \beta)$ are arbitrarily selected in advance in such a way that the surface is non-singular and the functions $\xi$, $\eta$, $\zeta$, $W$ have continuous partial derivatives of the third order, then a set of elements (20·6) related to them as described in the last paragraph, can be determined by solving for $\eta'$ and $\zeta'$, as functions of $\alpha$ and $\beta$, the equations

$$(20\cdot 7)\quad \begin{aligned} f\xi_\alpha + (\eta_\alpha - \eta'\xi_\alpha) f_{y'} + (\zeta_\alpha - \zeta'\xi_\alpha) f_{z'} &= W_\alpha, \\ f\xi_\beta + (\eta_\beta - \eta'\xi_\beta) f_{y'} + (\zeta_\beta - \zeta'\xi_\beta) f_{z'} &= W_\beta, \end{aligned}$$

in which the arguments of $f$ and its derivatives are $\xi(\alpha, \beta)$, $\eta(\alpha, \beta)$, $\zeta(\alpha, \beta)$, and the variables $\eta'$, $\zeta'$. Implicit function theorems assure us that solutions $\eta'(\alpha, \beta)$, $\zeta'(\alpha, \beta)$ exist, provided that equations (20·7) have an initial solution ($\alpha_0$, $\beta_0$, $\eta_0'$, $\zeta_0'$) with a direction $\eta_0'$, $\zeta_0'$ not tangent to $S$ at the point defined by the values ($\alpha_0$, $\beta_0$), and such that the element

$$[\xi(\alpha_0, \beta_0),\ \eta(\alpha_0, \beta_0),\ \zeta(\alpha_0, \beta_0),\ \eta_0',\ \zeta_0']$$

is admissible and makes the determinant $f_{y'y'}f_{z'z'} - (f_{y'z'})^2$ different from zero. For the functional determinant of the first members of equations (20·7) with respect to the variables $\eta'$, $\zeta'$ is the product

$$\begin{vmatrix} \eta_\alpha - \eta'\xi_\alpha & \zeta_\alpha - \zeta'\xi_\alpha \\ \eta_\beta - \eta'\xi_\beta & \zeta_\beta - \zeta'\xi_\beta \end{vmatrix} \begin{vmatrix} f_{y'y'} & f_{y'z'} \\ f_{z'y'} & f_{z'z'} \end{vmatrix};$$

and this is different from zero when the direction determined by $\eta_0'$, $\zeta_0'$ in $xyz$-space is not tangent to $S$ at the point defined by $\alpha_0$, $\beta_0$, since the condition for non-tangency is the non-vanishing of the determinant

$$\begin{vmatrix} 1 & \eta' & \zeta' \\ \xi_\alpha & \eta_\alpha & \zeta_\alpha \\ \xi_\beta & \eta_\beta & \zeta_\beta \end{vmatrix} = \begin{vmatrix} \eta_\alpha - \eta'\xi_\alpha & \zeta_\alpha - \zeta'\xi_\alpha \\ \eta_\beta - \eta'\xi_\beta & \zeta_\beta - \zeta'\xi_\beta \end{vmatrix}$$

at the values $(\alpha_0, \beta_0, \eta_0', \zeta_0')$.

An important special case of a family with the properties described in Theorem 20·1 is a two-parameter family of extremals passing through a fixed point $0$. In this case the point $0$ is a degenerate surface $S$ on which the Hilbert integral is certainly independent of the path. In the proofs of the sufficiency theorems of Weierstrass in Section 16 use was made of a field simply covered by such a family.

It is frequently convenient to choose the function $W(\alpha, \beta)$ equal to a constant for the equations (20·7), in which case the second members of these equations are zero. Every arc $\alpha = \alpha(t)$, $\beta = \beta(t)$ on the surface $S$ then cuts transversally the extremal arcs with initial elements (20·6) by which it is intersected, according to the definition of transversality in Section 10. In this case the surface $S$ is said to be a *transversal surface* of the family of extremals.

When the surface $S$ is a plane $x = x_0$, its defining functions (20·5) take the form $x_0$, $\alpha$, $\beta$, and equations (20·7) reduce to the simpler pair

$$(20\cdot8) \qquad f_{y'}(x_0, \alpha, \beta, \eta', \zeta') = W_\alpha, \qquad f_{z'}(x_0, \alpha, \beta, \eta', \zeta') = W_\beta.$$

If one solution $(\alpha_0, \beta_0, \eta_0', \zeta_0')$ of these equations is known, at which the determinant $f_{y'y'}f_{z'z'} - (f_{y'z'})^2$ is different from zero, then the implicit function theorems are applicable and assure us of the existence of other neighboring solutions $\eta'(\alpha, \beta)$, $\zeta'(\alpha, \beta)$.

**21. Sufficient conditions for an integral to be independent of the path.** The integral to be considered in this section has the form

$$(21\cdot1) \qquad \int (A\,dx + B\,dy + C\,dz),$$

where $A$, $B$, $C$ are functions of $x$, $y$, $z$, which are single valued and have continuous partial derivatives of at least the first order in a region $F$ of $xyz$-space.

An arc

$$(21\cdot2) \qquad x(t), \quad y(t), \quad z(t) \qquad (t_1 \leqq t \leqq t_2)$$

is said to be regular if the functions $x(t)$, $y(t)$, $z(t)$ defining it are continuous and have continuous derivatives such that $x'^2 + y'^2 + z'^2 \neq 0$ everywhere on the arc. A transformation of the parameter $t$ is defined by a function $t = \varphi(\tau)$

having a continuous derivative $\varphi'(\tau) > 0$ on an interval $\tau_1\tau_2$ whose ends $\tau_1$ and $\tau_2$ are such that $t_1 = \varphi(\tau_1)$, $t_2 = \varphi(\tau_2)$. It is easy to see that the value of the integral (21·1) is unchanged when the parametric representation is transformed in this way.

A regular arc $C_1$ in $F$ is deformable into a second such arc $C_2$ with the same end-points if the two arcs are members for $a = a_1$ and $a = a_2$, respectively, of a one-parameter family of arcs in $F$ through the same two end-points and defined by functions of the form

$$(21\cdot 3) \qquad x(t, a), \; y(t, a), \; z(t, a) \quad [a_1 \leqq a \leqq a_2, \; t_1(a) \leqq t \leqq t_2(a)].$$

These functions and their derivatives $x_t$, $y_t$, $z_t$ and the functions $t_1(a)$, $t_2(a)$ are supposed to be single valued and to have continuous first partial derivatives with respect to $a$ for all values $t$, $a$ satisfying the conditions in the parenthesis. The region $F$ is said to be *simply connected* if every regular arc $C_1$ in $F$ is deformable into every other such arc with the same end-points by a sequence of such deformations.

THEOREM 21·1. *If the identities*

$$(21\cdot 4) \qquad B_z - C_y \equiv 0, \qquad C_x - A_z \equiv 0, \qquad A_y - B_x \equiv 0$$

*hold in the region* F *for an integral (21·1) with the continuity properties described above and if* F *is simply connected according to the definition just given, then the integral is independent of the path in* F.

The first step in the proof of this theorem is to show that on all arcs of a family of the type (21·3) the values of the integral (21·1) are the same. The derivative with respect to $a$ of the integrand of (21·1), when the functions (21·3) are substituted, is readily calculated, with the help of the identities (21·4), to be

$$\partial \frac{Ax_a + By_a + Cz_a}{\partial t}.$$

Hence, the derivative with respect to $a$ of the value of the integral itself is

$$[A(x't_a + x_a) + B(y't_a + y_a) + C(z't_a + z_a)]_{t_1}^{t_2};$$

and this is zero, since the arcs of the family all pass through the same end-points for $t = t_1(a)$ and $t = t_2(a)$, and $x't_a + x_a$ and the similar expressions for $y$ and $z$ therefore vanish at these values.

Since the integral (21·1) has the same value on all arcs of a family of the form (21·3), it follows readily, since $F$ is simply connected, that it has the same value on all regular arcs in $F$ which have their end-points in common. Consequently, if a fixed point *1* is chosen in $F$, the value of the integral (21·1) on regular arcs joining *1* to a second point $(x, y, z)$ in $F$ is a single-valued function $W(x, y, z)$. By integrating up to $(x, y, z)$ on regular arcs starting at the point *1* and ending with straight end-segments parallel to the axes near $(x, y, z)$, it is readily provable that the three first partial derivatives of $W$ are $A$, $B$, $C$.

Hence the integral (21·1) is the integral of the differential $dW$ and is independent of the path, not only for regular arcs, but also for all arcs in $F$ of the type (21·2) which are continuous and which furthermore consist of a finite number of regular arcs.

It is interesting, though not essential for the sequel, to note that the only integrals of the form

$$I = \int f(x, y, z, y' z')\, dx$$

which can be independent of the path are those of the type (21·1) with coefficients $A$, $B$, $C$ satisfying the conditions (21·4). For if $I$ is independent of the path, every admissible arc must be a minimizing arc, and Euler's equations (7·1) must be satisfied identically in the variables $x$, $y$, $z$, $y'$, $z'$, $y''$, $z''$. The coefficients of $y''$, $z''$ in these equations are the derivatives $f_{y'y'}$, $f_{y'z'}$, $f_{z'z'}$. Their vanishing implies that $f$ is linear in $y'$, $z'$, and the relations (21·4) are then easily deducible as further consequences of the identical vanishing of the first members of Euler's equations.

**22. Further properties of the slope functions and extremals of a field.** The methods which have been described in Section 20 are usually the most effective ones for the construction of fields for special problems. It is interesting, however, and for theoretical purposes sometimes important, to have the further criteria for fields which will be developed in this section.

The slope functions $p(x, y, z)$, $q(x, y, z)$ are an essential part of a field, and one should seek to find the equations which characterize them independently of the extremals of the field. The desired equations are deducible from equations (18·6) formed for the functions (18·4). With the help of the identities (18·5) it is evident that these three equations are equivalent to $B_z - C_y = 0$ and the two further equations found by setting the expressions (18·8) equal to zero. After some manipulations these three equations take the form

$$\begin{aligned} &f_y - f_{y'x} - f_{y'y}p - f_{y'z}q - f_{y'y'}(p_x + p_y p + p_z q) \\ &\qquad\qquad - f_{y'z'}(q_x + q_y p + q_z q) = 0 \\ (22\cdot 1)\quad &f_z - f_{z'x} - f_{z'y}p - f_{z'z}q - f_{z'y'}(p_x + p_y p + p_z q) \\ &\qquad\qquad - f_{z'z'}(q_x + q_y p + q_z q) = 0 \\ &B_z - C_y = f_{y'z} + f_{y'y'}p_z + f_{y'z'}q_z - f_{z'y} - f_{z'y'}p_y - f_{z'z'}q_y = 0 \end{aligned}$$

in which the arguments of the derivatives of $f$ are $x$, $y$, $z$, $p$, $q$.

THEOREM 22·1. *The slope functions* p(x, y, z), q(x, y, z) *of every field* F *satisfy the three equations (22·1). Conversely, every simply connected region* F *of* xyz-*space is a field with the slope functions* p(x, y, z), q(x, y, z), *provided that in* F *these functions are single valued, have continuous first derivatives, define elements* (x, y, z, p, q) *which are admissible, and satisfy equations (22·1).*

The last part of the theorem is an immediate consequence of Theorem 21·1, since equations (22·1) imply the identities (21·4) for the coefficients $A$, $B$, $C$ of the Hilbert integral given in equations (18·4).

The value of the integral $I$, taken along the extremals of a family (20·1) between fixed limits $x_1$ and $x_2$, is a function $I(\alpha, \beta)$ of the parameters of the family. If $\beta$ is kept fixed while $\alpha$ varies, the resulting one-parameter family of extremals is of the type to which Theorem 8·1 is applicable, and the formula (8·4) of that theorem shows that the partial derivative of $I(\alpha, \beta)$ with respect to $\alpha$ is

$$I_\alpha = \left[ f_{y'} \frac{\partial y}{\partial \alpha} + f_{z'} \frac{\partial z}{\partial \alpha} \right]_{x_1}^{x_2}.$$

A similar formula holds for the derivative with respect to $\beta$. If the two second derivatives $I_{\alpha\beta}$, $I_{\beta\alpha}$ are now calculated and equated, it is found that

$$(22\cdot 2) \quad \left[ \frac{\partial y}{\partial \alpha} \frac{\partial}{\partial \beta} f_{y'} + \frac{\partial z}{\partial \alpha} \frac{\partial}{\partial \beta} f_{z'} - \frac{\partial y}{\partial \beta} \frac{\partial}{\partial \alpha} f_{y'} - \frac{\partial z}{\partial \beta} \frac{\partial}{\partial \alpha} f_{z'} \right]_{x_1}^{x_2} = 0.$$

When $x_1$ is kept fixed and $x_2$ is allowed to vary, it follows that on every extremal arc of a family (20·1) the expression between the brackets is constant.

If the extremals of a family (20·1) simply cover a field $F$, the integral $I^*$ of the field must be independent of the path on the section of $F$ by a fixed plane $x = x_1$, and also in the region of points $(\alpha, \beta)$ which correspond to this section by means of the equations $y = y(x_1, \alpha, \beta)$, $z = z(x_1, \alpha, \beta)$. In this $\alpha\beta$-region the integral $I^*$ in (18·1) is readily seen to have the form

$$I^* = \int \left[ \left( f_{y'} \frac{\partial y}{\partial \alpha} + f_{z'} \frac{\partial z}{\partial \alpha} \right) d\alpha + \left( f_{y'} \frac{\partial y}{\partial \beta} + f_{z'} \frac{\partial z}{\partial \beta} \right) d\beta \right],$$

where the arguments of the derivatives of $f$ are the functions (20·1) and their derivatives with respect to $x$ evaluated at $x = x_1$. In order that this integral in the $\alpha\beta$-region shall be independent of the path, it is necessary that

$$\frac{\partial}{\partial \beta} \left( f_{y'} \frac{\partial y}{\partial \alpha} + f_{z'} \frac{\partial z}{\partial \alpha} \right) = \frac{\partial}{\partial \alpha} \left( f_{y'} \frac{\partial y}{\partial \beta} + f_{z'} \frac{\partial z}{\partial \beta} \right);$$

and this result shows that along the extremals of the field the expression between brackets in (22·2) is not only constant but vanishes identically. The following theorem can now be readily established:

THEOREM 22·2. *Along each extremal of every two-parameter family of extremals of the form (20·1) the expression*

$$(22\cdot 3) \qquad \frac{\partial y}{\partial \alpha} \frac{\partial}{\partial \beta} f_{y'} + \frac{\partial z}{\partial \alpha} \frac{\partial}{\partial \beta} f_{z'} - \frac{\partial y}{\partial \beta} \frac{\partial}{\partial \alpha} f_{y'} - \frac{\partial z}{\partial \beta} \frac{\partial}{\partial \alpha} f_{z'}$$

*remains constant. If the family simply covers a field* F, *then the constant values of this expression on the extremals of the field are all zero. Conversely, if the values of*

*(22·3) on the extremals of a family (20·1) are all zero, then every simply connected region* F *simply covered by the extremals and having the determinant* $\Delta = y_\alpha z_\beta - y_\beta z_\alpha$ *of the family different from zero in it, is a field with the slope functions* p(x, y, z), q(x, y, z) *of the family.*

Only the last sentence of the theorem remains to be proved. The slope functions $p$, $q$ of the family satisfy the first two of equations (22·1), since they are the slope functions of a family of extremals satisfying equations (18·7). To show that they also satisfy the third equation (22·1), one can first find the derivatives with respect to $y$ and $z$ of the solutions $\alpha(x, y, z)$, $\beta(x, y, z)$ of equations (20·1) by solving the equations

$$1 = y_\alpha \alpha_y + y_\beta \beta_y\,, \qquad 0 = y_\alpha \alpha_z + y_\beta \beta_z\,,$$

$$0 = z_\alpha \alpha_y + z_\beta \beta_y\,, \qquad 1 = z_\alpha \alpha_z + z_\beta \beta_z\,.$$

The result is

$$(22\cdot4) \quad \Delta\alpha_y = z_\beta\,, \qquad \Delta\beta_y = -z_\alpha\,, \qquad \Delta\alpha_z = -y_\beta\,, \qquad \Delta\beta_z = y_\alpha\,,$$

where $\Delta$ is, as before, the determinant $y_\alpha z_\beta - y_\beta z_\alpha$. The coefficients $B = f_{y'}$, $C = f_{z'}$ in the integral $I^*$ have the arguments $x, y, z, p, q$, which are, however, the same as the functions

$$x\,, \quad y(x, \alpha, \beta)\,, \quad z(x, \alpha, \beta)\,, \quad y'(x, \alpha, \beta)\,, \quad z'(x, \alpha, \beta)$$

with $\alpha$, $\beta$ replaced by the functions $\alpha(x, y, z)$, $\beta(x, y, z)$. With the help of equations (22·4) the expression $B_z - C_y$ is then found to have the value

$$B_z - C_y = \frac{\partial \alpha}{\partial z}\frac{\partial}{\partial \alpha} f_{y'} + \frac{\partial \beta}{\partial z}\frac{\partial}{\partial \beta} f_{y'} - \frac{\partial \alpha}{\partial y}\frac{\partial}{\partial \alpha} f_{z'} - \frac{\partial \beta}{\partial y}\frac{\partial}{\partial \beta} f_{z'}$$

$$= \frac{1}{\Delta}\left( -\frac{\partial y}{\partial \beta}\frac{\partial}{\partial \alpha} f_{y'} + \frac{\partial y}{\partial \alpha}\frac{\partial}{\partial \beta} f_{y'} - \frac{\partial z}{\partial \beta}\frac{\partial}{\partial \alpha} f_{z'} + \frac{\partial z}{\partial \alpha}\frac{\partial}{\partial \beta} f_{z'} \right),$$

which vanishes identically by hypothesis. Hence the result desired in the last theorem is a consequence of the theorem which precedes it.

A two-parameter family of extremals (20·1) whose slope functions form a field in every region $F$ which the family simply covers with determinant $\Delta(x, \alpha, \beta)$ different from zero is sometimes called a *Mayer family of extremals*, after the man who first studied the theory of fields in higher spaces.[9] Such a family is a generalization of a normal congruence of straight lines, a two-parameter family of straight lines which is cut orthogonally by a one-parameter family of surfaces. It is well known that not every two-parameter family of straight lines in space has this property but that, if the lines of the family are all intersected by a single orthogonal surface, then there is a one-parameter family of such orthogonal surfaces and the family is a normal congruence. Similarly we know, from the results of Theorem 20·1, that if a two-parameter family of extremals is cut transversally by a single surface $S$, then the family

[9] For references see Bolza, *Vorlesungen*, p. 648.

is a Mayer family; and we shall see in Section 28 that there is a one-parameter family of such transversal surfaces in every region $F$ which the family simply covers.

Theorems 20·1 and 22·2 give criteria for a two-parameter family of extremals to be a Mayer family. A particular case is a two-parameter family of extremals all passing through a single fixed point.

**23. The theory of the second variation.** Before the time of Weierstrass, writers on the calculus of variations inferred without proof that an arc $E_{12}$ surely gave the integral $I$ a minimum value if the first variation $I_1(\eta, \zeta)$ along $E_{12}$ vanished and the second variation $I_2(\eta, \zeta)$ was positive for all admissible variations $\eta$, $\zeta$ vanishing at $x_1$ and $x_2$ but not identically zero between these values. Their instinctive conclusion was correct for the case of a weak relative minimum, provided that $E_{12}$ also satisfies the strengthened Legendre condition III′. For in that case the positiveness of the second variation implies the strengthened Jacobi condition IV′ along $E_{12}$, as one sees with the help of the reasoning in Section 11; and the hypotheses of Theorem 16·1, the sufficiency theorem for a weak relative minimum, are therefore all satisfied along $E_{12}$. The proof of this theorem in Section 16 uses the notation of a field, but the first proof was made by Weierstrass[10] with the aid of an expansion by Taylor's formula and without the use of a field. Proofs of this latter type, the so-called "expansion proofs," have also been given for a strong relative minimum;[11] but they are much more complicated than the corresponding proofs for a weak relative minimum.

The impressions of the early writers mentioned above were the cause of the development of an elaborate theory of the second variation, the purpose of which was to specify the circumstances under which the second variation could be transformed into an expression which was surely positive. The literature of this theory is extensive and complicated, but many of the methods used can be greatly simplified by correlating them with the theory of the accessory minimum problem of the second variation described in Section 11 of the preceding chapter.[12] It is to be shown in this section that by this correlation the result of the transformation theory of the second variation appears as an immediate consequence of the notion of a field and the integral formula (19·1). The suffi-

[10] *Op. cit.*, pp. 173–77. This proof seems to have been first presented by Weierstrass about the year 1877. See Duren, *op. cit.*, pp. 245–349.

[11] See Levi, "Sui criterii sufficiente per il massimo e per il minimo nel calcolo delle variazioni," *Annali di matematica*, XXI (1913), 173–218; Malnate, "Sui criterii sufficiente per il massimo e minimo nel calcolo delle variazioni," *Giornale di matematiche di Battaglini*, LVII (1919), 79–102; and especially Reid, "Sufficient Conditions by Expansion Methods for the Problem of Bolza in the Calculus of Variations," *Annals of Mathematics*, XXXVIII (1937), 662–78.

[12] Bliss, "The Transformation of Clebsch in the Calculus of Variations," *Proceedings of the International Mathematical Congress, Toronto, 1924*, I, 589.

ciency proof for a weak relative minimum, of Section 24 below, makes use of these results.

Let $E_{12}$ be a non-singular extremal arc for the original integral $I$. The extremals of the problem of minimizing the second variation

$$I_2(\eta, \zeta) = \int_{x_1}^{x_2} 2\omega(x, \eta, \zeta, \eta', \zeta')\, dx$$

along $E_{12}$, in the class of admissible variations $\eta$, $\zeta$ joining the points $(x_1, 0, 0)$ and $(x_2, 0, 0)$ in $x\eta\zeta$-space, are solutions of the accessory equations (11·1), which may be written with the notations

$$(23\cdot 1) \qquad \begin{aligned} J(\eta, \zeta) &= \frac{d\omega_{\eta'}}{dx} - \omega_\eta = 0, \\ K(\eta, \zeta) &= \frac{d\omega_{\zeta'}}{dx} - \omega_\zeta = 0. \end{aligned}$$

The homogeneous quadratic form $2\omega$ satisfies the well-known identity

$$\eta\omega_u + \zeta\omega_v + \eta'\omega_{u'} + \zeta'\omega_{v'} = u\omega_\eta + v\omega_\zeta + u'\omega_{\eta'} + v'\omega_{\zeta'},$$

where $\omega_u$, for example, is a symbol for $\omega_\eta(x, u, v, u', v')$. By means of this formula one readily establishes the identity

$$(23\cdot 2) \qquad \begin{aligned} &\eta J(u, v) + \zeta K(u, v) - uJ(\eta, \zeta) - vK(\eta, \zeta) \\ &\qquad = \frac{d}{dx}(\eta\omega_{u'} + \zeta\omega_{v'} - u\omega_{\eta'} - v\omega_{\zeta'}), \end{aligned}$$

with the help of which the following theorem is justified:

THEOREM 23·1. *For every pair of solutions* $(\eta, \zeta)$ *and* (u, v) *of the accessory equations (23·1) the expression*

$$(23\cdot 3) \qquad L(\eta, \zeta; u, v) = \eta\omega_{u'} + \zeta\omega_{v'} - u\omega_{\eta'} - v\omega_{\zeta'}$$

*is a constant. When it vanishes, the two solutions* $(\eta, \zeta)$ *and* (u, v) *are said to be conjugate.*

The constancy of the expression (22·3) along an extremal is an instance of this theorem, since $(y_a, z_a)$ and $(y_b, z_b)$ are two solutions of the accessory equations, and since the derivative $\partial f_{y'}/\partial a$, for example, is readily identifiable with the expression $\omega_{\eta'}(x, y_a, z_a, y_a', z_a')$.

If $(u, v)$, $(u_1, v_1)$, and $(u_2, v_2)$ are three solutions of the accessory equations such that the last two are conjugate and have their determinant $u_1v_2 - u_2v_1$ different from zero on the interval $x_1x_2$, the two-parameter family of extremals of the second variation

$$(23\cdot 4) \qquad \begin{aligned} \eta &= u + au_1 + bu_2 = \eta(x, a, b), \\ \zeta &= v + av_1 + bv_2 = \zeta(x, a, b) \end{aligned}$$

simply covers the region of $x\eta\zeta$-space bounded by the planes $x = x_1$ and $x = x_2$ and forms a field there. The expression

$$\frac{\partial \eta}{\partial a}\frac{\partial}{\partial b}\omega_{\eta'} + \frac{\partial \zeta}{\partial a}\frac{\partial}{\partial b}\omega_{\zeta'} - \frac{\partial \eta}{\partial b}\frac{\partial}{\partial a}\omega_{\eta'} - \frac{\partial \zeta}{\partial b}\frac{\partial}{\partial a}\omega_{\zeta'},$$

analogous to the expression (22·3), is in fact $L(u_1, v_1; u_2, v_2)$; and it vanishes because the solutions $(u_1, v_1)$ and $(u_2, v_2)$ are conjugate. The slope functions $\pi(x, \eta, \zeta)$, $\kappa(x, \eta, \zeta)$ of the field in $x\eta\zeta$-space are found by solving equations (23·4) for $a$ and $b$ and substituting in the derivatives

$$\eta_x(x, a, b) = u' + au_1' + bu_2',$$
$$\zeta_x(x, a, b) = v' + av_1' + bv_2'.$$

If the determinant $u_1v_2 - u_2v_1$ is denoted by $\Delta$, the slope functions have the values

$$(23\cdot 5)\qquad \begin{aligned} \pi(x, \eta, \zeta) &= \frac{1}{\Delta}\begin{vmatrix} u' & u_1' & u_2' \\ u-\eta & u_1 & u_2 \\ v-\zeta & v_1 & v_2 \end{vmatrix}, \\ \kappa(x, \eta, \zeta) &= \frac{1}{\Delta}\begin{vmatrix} v' & v_1' & v_2' \\ u-\eta & u_1 & u_2 \\ v-\zeta & v_1 & v_2 \end{vmatrix}. \end{aligned}$$

A new form for the second variation can now be easily deduced with the help of the formula (19·1). Since $(u, v)$ is an extremal of the family (23·4), it follows from (19·1) that for an arbitrary admissible arc in $x\eta\zeta$-space joining the end-points $[x_1, u(x_1), v(x_1)]$ and $[x_2, u(x_2), v(x_2)]$ of this extremal we have

$$I_2(\eta, \zeta) - I_2(u, v) = \int_{x_1}^{x_2} E_{2\omega}(x, \eta, \zeta, \pi, \kappa, \eta', \zeta')\,dx,$$

where the $E$-function, calculated for the quadratic form $2\omega$ from the formula (9·2), has the value

$$E_{2\omega} = (\eta' - \pi)^2\omega_{\eta'\eta'} + 2(\eta' - \pi)(\zeta' - \kappa)\omega_{\eta'\zeta'} + (\zeta' - \kappa)^2\omega_{\zeta'\zeta'}.$$

This justifies the following theorem:

THEOREM 23·2. *If* $(u, v)$, $(u_1, v_1)$, *and* $(u_2, v_2)$ *are solutions of the accessory equations (23·1) such that the last two are conjugate and have their determinant* $u_1v_2 - u_2v_1$ *different from zero on the interval* $x_1x_2$, *then for every pair of admissible variations* $\eta$, $\zeta$ *with end-values at* $x_1$ *and* $x_2$ *the same as those of* $(u, v)$ *the second variation has the value*

$$(23\cdot 6)\qquad \begin{aligned} I_2(\eta, \zeta) = I_2(u, v) + \int_{x_1}^{x_2} [&(\eta' - \pi)^2 f_{y'y'} \\ &+ 2(\eta' - \pi)(\zeta' - \kappa) f_{y'z'} + (\zeta' - \kappa)^2 f_{z'z'}]\,dx \end{aligned}$$

*in which* $\pi$ *and* $\kappa$ *are the slope functions defined by equations* (23·5).

In the literature on the second variation the differences $\eta' - \pi$, $\zeta' - \kappa$ are usually given in the forms

$$\eta' - \pi = \frac{1}{\Delta}\begin{vmatrix} \eta' - u' & u_1' & u_2' \\ \eta - u & u_1 & u_2 \\ \zeta - v & v_1 & v_2 \end{vmatrix},$$

$$\zeta' - \kappa = \frac{1}{\Delta}\begin{vmatrix} \zeta' - v' & v_1' & v_2' \\ \eta - u & u_1 & u_2 \\ \zeta - v & v_1 & v_2 \end{vmatrix},$$

which are readily deducible from equations (23·5).

If the non-singular extremal arc $E_{12}$ for the original integral $I$ has on it no point conjugate to *1*, there is always a pair of conjugate solutions $(u_1, v_1)$ and $(u_2, v_2)$ with determinant different from zero on the interval $x_1x_2$. For, according to Theorem 12·2, there is then a value $x_0$ less than $x_1$ which has no conjugate value on $x_1x_2$. The solutions $(u_1, v_1)$ and $(u_2, v_2)$ of the accessory equations, whose elements vanish at $x_0$ and whose derivatives at $x_0$ form the identity matrix, are a conjugate pair, as one readily verifies. The determinant $\Delta = u_1v_2 - u_2v_1$ has a factor $(x - x_0)^2$ only, and hence does not vanish identically, as one sees by applying Taylor's formula at $x = x_0$ to the elements of $\Delta$ separately. Theorem 12·3 then shows that $\Delta$ does not vanish on the interval $x_1x_2$ since the zeros of $\Delta$ are the values conjugate to $x_0$ and since there are, by hypothesis, none such on that interval. The truth of the following statement is thus established:

THEOREM 23·3. *For a non-singular extremal arc* $E_{12}$ *having on it no point conjugate to* 1 *there exists a pair of conjugate solutions* $(u_1, v_1)$ *and* $(u_2, v_2)$ *of the accessory equations with determinant different from zero on the interval* $x_1x_2$. *For every other solution* $(u, v)$ *of the accessory equations the second variation* $I_2(\eta, \zeta)$ *along* $E_{12}$ *is expressible in the form (23·6) for all admissible variations* $\eta, \zeta$ *having the end-values of* $u, v$ *at* $x_1$ *and* $x_2$. *If* $E_{12}$ *satisfies Legendre's condition in the stronger form III′, then* $I_2(\eta, \zeta)$ *is always greater than* $I_2(u, v)$ *for such variations unless* $\eta - u \equiv \zeta - v \equiv 0$ *on* $x_1x_2$.

An important special case is the one for which $(u, v)$ is the particular solution $(0, 0)$ of the accessory equations. It follows in that case that under the hypotheses of the theorem the second variation is non-negative for every pair of admissible variations $(\eta, \zeta)$ vanishing at $x_1$ and $x_2$, and that for such variations the second variation vanishes only when $(\eta, \zeta) \equiv (0, 0)$.

COROLLARY 23·1. *If* $E_{12}$ *satisfies condition III′ and has conjugate end-points but no point conjugate to* 1 *between* 1 *and* 2, *then for every accessory extremal* $(u, v)$ *the value* $I_2(u, v)$ *is at least an improper minimum relative to the values of* $I_2$ *on admissible arcs in* $\eta\zeta$*-space joining its ends.*

The corollary is an easy consequence of the theorem, as can be seen with the help of suitable approximation functions. An arbitrary admissible set of variations $(\eta, \zeta)$ is approximated both in position and direction on the interval $x_3 \leqq x \leqq x_2 - \epsilon$, as $\epsilon > 0$ approaches zero, by the set

$$H(x) = \eta(x) + (x - x_3)\frac{u(x_2-\epsilon) - \eta(x_2-\epsilon)}{x_2-\epsilon-x_3},$$

$$Z(x) = \zeta(x) + (x - x_3)\frac{v(x_2-\epsilon) - \zeta(x_2-\epsilon)}{x_2-\epsilon-x_3}.$$

The set of variations identical with $\eta$, $\zeta$ on the interval $x_1 \leqq x \leqq x_3$, with $H$, $Z$ on $x_3 \leqq x \leqq x_2 - \epsilon$, and with $u$, $v$ on $x_2 - \epsilon \leqq x \leqq x_2$, gives the second variation a value greater than $I_2(u, v)$, by Theorem 23·3, since there is no value conjugate to $x_1$ on the interval $x_1 < x \leqq x_2 - \epsilon$. By letting $\epsilon$ approach zero we see that $I_2(\eta, \zeta) \geqq I_2(u, v)$.

In deducing the formula (23·6) for the second variation, use has been made in this section of the notion of a field and the integral formula of Weierstrass. It is interesting, however, to know that the formula (23·6) can be obtained without these aids, though the argument is rather an artificial one. The notations

$$(23\cdot 7)\qquad \begin{aligned} \eta - u &= au_1 + bu_2, & \zeta - v &= av_1 + bv_2, \\ \pi - u' &= au_1' + bu_2', & \kappa - v' &= av_1' + bv_2', \\ U &= a'u_1 + b'u_2, & V &= a'v_1 + b'v_2, \\ P &= a'u_1' + b'u_2', & Q &= a'v_1' + b'v_2' \end{aligned}$$

will be helpful, where the notations of the first two rows are the same as those of preceding pages and where the last two rows define $U, P, V, Q$. It will be remembered that $a$, $b$ are functions of $x$ with the derivatives $a'$, $b'$. We shall denote $\omega_\eta(x, u, v, u', v')$ by $\omega_\eta(u, u')$, with similar notations for other derivatives and sets of arguments. Then if $\eta(x)$ and $\zeta(x)$ are given and $a$ and $b$ are determined as functions of $x$ by means of equations (23·4), which are the same as the first two equations of the system (23·7), we have

$$(23\cdot 8)\qquad \begin{aligned} \frac{d}{dx}\omega_{\eta'}(\eta - u, \pi - u') &= \frac{d}{dx}\omega_{\eta'}(au_1 + bu_2, au_1' + bu_2') \\ &= \omega_\eta(\eta - u, \pi - u') + \omega_{\eta'}(U, P), \end{aligned}$$

with similar equations for $\omega_\zeta$, since $(u_1, v_1)$ and $(u_2, v_2)$ are solutions of the accessory equations and the derivatives of $\omega$ involved are linear in $a$, $b$. Furthermore, since the solutions $(u_1, v_1)$ and $(u_2, v_2)$ of the accessory equations are conjugate, the same is true of every pair of linear combinations of them, and it follows with the help of equations (23·7) and the expression (23·3) that

$$(23\cdot 9)\qquad \Sigma(\eta - u)\,\omega_{\eta'}(U, P) - \Sigma U \omega_{\eta'}(\eta - u, \pi - u') \equiv 0$$

where the meaning of the sums is evident. This formula holds even when $a$, $b$, $a'$, $b'$ are arbitrary functions of $x$, since its first member is a bilinear form in $a$, $b$, $a'$, $b'$ with coefficients all zero.

With the help of Taylor's formula,

$$2\omega(\eta, \eta') - 2\omega(u, u') = 2\Sigma[(\eta - u)\omega_\eta(u, u') + (\eta' - u')\omega_{\eta'}(u, u')] + 2\omega(\eta - u, \eta' - u'),$$

$$2\omega(\eta - u, \eta' - u') = 2\omega(\eta - u, \pi - u') + 2\Sigma(\eta' - \pi)\omega_{\eta'}(\eta - u, \pi - u') + 2\omega(0, \eta' - \pi).$$

The first member of the first of these equations is, therefore, equal to the sum of $2\omega(0, \eta' - \pi)$ and the expression

$$2\Sigma[(\eta - u)\omega_\eta(u, u') + (\eta' - u')\omega_{\eta'}(u, u')] + 2\Sigma(\eta' - \pi)\omega_{\eta'}(\eta - u, \pi - u') + 2\omega(\eta - u, \pi - u').$$

But this last expression is the derivative of

$$\Sigma(\eta - u)[2\omega_{\eta'}(u, u') + \omega_{\eta'}(\eta - u, \pi - u')],$$

as one sees with the help of equations (11·1), (23·8), (11·3), (23·9), and (23·7). Hence, for an arbitrary pair of admissible variations $\eta$, $\zeta$ the formula

$$2\omega(\eta, \eta') - 2\omega(u, u') = 2\omega(0, \eta' - \pi) + \frac{d}{dx}\Sigma(\eta - u)[2\omega_{\eta'}(u, u') + \omega_{\eta'}(\eta - u, \pi - u')] \tag{23·10}$$

is valid, the last term $2\omega(0, \eta' - \pi)$ being the quadratic form $E_{2\omega}$ just preceding Theorem 23·2. An integration of this formula gives equation (23·6). For the particular accessory extremal $(u, v) \equiv (0, 0)$ equation (23·10) becomes

$$2\omega(\eta, \eta') = \frac{d}{dx}\Sigma\eta\omega_{\eta'}(\eta, \pi) + 2\omega(0, \eta' - \pi). \tag{23·11}$$

This is a variation of a formula which has often proved useful in the theory of the calculus of variations.[13]

**24. Sufficiency proofs without the use of fields.** In the following paragraphs two proofs of the sufficiency of the conditions in Theorem 16·1 for a weak relative minimum are first given, neither of which depends upon the notion of a field. The first proof is modeled after that of Weierstrass for parametric problems in the plane, to which reference was made in Section 14. The second depends upon continuity properties of the solutions of differential equations con-

[13] Von Escherich, *Wiener Berichte*, CVIII (1899), 1283, eq. (9); Bolza, *op. cit.*, p. 630, eq. (68); Hahn, *Rendiconti del circolo matematico di Palermo*, XXIX (1910), 64, eq. (48); Bliss, *Bulletin of the American Mathematical Society*, XXVI (1920), 359, and *Proceedings of the International Mathematical Congress, Toronto, 1924*, I, 589.

taining arbitrary functions established by Bliss[14] and is simpler than the first proof, provided that these properties are presupposed as known. Both proofs make use of the transformation of the second variation in Theorem 23·2 of the preceding section. As was seen in the concluding paragraphs of the last section, this transformation can be justified without the use of the notion of a field, and the sufficiency proofs here given can therefore also be regarded as independent of that notion.

In the concluding paragraphs of this section a sketch is given of a similar proof, not depending upon the notion of a field, for the sufficiency of the conditions in Theorem 16·2 for a strong relative minimum. The details of this somewhat complicated proof may be found in the papers of Levi, Malnate, and Reid, to which reference was made in Section 23.

Let $E_{12}$ be an admissible arc

$$y(x), \qquad z(x) \qquad (x_1 \leqq x \leqq x_2)$$

without corners and satisfying the conditions I, III′, IV′, as presupposed in Theorem 16·1; and let

$$(24\cdot 1) \qquad Y(x) = y(x) + \eta(x), \quad Z(x) = z(x) + \zeta(x) \qquad (x_1 \leqq x \leqq x_2)$$

be an admissible arc $C_{12}$ joining the ends of $E_{12}$ and lying in a neighborhood $R_1$ of the values $(x, y, z, y', z')$ belonging to $E_{12}$. It is desired to show that when $R_1$ is sufficiently small the difference

$$(24\cdot 2) \qquad \Delta I = \int_{x_1}^{x_2} [f(x, y+\eta, z+\zeta, y'+\eta', z'+\zeta') - f(x, y, z, y', z')]\,dx$$

will be positive or zero and will vanish only when $\eta \equiv \zeta \equiv 0$ on $x_1x_2$.

The difference (24·2) can be expressed by means of Taylor's formula with integral remainder in the form

$$(24\cdot 3) \qquad \begin{aligned} \Delta I &= \int_{x_1}^{x_2} [f_y\eta + f_{y'}\eta' + f_z\zeta + f_{z'}\zeta']\,dx \\ &\quad + \int_{x_1}^{x_2} \omega(x, \eta, \zeta, \eta', \zeta')\,dx + \int_{x_1}^{x_2} \Omega(x, \eta, \zeta, \eta', \zeta')\,dx, \end{aligned}$$

where $\Omega$ is a homogeneous quadratic form in $\eta, \zeta, \eta', \zeta'$ having the coefficient

$$\int_0^1 (1-\theta)\,[f_{yy}(x, y+\theta\eta, z+\theta\zeta, y'+\theta\eta', z'+\theta\zeta') - f_{yy}(x, y, z, y', z')]\,d\theta$$

14 "Differential Equations Containing Arbitrary Functions," *Transactions of the American Mathematical Society*, XXI (1920), 79.

for $\eta^2$, and other similar coefficients. The first integral in the expression (24·3) vanishes, as one readily sees with the help of the Euler equations of Corollary 6·1, which are consequences of the property $I$ of $E_{12}$. Let

$$2\phi = k_1\eta^2 + k_2\zeta^2 + k_3\eta'^2 + k_4\zeta'^2$$

be a quadratic form with distinct positive constant coefficients $k_i$ ($i = 1, \ldots, 4$). Then $\Delta I$ is expressible in the form

$$\Delta I = \int_{x_1}^{x_2} (\omega - \phi)\, dx + \int_{x_1}^{x_2} (\Omega + \phi)\, dx\,. \qquad (24\cdot 4)$$

When the constants $k_i$ are fixed with sufficiently small values, the first integral in the formula (24·4) for $\Delta I$ is positive unless $\eta \equiv \zeta \equiv 0$ on $x_1x_2$. This can be seen with the help of the results of Section 23. The conditions III′, IV′ on $E_{12}$ and Theorem 23·3, in fact, imply that the accessory equations (23·1) for $\omega$ have a conjugate system of solutions $u_i$, $v_i$ ($i = 1, 2$) with determinant $u_1v_2 - u_2v_1$ different from zero on $x_1x_2$. From well-known theorems concerning differential equations containing parameters the solutions of the accessory equations

$$\frac{d}{dx}(\omega_{\eta'} - k_3\eta') - (\omega_\eta - k_1\eta) = 0\,,$$

$$\frac{d}{dx}(\omega_{\zeta'} - k_4\zeta') - (\omega_\zeta - k_2\zeta) = 0$$

for $\omega - \phi$ with the initial values of $u_1, v_1, \omega_{u_1'}, \omega_{v_1'}$ and $u_2, v_2, \omega_{u_2'}, \omega_{v_2'}$ at $x = x_1$ will be continuous in the parameters $k_1, k_2, k_3, k_4$; and it can be seen therefore that they will also be a conjugate system, with determinant different from zero on $x_1x_2$ if the constants $k_i$ are sufficiently small. Furthermore, the quadratic form with the coefficients

$$\begin{matrix} f_{y'y'} - k_3 & f_{y'z'} \\ f_{y'z'} & f_{z'z'} - k_4 \end{matrix}$$

is surely positive definite for small values $k_i$, since this same quadratic form with $k_3 = k_4 = 0$ is positive definite on account of the property III′. The transformation of Theorem 23·2 therefore shows that the first integral in equation (24·4) is positive, as stated above. The quadratic form $\Omega + \phi$ is positive definite in the variables $\eta$, $\zeta$, $\eta'$, $\zeta'$ when $R_1$ is taken sufficiently small, since its coefficients will then differ very little from those of $\phi$. This completes the proof of Theorem 16·1.

For the second proof of Theorem 16·1 we may denote by $\Omega(x, u, v, u', v')$ the homogeneous quadratic form in $u, v, u', v'$ with the coefficient for $u^2$ equal to

$$\int_0^1 (1 - \theta)\, f_{yy}(x,\ y + \theta\eta,\ z + \theta\zeta,\ y' + \theta\eta',\ z' + \theta\zeta')\, d\theta$$

and other similar coefficients. The difference $\Delta I$ is then expressible by Taylor's formula in the form

$$\Delta I = \int_{x_1}^{x_2} \Omega(x, \eta, \zeta, \eta', \zeta')\, dx ,$$

since the first variation vanishes, as before. The conditions III′, IV′ and Theorem 23·3 imply again the existence of a conjugate pair of solutions $(u_i, v_i)$ $(i = 1, 2)$ of the accessory equations for $\omega$ with a determinant $u_1v_2 - u_2v_1$ different from zero on $x_1x_2$. The pair of solutions of the accessory equations for $\Omega(x, u, v, u', v')$ with the initial values of $(u_i, v_i, \omega_{u_i'}, \omega_{v_i'})$ $(i = 1, 2)$ at $x = x_1$ is a conjugate pair and also has its determinant different from zero on $x_1x_2$ when the neighborhood $R_1$ is sufficiently small, since these solutions are continuous functionals in $\eta(x)$, $\zeta(x)$, $\eta'(x)$, $\zeta'(x)$ and can be made to differ as little as is desired from $(u_i, v_i)$ $(i = 1, 2)$ by restricting $R_1$, according to the theorems of Bliss referred to above. Furthermore, the quadratic form $\Omega(x, 0, 0, u', v')$ is positive definite when $R_1$ is small, since the same is true of the corresponding form $\omega(x, 0, 0, u', v')$. Theorem 23·2 then assures the inequality $\Delta I > 0$ for all admissible arcs (24·1) in the nieghborhood $R_1$ joining the ends of $E_{12}$ and not vanishing identically.

In order to make a proof by expansion methods of the sufficient conditions of Theorem 16·2 for a strong relative minimum, we may use the notations (24·1) for the arc $C_{12}$ and express the integrand of $\Delta I$ in (24·2) in the form

$$\begin{aligned} &E(x, Y, Z, p, q, Y', Z') \\ &+ f_y\eta + f_z\zeta + f_{y'}\eta' + f_{z'}\zeta' \\ &+ \omega(x, \eta, \zeta, \eta', \zeta') - Q(x, Y' - p, Z' - q) \\ &+ B + (Y' - p)C + (Z' - q)D . \end{aligned} \tag{24·5}$$

In this expression the arguments of the derivatives of $f$, where not otherwise specified, are the functions $x$, $y(x)$, $z(x)$, $y'(x)$, $z'(x)$ belonging to the arc $E_{12}$ whose minimizing properties are to be established, and

$$2Q = f_{y'y'}(Y' - p)^2 + 2f_{y'z'}(Y' - p)(Z' - q) + f_{z'z'}(Z' - q)^2 .$$

The arguments $p$, $q$ will be specified presently. The symbols $B$, $C$, $D$ have the values defined by the equations

$$\begin{aligned} f(x, Y, Z, p, q) - f(x, y, z, y', z') &= f_y\eta + f_z\zeta + f_{y'}(p - y') \\ &\quad + f_{z'}(q - z') + \omega(x, \eta, \zeta, p - y', q - z') + B \end{aligned}$$

$$\begin{aligned} f_{y'}(x, Y, Z, p, q) &= f_{y'} + f_{y'y}\eta + f_{y'z}\zeta + f_{y'y'}(p - y') \\ &\quad + f_{y'z'}(q - z') + C , \end{aligned}$$

$$\begin{aligned} f_{z'}(x, Y, Z\ \ p, q) &= f_{z'} + f_{z'y}\eta + f_{z'z}\zeta + f_{z'y'}(p - y') \\ &\quad + f_{z'z'}(q - z') + D . \end{aligned}$$

It is evident that they are also expressible as integral forms of remainders in three applications of Taylor's formula.

The integral of the terms in the second row of the expression (24·5) vanishes by the usual integration by parts. Since the extremal arc $E_{12}$ satisfies the conditions III′ and IV′, it follows, as for Theorem 23·3, that there exists a conjugate pair of solutions $(u_1, v_1)$ and $(u_2, v_2)$ of the accessory equations along $E_{12}$ with determinant different from zero on the interval $x_1x_2$. The integral of the third row in the expression (24·5) vanishes as a result of the transformation (23·6) applied to the integral of $\omega$, provided that we determine $a$, $b$, $\pi$, $\kappa$, $p$, $q$ by the equations

$$(24\cdot6) \qquad \eta = au_1 + bu_2\,, \qquad \zeta = av_1 + bv_2\,,$$

$$(24\cdot7) \qquad \pi = au_1' + bu_2' \qquad \kappa = av_1' + bv_2'\,,$$

$$(24\cdot8) \qquad p = y' + \pi\,, \qquad q = z' + \kappa\,.$$

The first two of these equations are equivalent to (23·4) when $u \equiv v \equiv 0$; and $\pi$ and $\kappa$ are the corresponding slope functions (23·5). Since $Y - y = \eta$, $Z - z = \zeta$, the variables $p$ and $q$ may be regarded as functions of $x$, $Y$, $Z$, the slope functions of the two-parameter family of curves defined in $xYZ$-space by the equations

$$Y = y(x) + au_1 + bu_2\,, \qquad Z = z(x) + av_1 + bv_2\,.$$

With the help of arguments like those used in the paper of Reid, to which reference was made in Section 23,[15] it can be shown that, as a consequence of the properties $\mathrm{II}_N'$ and III′, presumed for the arc $E_{12}$, there exists a neighborhood $F$ of $E_{12}$ in $xYZ$-space so small that along every admissible arc $C_{12}$ in $F$

$$(24\cdot9) \qquad E(x,\ Y,\ Z,\ p,\ q,\ Y'\ \ Z') \geqq \tau R\,[\mathrm{mod}\,(a',\ b')\,]\,,$$

where $\tau$ is a positive constant and

$$\mathrm{mod}\,(a',\ b') = (a'^2 + b'^2)^{1/2}\,, \qquad R(t) = \frac{t^2}{1+t}\,.$$

In securing this result one must have regard for the relations

$$Y' - p = \eta' - \pi = a'u_1 + b'u_2\,, \qquad Z' - q = \zeta' - \kappa = a'v_1 + b'v_2\,.$$

The form $B$ contains $a$, $b$ in a polynomial which is homogeneous and of the third degree, as one sees from the equations (24·6)–(24·8); and the last two terms in the fourth line of the expression (24·5) contain $a$, $b$, $a'$, $b'$ in polynomials which are homogeneous and of the second degree in $a$, $b$ and linear and homogeneous in $a'$, $b'$. Consequently, the region $F$ may be still further restricted, if necessary, so that along every admissible arc $C_{12}$ in $F$

$$|B| \leqq \epsilon\,[\mathrm{mod}\,(a,\ b)\,]^2\,,$$

$$|\,(Y' - p)C + (Z' - q)\,D\,| \leqq \epsilon\,\mathrm{mod}\,(a,\ b)\,\mathrm{mod}\,(a',\ b')\,.$$

[15] See also Tonelli, *Fondamenti di calcolo delle variazioni*, I, 351, and the reference to Levi there given.

But Reid has also shown[16] that if mod $(a, b) \leqq 1$

$$\int_{x_1}^{x_2} \text{mod}\,(a,\; b)\,\text{mod}\,(a',\; b')\,dx \leqq k_1 \int_{x_1}^{x_2} R\,[\text{mod}\,(a',\; b')\,]\,dx\,,$$

$$\int_{x_1}^{x_2} [\text{mod}\,(a,\; b)\,]^2 dx \leqq k_2 \int_{x_1}^{x_2} R\,[\text{mod}\,(a',\; b')\,]\,dx\,,$$

where $k_1$ and $k_2$ are positive constants. Hence for admissible arcs $C_{12}$ in a sufficiently restricted neighborhood $F$ of the extremal $E_{12}$ we have

$$\Delta I \geqq (\tau - \epsilon k_1 - \epsilon k_2) \int_{x_1}^{x_2} R\,[\text{mod}\,(a',\; b')\,]\,dx \geqq 0\,,$$

and the last equality sign holds only if $a' \equiv b' \equiv 0$, in which case $a \equiv b \equiv 0$ and $C_{12}$ coincides with $E_{12}$.

The account just given of Reid's justification of the conditions for a strong relative minimum by expansion methods is incomplete in details. In particular, the proofs of the inequality (24·9) and of the last three integral inequalities above, require more attention. For problems with no side conditions, such as the three-dimensional one here discussed, Reid's published proof of the inequalities leading to (24·9) can be greatly simplified, as he himself has indicated.

[16] See section 5 of his paper last cited above. Note that $a(x_1) = b(x_1) = 0$. Reid uses the function $R(t) = (1 + t^2)^{1/2} - 1$, but has also suggested the one in the text here.

# CHAPTER III

## FIELDS AND THE HAMILTON-JACOBI THEORY

**25. Introduction.** In Section 7 of Chapter I above, it has been shown that for the problem of the calculus of variations in $xyz$-space the solutions of Euler's differential equations form a four-parameter family of curves. When a particular problem is to be solved, the integration of these equations and the determination of the extremals through the two given points *1* and *2* are of paramount importance and are frequently very difficult to carry out. For the development of the theory, however, it is sufficient, for the most part, to know the function-theoretic characteristics of the family of extremals neighboring a given one. These are described in the so-called "imbedding theorems" of Section 7, which are to be re-proved by a different method in Section 27 below.

The development of the theory of extremals has been greatly aided by the introduction of so-called "canonical variables" $(x, y, z, u, v)$ in place of the original variables $(x, y, z, y', z')$ of the problem. We shall see that in terms of the canonical variables the differential equations of the extremals take a remarkably simple canonical form and that with the help of these new variables it is possible to show that the extremals themselves are the characteristic curves of a partial-differential equation of the first order. These theories, due to Hamilton and Jacobi, are explained in this chapter. They not only have been of assistance in the development of the theory of the calculus of variations but also have played a fundamental role in the applications of the theory to classical mechanics and to the recently developed quantum theories. A simple example of these applications in dynamics is given in Section 30.

Carathéodory has devised a quite new approach to a considerable portion of the theory of the calculus of variations. In his theory the extremals appear as so-called "curves of quickest descent." A brief introduction to his point of view is given in Section 31.

**26. Canonical variables and canonical equations for extremals.** When the variables $x, y, z, y', z'$ are replaced by a new set $x, y, z, u, v$ for which $u$ and $v$ are defined by the equations

$$(26\cdot1)\qquad u = f_{y'}(x, y, z, y', z'), \qquad v = f_{z'}(x, y, z, y', z'),$$

the differential equations of the extremals can be put into a remarkably simple form. The new variables $x, y, z, u, v$ are called *canonical variables*, and the equations of the extremals in terms of them are called *canonical equations.*

In order to carry through the discussion, it will be assumed that the region $R$ of Section 3 consists only of interior points $(x, y, z, y', z')$ at which the determinant $f_{y'y'}f_{z'z'} - (f_{y'z'})^2$ is different from zero, and that the equations (26·1) define a one-to-one correspondence between the points $(x, y, z, y', z')$ of $R$ and the points $(x, y, z, u, v)$ of the region $S$ into which $R$ is transformed by means of these equations. Equations (26·1) have then single-valued solutions

$$(26\cdot 2) \qquad y' = P(x, y, z, u, v), \qquad z' = Q(x, y, z, u\ v),$$

which also relate corresponding points of $R$ and $S$.

A set $(x, y, z, u, v)$ will be called *admissible* if it lies in the region $S$, and an arc defined by functions

$$y(x), \qquad z(x), \qquad u(x), \qquad v(x) \qquad (x_1 \leqq x \leqq x_2)$$

will be called an *admissible arc* if it is the image of an admissible arc in $R$.

The arguments in this chapter are based upon the assumption that the integrand function $f$ has continuous derivatives in the region $R$ at least up to and including those of order $m = 3$, in accordance with remarks in footnotes 5 and 11 on pages 7 and 17. According to well-known theorems concerning implicit functions,[1] the functions $P$ and $Q$ in equations (26·2) then have continuous partial derivatives of at least the second order, since, when the integrand function $f$ has continuous third derivatives, the second members of equations (26·1) have continuous second derivatives. Furthermore, every point $(x_0, y_0, z_0, u_0, v_0)$ of $S$ is an interior point, since for every point $(x, y, z, u, v)$ sufficiently near to $(x_0, y_0, z_0, u_0, v_0)$ equations (26·1) have a solution $y'$, $z'$ defining a set $(x, y, z, y', z')$ interior to $R$.

A function $H(x, y, z, u, v)$ can be defined by means of the equations

$$(26\cdot 3) \qquad \begin{aligned} H(x, y, z, u, v) &= [y' f_{y'} + z' f_{z'} - f]^{y'=P,\ z'=Q} \\ &= Pu + Qv - f(x, y, z, P, Q). \end{aligned}$$

The two forms for $H$ are readily identifiable by means of the identities

$$u = f_{y'}(x, y, z, P, Q), \qquad v = f_{z'}(x, y, z, P, Q),$$

with the help of which one can also deduce readily the following partial derivatives for $H$:

$$(26\cdot 4) \qquad \begin{aligned} H_u &= P(x, y, z, u, v), & H_x &= -f_x(x, y, z, P, Q), \\ H_v &= Q(x, y, z, u, v), & H_y &= -f_y(x, y, z, P, Q), \\ & & H_z &= -f_z(x, y, z, P, Q). \end{aligned}$$

From these formulas it follows that $H$ has continuous derivatives of order at least three when the function $f$ has that property.

[1] See the Appendix below.

THEOREM 26·1. *Every extremal arc*

$$(26{\cdot}5) \qquad y(x), \quad z(x) \qquad (x_1 \leqq x \leqq x_2)$$

*defines by means of equations (26·1) an admissible continuous solution*

$$(26{\cdot}6) \qquad y(x) \quad z(x), \quad u(x), \quad v(x) \qquad (x_1 \leqq x \leqq x_2)$$

*of the equations*

$$(26{\cdot}7) \qquad \frac{dy}{dx} = H_u, \quad \frac{dz}{dx} = H_v, \quad \frac{du}{dx} = -H_y, \quad \frac{dv}{dx} = -H_z.$$

*Conversely, for every admissible continuous solution of these equations the functions* y(x), z(x) *belong to an extremal.*

Equations (26·7) are called the *canonical equations* of the extremals.[2]

The first part of the theorem is easily proved; for the functions $u(x)$, $v(x)$, corresponding to the extremal arc (26·5) by means of equations (26·1), necessarily satisfy equations (26·2), so that

$$\frac{dy}{dx} = P = H_u, \qquad \frac{dz}{dx} = Q = H_v.$$

Furthermore, equations (26·1), (26·4), and the Euler equations of Corollary 6·1 show that

$$\frac{du}{dx} = f_y = -H_y, \qquad \frac{dv}{dx} = f_z = -H_z.$$

Conversely, if an admissible arc (26·6) satisfies the first two equations (26·7), it must satisfy equations (26·1), and the last two equations (26·7) then imply Euler's equations.

The preceding results can be applied to the accessory minimum problem of the second variation. The equations defining canonical accessory variables $x, \eta, \zeta, \varphi, \psi$, analogous to equations (26·1) for the variables $x$, $y$, $z$, $u$, $v$, are

$$(26{\cdot}8) \qquad \varphi = \omega_{\eta'}(x, \eta, \zeta, \eta', \zeta'), \qquad \psi = \omega_{\zeta'}(x, \eta, \zeta, \eta', \zeta'),$$

where $2\omega$ is the quadratic form in the integrand of the second variation, as described in Section 4 above. The equations (26·8) are linear in the variables $\eta, \zeta, \eta', \zeta'$ and have as their matrix of coefficients of $\eta', \zeta'$ the matrix (6·3). Hence, for a non-singular extremal arc they have solutions

$$(26{\cdot}9) \qquad \eta' = \Pi(x, \eta, \zeta, \varphi, \psi), \qquad \zeta' = \mathrm{K}(x, \eta, \zeta, \varphi, \psi),$$

[2] The introduction of canonical variables and equations into the problems of the calculus of variations associated with theories of mechanics is ascribed by Jacobi to Hamilton. See Jacobi, *Vorlesungen über Dynamik*, p. 143. These lectures of Jacobi were delivered at the University of Königsberg during the year 1842–43. See also Hamilton, "Second Essay on a General Method in Dynamics," *Philosophical Transactions of the Royal Society of London, 1835*, p. 98. Lagrange had used differential equations of the canonical form in his theory of perturbations; see his *Mécanique analytique* (1811), p. 336.

which are linear and homogeneous in $\eta$, $\zeta$, $\varphi$, $\psi$. The Hamiltonian function for the accessory minimum problem is defined by the equation

$$(26\cdot 10)\qquad \begin{aligned} \mathfrak{H}(x,\ \eta,\ \zeta,\ \varphi,\ \psi) &= [\eta'\omega_{\eta'}+\zeta'\omega_{\zeta'}-\omega]^{\eta'=\Pi,\ \zeta'=K} \\ &= \Pi\varphi+K\psi-\omega(x,\ \eta,\ \zeta,\ \Pi,\ K)\,. \end{aligned}$$

It is homogeneous and quadratic in the variables $\eta$, $\zeta$, $\varphi$, $\psi$ and has derivatives

$$\mathfrak{H}_\varphi=\Pi\,,\qquad \mathfrak{H}_\psi=K\,,$$

$$\mathfrak{H}_x=-\omega_x\,,\qquad \mathfrak{H}_\eta=-\omega_\eta\,,\qquad \mathfrak{H}_\zeta=-\omega_\zeta\,,$$

analogous to (26·4), in which the arguments of the derivatives of $\omega$ are $x$, $\eta$, $\zeta$, $\Pi$, $K$. The canonical accessory equations have the form

$$(26\cdot 11)\qquad \frac{d\eta}{dx}=\mathfrak{H}_\varphi\,,\qquad \frac{d\zeta}{dx}=\mathfrak{H}_\psi\,,\qquad \frac{d\varphi}{dx}=-\mathfrak{H}_\eta\,,\qquad \frac{d\psi}{dx}=-\mathfrak{H}_\zeta\,.$$

Every accessory extremal $\eta(x)$, $\zeta(x)$ defines by means of the equations (26·8) a continuous solution of equations (26·11), and conversely.

Equations (26·11) have second members linear and homogeneous in $\eta$, $\zeta$, $\varphi$, $\psi$. There is one and but one solution of these equations taking given initial values $\eta_0$, $\zeta_0$, $\varphi_0$, $\psi_0$ at a value $x = x_0$. In particular, if these initial values are all zero, the unique corresponding solution is $\eta\equiv\zeta\equiv\varphi\equiv\psi\equiv 0$. If $\eta_\nu(x)$, $\zeta_\nu(x)$, $\varphi_\nu(x)$, $\psi_\nu(x)$ $(\nu = 1, \ldots, 4)$ are four linearly independent solutions of equations (26·11), then every other solution $\eta(x)$, $\zeta(x)$, $\varphi(x)$, $\psi(x)$ is expressible linearly with constant coefficients in terms of them. The determinant

$$\begin{vmatrix} \eta_1(x) & \eta_2(x) & \eta_3(x) & \eta_4(x) \\ \zeta_1(x) & \zeta_2(x) & \zeta_3(x) & \zeta_4(x) \\ \varphi_1(x) & \varphi_2(x) & \varphi_3(x) & \varphi_4(x) \\ \psi_1(x) & \psi_2(x) & \psi_3(x) & \psi_4(x) \end{vmatrix}$$

of four solutions is either identically zero or everywhere different from zero, and a necessary and sufficient condition that the four solutions be linearly independent is that it be different from zero. These are results which are well known from the theory of systems of linear differential equations.[3]

**27. A second proof of the imbedding theorem.** By means of the canonical equations the imbedding Theorem 7·1 for a non-singular extremal arc $E_{12}$ can be proved under the hypothesis that the integrand function $f$ has continuous partial derivatives of the third order, instead of the fourth order as originally presupposed in Section 3. To justify this statement it can be shown, in the first place, that the elements $(x, y, z, y', z')$ on a non-singular extremal arc $E_{12}$ are

[3] See Sec. 12, above; or, e.g., Goursat-Hedrick, *A Course in Analysis*, II, Part II, 152 ff.; Kamke, *Differentialgleichungen reeler Funktionen*, chap. v.

always contained in a region $R$ which is transformed in a one-to-one way into a region $S$ of points $(x, y, z, u, v)$ by means of the equations

$$u = f_{y'}(x, y, z, y', z'), \qquad v = f_{z'}(x, y, z, y', z') \tag{27·1}$$

in the manner described in Section 26. This is an immediate consequence of a theorem of Bolza[4] concerning implicit functions. The solutions

$$y' = P(x, y, z, u, v), \qquad z' = Q(x, y, z, u, v) \tag{27·2}$$

of equations (27·1), thus defined in $R$, will have continuous derivatives of the second order at least, since the second members of equations (27·1) have this property; and it is easy to see that the same will be true of the second members of the canonical equations

$$\frac{dy}{dx} = H_u, \qquad \frac{dz}{dx} = H_v, \qquad \frac{du}{dx} = -H_y, \qquad \frac{dv}{dx} = -H_z. \tag{27·3}$$

The existence theorems for differential equations now justify the statement that through each initial element $(x, y, z, u, v) = (x_0, a, b, c, d)$ in a sufficiently small neighborhood of the elements belonging to $E_{12}$ there passes one and but one solution of the canonical equations (27·3), $x_0$ being a fixed value on the interval $x_1x_2$. The functions defining these solutions have the form

$$\begin{aligned} &y(x, a, b, c, d), \qquad z(x, a, b, c, d), \\ &u(x, a, b, c, d), \qquad v(x, a, b, c, d); \end{aligned} \tag{27·4}$$

and the family contains $E_{12}$ for

$$x_1 \leqq x \leqq x_2, \qquad a = a_0, \qquad b = b_0, \qquad c = c_0, \qquad d = d_0,$$

where $(x_0, a_0, b_0, c_0, d_0)$ is the element $(x, y, z, u, v)$ belonging to $E_{12}$ at $x = x_0$. The functions (27·4) and their derivatives $y_x, z_x, u_x, v_x$ have continuous partial derivatives of at least the second order in a neighborhood of the values $(x, a, b, c, d)$ belonging to $E_{12}$, since the second members of equations (27·3) have this property when $f$ has continuous third derivatives, as was presupposed at the beginning of this section. The first two functions (27·4) define a four-parameter family of extremals, as was seen in Theorem 26·1.

The determinant (7·6) for this family is different from zero at $x = x_0$, since the product of the determinants

$$\begin{vmatrix} 1 & 0 & 0 & 0 \\ 0 & 1 & 0 & 0 \\ f_{y'y} & f_{y'z} & f_{y'y'} & f_{y'z'} \\ f_{z'y} & f_{z'z} & f_{z'y'} & f_{z'z'} \end{vmatrix} \begin{vmatrix} y_a & y_b & y_c & y_d \\ z_a & z_b & z_c & z_d \\ y_{ax} & y_{bx} & y_{cx} & y_{dx} \\ z_{ax} & z_{bx} & z_{cx} & z_{dx} \end{vmatrix} \tag{27·5}$$

[4] *Vorlesungen über Variationsrechnung*, p. 160, or *Mathematische Annalen*, LXIII (1906), 246. See also Mason and Bliss, "Fields of Extremals in Space," *Transactions of the American Mathematical Society*, XI (1910), 326, or Bliss, *Princeton Colloquium Lectures*, p. 20 and Sec. 8.

is the Jacobian $\partial(y, z, u, v)/\partial(a, b, c, d)$, which has the value 1 at $x = x_0$, as one readily verifies from the identities expressing the fact that the curve (27·4) passes through the initial element $(x_0, a, b, c, d)$. It follows, as in Section 12, that the determinant (7·6) is everywhere different from zero on the curves of the family (27·4).

It can be proved directly, by a method similar to that in Section 12, that the Jacobian $\partial(y, z, u, v)/\partial(a, b, c, d)$ is everywhere different from zero, since by substituting the functions (27·4) in the equations (27·3) and differentiating with respect to the constants $a, b, c, d$ we find that the columns of the Jacobian are solutions $(\eta, \zeta, \varphi, \psi)$ of the linear equations

$$(27\cdot 6)\qquad \begin{aligned} \frac{d\eta}{dx} &= \quad H_{uy}\eta + H_{uz}\zeta + H_{uu}\varphi + H_{uv}\psi\,, \\ \frac{d\zeta}{dx} &= \quad H_{vy}\eta + H_{vz}\zeta + H_{vu}\varphi + H_{vv}\psi\,, \\ \frac{d\varphi}{dx} &= -H_{yy}\eta - H_{yz}\zeta - H_{yu}\varphi - H_{yv}\psi\,, \\ \frac{d\psi}{dx} &= -H_{zy}\eta - H_{zz}\zeta - H_{zu}\varphi - H_{zv}\psi\,. \end{aligned}$$

By an argument quite similar to that for $d(x)$ in Section 12 or by known theorems concerning linear differential equations,[5] it can now be shown that the determinant of four solutions of equations (27·6) is different from zero everywhere if it is different from zero at a single point.

**28. Transversal surfaces of a field and the Hamilton-Jacobi equation.** A surface $W(x, y, z) =$ constant is said to be *transversal to the direction* $1 : y' : z'$ at a point $(x, y, z)$ if the equation

$$(28\cdot 1)\qquad (f - y'f_{y'} - z'f_{z'})\,dx + f_{y'}dy + f_{z'}dz = 0$$

is satisfied by every set of differentials $dx : dy : dz$ which satisfies the equation

$$28\cdot 2)\qquad W_x dx + W_y dy + W_z dz = 0\,.$$

This property of transversality is equivalent to saying that every curve on the surface through the point $(x, y, z)$ is transversal at that point to the direction $1 : y' : z'$, according to the definition of transversality in Section 10.

In a field $F$ the Hilbert integral

$$(28\cdot 3)\qquad I^* = \int [\,(f - pf_{y'} - qf_{z'})\,dx + f_{y'}dy + f_{z'}dz\,]\,,$$

formed with the slope functions of the field, is independent of the path in $F$. Taken from a fixed point $(x_0, y_0, z_0)$ in the field to a variable point $(x, y, z)$, its

[5] Goursat-Hedrick, *op. cit.*, p. 154, eq. (125). See also the footnote on p. 68, above.

values define a single-valued function $W(x\ y, z)$ whose derivatives are readily found, by the method used in proving Theorem 21·1, to be

$$(28\cdot4)\qquad W_x = f - pf_{y'} - qf_{z'}\,, \qquad W_y = f_{y'}\,, \qquad W_z = f_{z'}\,.$$

From the definition in the preceding paragraph it is evident that at every point $(x, y, z)$ of the field the surface $W$ = constant through $(x, y, z)$ cuts transversally the extremal of the field through that point. The surfaces $W$ = constant are called the *transversal surfaces* of the field.

Under the circumstances described in Section 26 the solutions $p$, $q$ of the last two equations (28·4) are the functions

$$(28\cdot5)\qquad p = P(x, y, z, W_y, W_z)\,, \qquad q = Q(x, y, z, W_y, W_z)\,,$$

where $P$ and $Q$ are the solutions (26·2) of equations (26·1). If these are substituted in the first equation (28·4), it follows from the definition of the function $H$ in equation (26·3) that the function $W$ satisfies the equation

$$(28\cdot6)\qquad W_x + H(x, y, z, W_y, W_z) = 0\,.$$

This is the so-called *Hamilton-Jacobi partial differential equation.*[6]

THEOREM 28·1. *In every field* F *the Hilbert invariant integral* I* *defines a function* W(x, y, z) *having continuous second partial derivatives in* F, *satisfying the Hamilton-Jacobi partial differential equation (28·6), and such that the surfaces of the one-parameter family* W(x, y, z) = constant *are transversal surfaces of the field. Conversely, let* W(x, y, z) *be a function which has continuous second partial derivatives and which defines only admissible elements* (x, y, z, u, v) = (x, y, z, $W_y$, $W_z$) *in a region* F *of* xyz-*space. Then, if* W *satisfies the Hamilton-Jacobi equation (28·6), the region* F *is a field with the slope functions (28·5), and the surfaces* W = constant *are the transversal surfaces of the field.*

It is evident that the function $W(x, y, z)$ defined by the Hilbert integral has continuous derivatives of order two at least, as stated in the theorem, since in the equations (28·4) the slope functions $p$ and $q$ of the field have by hypothesis continuous first derivatives at least.

The last part of the theorem is easily provable, since every solution $W$ of equation (28·6) with the properties described in the theorem defines slope functions $p$ and $q$ by means of equations (28·5), which with $W$ satisfy the equations (28·4). But if these equations are true, the integral $I^*$ formed with the slope functions (28·5) is the integral of $dW$ and hence is independent of the path. Thus, the region $F$ is a field with the slope functions $p$ and $q$, according to the definition of a field in Section 18.

[6] This equation was apparently first introduced by Hamilton for problems of mechanics in 1835 (*op. cit.*, p. 100). Jacobi exhibited the relationship between its solutions and those of the canonical equations (*op. cit.*, pp. 157 ff.). The corresponding partial differential equation for more general problems of the calculus of variations was suggested by Beltrami, "Sulla teoria delle linee geodetische," *Rendiconti del Reale Istituto Lombardo*, Ser. 2, I (1868), 708–18, or in his *Opere matematiche*, I, 368.

Theorems 20·1 and 22·2 give criteria for a two-parameter family of extremals to be a Mayer family. With the help of the canonical extremals (27·4) such a family can be constructed as described in the following useful theorem:

THEOREM 28·2. *If* $W(a, b)$ *is a function having continuous second derivatives in a region* A *of points* $(a, b)$ *and defining only admissible elements* $(x, y, z, u, v) = (x_0, a, b, W_a, W_b)$ *for points* $(a, b)$ *in* A, *then the two-parameter family of extremals defined by the functions*

$$y(x, a, b, W_a, W_b), \qquad z(x, a, b, W_a, W_b),$$

*found by substituting* $c = W_a$, $d = W_b$ *in the functions (27·4), is a Mayer family, according to the definition of Section 22.*

This follows because $a, b, c = W_a, d = W_b$ are the initial values at $x = x_0$ of the four functions (27·4); and for an arc on the plane $x = x_0$ the integral $I^*$ therefore reduces to the form

$$I^* = \int (f_{y'}dy + f_{z'}dz) = \int (W_a da + W_b db),$$

which is independent of the path. Theorem 20·1 now justifies the last theorem.

The transversal surfaces and extremals of a field have a variety of properties which are deducible from the two fundamental ones in the following theorem:

THEOREM 28·3. *On an extremal arc* $E_{12}$ *of a field the value of the invariant integral* $I^*$ *is equal to the value of the original integral* I. *On an arc* $C_{12}$ *lying in a transversal surface of a field the value of the integral* $I^*$ *is zero. On all arcs* $C_{12}$ *in a field* F *with end-points on the same two transversal surfaces the values of the integral* $I^*$ *are the same.*

The first of these properties follows from the fact that the differential equations

$$\frac{dy}{dx} = p(x, y, z), \qquad \frac{dz}{dx} = q(x, y, z)$$

are satisfied by every extremal of the field, and it is readily seen that on every solution of these equations the integrand of the integral (28·3) reduces simply to $f(x, y, z, p, q)$. To prove the second property we need only to note that the differentials $dx : dy : dz$ of an arc on a transversal surface $W =$ constant satisfy equation (28·2) and hence also equation (28·1), as a consequence of equations (28·4). But the first member of (28·1) is the integrand of the invariant integral (28·3). The third property of the theorem is a consequence of the equations

$$I^*(C_{12}) = \int_{C_{12}} dW = W(x_2, y_2, z_2) - W(x_1, y_1, z_1).$$

It further follows from this, with the help of the first statement of the theorem, that if there is an extremal arc $E_{34}$ of the field joining the two surfaces, then $I^*(C_{12}) = I(E_{12})$.

**29. Extremals as characteristics of a partial differential equation.** The results described in the preceding section justify the introduction of the partial differential equation (28·6) at this stage of the theory. It is evident from Theorem 28·1 that a solution $W(x, y, z, a, b)$ of equation (28·6), containing two arbitrary constants $a$ and $b$, determines a two-parameter family of fields with their corresponding two-parameter Mayer families of extremals; and the totality of these extremals should therefore form the complete four-parameter family of extremals of the problem. The proof of this result in the following paragraphs is independent of the developments in Section 28.

The function $W(x, y, z, a, b)$ in the following theorem is supposed to have continuous partial derivatives of the second order and to have its determinant $W_{ay}W_{bz} - W_{az}W_{by}$ different from zero for all points $(x, y, z, a, b)$ satisfying conditions of the form

$$(x,\ y,\ z) \text{ in a region } F, \qquad (a,\ b) \text{ in a region } A. \tag{29·1}$$

Furthermore, the sets $(x, y, z, u, v) = (x, y, z, W_y, W_z)$ corresponding to these arguments are all supposed to be admissible.

Theorem 29·1.[7] *If a function* W(x, y, z, a, b) *has the properties described above and satisfies the partial differential equation*

$$W_x + H(x,\ y,\ z,\ W_y,\ W_z) = 0 \tag{29·2}$$

*in a region (29·1), then every admissible arc* $E_{12}$ *interior to* F, *having no corners and satisfying the equations*

$$W_a = c\,, \qquad W_b = d \tag{29·3}$$

*for particular constant values* $a_0$, $b_0$, $c_0$, $d_0$, *is an extremal. Furthermore, equations (29·3) have a family of solutions*

$$y(x,\ a,\ b,\ c,\ d)\,, \qquad z(x,\ a,\ b,\ c,\ d) \tag{29·4}$$

*containing* $E_{12}$ *for values* (x, a, b, c, d) *satisfying conditions of the form*

$$x_1 \leqq x \leqq x_2\,, \qquad a = a_0\,, \qquad b = b_0\,, \qquad c = c_0\,, \qquad d = d_0 \tag{29·5}$$

*and forming a four-parameter family of extremals with properties similar to those described in Theorem 7·1.*

To prove the first part of the theorem, it should first be noted that the identities

$$\begin{aligned} W_{xa} + H_u W_{ya} + H_v W_{za} &= 0\,, \qquad & W_{xy} + H_y + H_u W_{yy} + H_v W_{zy} &= 0\,, \\ W_{xb} + H_u W_{yb} + H_v W_{zb} &= 0\,, \qquad & W_{xz} + H_z + H_u W_{yz} + H_v W_{zz} &= 0 \end{aligned} \tag{29·6}$$

are consequences of the fact that $W$ satisfies the Hamilton-Jacobi equation (29·2). They are found by differentiation of that equation with respect to $a$, $b$, $y$, $z$. If the functions

$$y(x)\,, \qquad z(x) \qquad\qquad (x_1 \leqq x \leqq x_2)$$

[7] See Jacobi, *op. cit.*, pp. 157 ff.

defining $E_{12}$ are substituted in $W_y$ and $W_z$ to form two new functions $u(x)$, $v(x)$, then it is readily seen, with the help of equations (29·3), that

$$W_{ax}+W_{ay}y'+W_{az}z'=0\ , \qquad u'=W_{yx}+W_{yy}y'+W_{yz}z'\ ,$$
$$W_{bx}+W_{by}y'+W_{bz}z'=0\ , \qquad v'=W_{zx}+W_{zy}y'+W_{zz}z'\ .$$

These equations and the set (29·6) show that $y(x)$, $z(x)$, $u(x)$, $v(x)$ satisfy the canonical equations (26·7) and hence that $E_{12}$ is an extremal.

The last part of the theorem is a consequence of the fact that the values $(x, y, z, a, b, c, d)$ belonging to $E_{12}$ form a set satisfying equations (29·3) on which the determinant $W_{ay}W_{bz} - W_{az}W_{by}$ is different from zero. Hence, equations (29·3) have solutions (29·4), including $E_{12}$ for values (29·5) and having continuous partial derivatives of at least the first order in a neighborhood of these values. The functions $u = W_x$, $v = W_y$, with (29·4) substituted, also have continuous first partial derivatives. Since from the first part of the theorem the functions (29·4) with $u = W_y$, $v = W_z$ satisfy the canonical equations (26·7), it follows that $y_x$, $z_x$, $u_x$, $v_x$ also have continuous first partial derivatives. These continuity properties are similar to those described in Theorem 7·1 but not so extensive. If the function $W$ has continuous third partial derivatives, the functions $y$, $z$, $u$, $v$ and their derivatives with respect to $x$ have continuous second partial derivatives, exactly as stated for $y$, $z$, $y_x$, $z_x$ in Theorem 7·1. By substituting the functions (29·4) in equations (29·3) and differentiating the resulting equations and $u = W_y$, $v = W_z$ with respect to $a$, $b$, $c$, $d$, it is readily seen that the product of the determinants

$$\begin{vmatrix} W_{ay} & W_{az} & 0 & 0 \\ W_{by} & W_{bz} & 0 & 0 \\ W_{yy} & W_{yz} & -1 & 0 \\ W_{zy} & W_{zz} & 0 & -1 \end{vmatrix} \begin{vmatrix} y_a & y_b & y_c & y_d \\ z_a & z_b & z_c & z_d \\ u_a & u_b & u_c & u_d \\ v_a & v_b & v_c & v_d \end{vmatrix}$$

is the determinant

$$\begin{vmatrix} -W_{aa} & -W_{ab} & 1 & 0 \\ -W_{ba} & -W_{bb} & 0 & 1 \\ -W_{ya} & -W_{yb} & 0 & 0 \\ -W_{za} & -W_{zb} & 0 & 0 \end{vmatrix}$$

and hence that the value of the functional determinant $\partial(y, z, u, v)/\partial(a, b, c, d)$ is everywhere different from zero. This establishes the fact that the final property of the family (7·5) also belongs to the family (29·4).

A brief sketch of well-known results concerning the solutions of a partial differential equation

$$(29\cdot7) \qquad F(x_1, \ldots, x_n, p_1, \ldots, p_n) = 0\ .$$

where $p_i = \partial W/\partial x_i$ $(i=1, \ldots, n)$, will indicate how the preceding results fit into the general theory of the characteristic strips of such an equation.[8] Let $W(x_1, \ldots, x_n, a_1, \ldots, a_{n-1})$ be a solution of equation (29·7) containing $n-1$ parameters $a_r$ $(r = 1, \ldots, n-1)$. It is evident that for every value $c$

$$W = W(x_1, \ldots, x_n, a_1, \ldots, a_{n-1}) - c$$

will also be a solution. If $C(a_1, \ldots, a_{n-1})$ is an arbitrarily selected function of $a_1, \ldots, a_{n-1}$ the $(n-1)$-parameter family of solutions

$$W = W(x_1, \ldots, x_n, a_1, \ldots, a_{n-1}) - C(a_1, \ldots, a_{n-1}) \tag{29·8}$$

will have an envelope determined by solving the equations

$$W_{a_r} - C_{a_r} = 0 \qquad (r = 1, \ldots, n-1) \tag{29·9}$$

for $a_1, \ldots, a_{n-1}$ as functions of $x_1, \ldots, x_n$ and substituting in equation (29·8). It is easy to see that this envelope is also a solution of equation (29·7). The curve in the space of $(n+1)$-dimensional points $(x_1, \ldots, x_n, W)$ and the strip of normals $p_1 : \ldots : p_n : -1$ associated with this curve by setting $p_i = W_{x_i}$, has the property that along it a particular solution (29·8) touches the enveloping space.[9] Such a strip is called a "characteristic strip" and is determined by equations (29·9) and (29·8). The differentials $dx_i$, $dp_i$ along a characteristic strip satisfy the equations

$$W_{a_r x_i} dx_i = 0, \qquad dp_k = W_{x_k x_i} dx_i,$$

where it is to be understood that terms containing a repeated subscript $i$ stand for the sum of these terms for $i = 1, \ldots, n$, in accordance with well-established notations of tensor analysis. By substituting $W(x, a)$ in equation (29·7) and differentiating with respect to $a_r$, $x_k$, it is found that

$$F_{p_i} W_{x_i a_r} = 0, \qquad F_{x_k} + F_{p_i} W_{x_i x_k} = 0.$$

These equations and the preceding ones show that the characteristic strips all satisfy the differential equations

$$\frac{dx_1}{F_{p_1}} = \ldots = \frac{dx_n}{F_{p_n}} = \frac{dp_1}{-F_{x_1}} = \ldots = \frac{dp_n}{-F_{x_n}}.$$

Since the function $C(a_1, \ldots, a_{n-1})$ may be selected arbitrarily, all strips determined by equations of the form

$$W_{a_r} - b_r = 0, \qquad p_i = W_{x_i}$$

are characteristic strips. The results stated in Theorems 26·1 and 29·1 now show that the extremals in the *xyzuv*-space are characteristic strips of the Hamilton-Jacobi partial differential equation.

[8] For this theory see, e.g., Goursat-Hedrick, *op. cit.*, Secs. 85–87.

[9] Goursat-Hedrick, *ibid.*, p. 262.

**30. An application in dynamics.** The differential equations

$$(30{\cdot}1) \qquad mx'' = -U_x\,, \qquad my'' = -U_y\,, \qquad mz'' = -U_z$$

are the equations of motion for a particle of mass $m$ moving in a field of force whose components are the partial derivatives of the function $-U(x, y, z, t)$ with respect to $x, y, z$. It is understood that the primes indicate derivatives with respect to the time $t$ and that the motion is described by three functions $x(t)$, $y(t)$, $z(t)$ which satisfy the equations, and which with their derivatives take initial values specified at a time $t_0$ by the initial position and velocity of the particle at that time. One may now readily verify the truth of the following theorem:

THEOREM 30·1. HAMILTON'S PRINCIPLE. *The differential equations (30·1) of the possible trajectories of the moving particle described above are also the differential equations of the extremals of the integral*

$$I = \int (T - U)\, dt\,,$$

*where* T *is the kinetic energy*

$$T = \tfrac{1}{2} m\,(x'^2 + y'^2 + z'^2)$$

*of the particle.*

The problem of the calculus of variations thus introduced is in the four-dimensional $txyz$-space instead of the $xyz$-space of the preceding sections, but for the calculation of the Euler differential equations this necessitates only a change in notation from $x$ to $t$ as independent variable and to three instead of two equations.

An important application of Hamilton's principle lies in the recognition of the fact that minimizing curves of the integral $I$ will go over into minimizing curves after a transformation of the coordinates $x, y, z$ into any other coordinates $q_1, q_2, q_3$ by means of equations of the form

$$(30{\cdot}2) \qquad x = x(q_1, q_2, q_3)\,, \qquad y = y(q_1, q_2, q_3)\,, \qquad z = z(q_1, q_2, q_3)\,.$$

Without the necessity of further analysis it is then clear that in the new coordinates the differential equations of motion are the equations

$$\frac{dT_{q_i'}}{dt} - \frac{\partial (T - U)}{\partial q_i} = 0\,,$$

where it is understood that the expressions (30·2) and their derivatives

$$x' = x_{q_i} q_i'\,, \qquad y' = y_{q_i} q_i'\,, \qquad z' = z_{q_i} q_i'$$

with respect to $t$ have been substituted in $T$ and $U$.

The canonical coordinates $t$, $q_i$, $p_i$ corresponding to $t$, $q_i$, $q_i'$ are defined by means of the equations

$$p_i = T_{q_i'}\,,$$

which are linear in the derivatives $q_i'$ and therefore easily solvable. The variables $p_i$ are called *moments*, since in terms of the original coordinates $x$, $y$, $z$ they are the products

$$p_1 = mx' , \qquad p_2 = my' , \qquad p_3 = mz'$$

of the mass times the projections $x'$, $y'$, $z'$ of the velocity. The kinetic energy $T$ is a homogeneous quadratic form in the variables $q_i'$, as in the original velocities $x'$, $y'$, $z'$; and Hamilton's function $H(t, q, p)$ is found, with the help of this fact, to have the value

$$H(t, q, p) = T + U .$$

The canonical equations of motion take the simple form

$$\frac{dq_i}{dt} = \frac{\partial H}{\partial p_i}, \qquad \frac{dp_i}{dt} = -\frac{\partial H}{\partial q_i}.$$

When the function $U$ does not contain $t$ explicitly, the same is true of $H$; and these equations imply readily the principle of the conservation of energy

$$\frac{dH}{dt} = H_{q_i}\frac{dq_i}{dt} + H_{p_i}\frac{dp_i}{dt} = 0 ,$$

which says that along every trajectory the sum $H$ of the kinetic energy $T$ and the potential energy $U$ is a constant.

The partial differential equation of Hamilton and Jacobi is

$$W_t + H(t, q, W_q) = 0 . \tag{30·3}$$

If a solution $W(t, q, a_1, a_2, a_3)$ is known, the equations of the trajectories are

$$W_{a_i} = b_i ,$$

where the $a_i$ and $b_i$ are arbitrary constants. The case when $U$ and therefore $H$ do not contain $t$ explicitly is again an important one. In this case, if $W(q, a_1, a_2, a_3)$ is a solution of the equation

$$H(q, W_q) = a_3 ,$$

then a solution of (30·3) is $W(q, a) - a_3 t$, and the equations of the extremals are

$$W_{a_1} = b_1 , \qquad W_{a_2} = b_2 , \qquad W_{a_3} = t + b_3 .$$

**31. Extremals as curves of quickest descent.** Carathéodory[10] has emphasized geometric properties of extremals which he makes the basis of a very interesting approach to the theory of the calculus of variations. In order to exhibit these properties for the three-dimensional case studied in the preceding pages, let

$$W(x, y, z) = \mu \tag{31·1}$$

[10] "Über diskontinuirliche Lösungen in der Variationsrechnung" (diss., Göttingen, 1904). See also chap. v, on "Variationsrechnung," by Carathéodory in Von Mises, *Die Differential- und Integral-gleichungen der Mechanik und Physik*, and Carathéodory, *Variationsrechnung und partielle Differentialgleichungen erster Ordnung* (1935), pp. 249–51.

be a one-parameter family of surfaces defined by a function $W(x, y, z)$ which has continuous partial derivatives of at least the second order in a region $F$ of $xyz$-space. Consider an admissible arc

$$y(x), \quad z(x) \qquad (x_1 \leqq x \leqq x_2) \tag{31·2}$$

in the region $F$, having no corners and nowhere tangent to one of the surfaces (31·1). The equation

$$W[x, y(x), z(x)] = \mu$$

then determines $x$ as a function $x(\mu)$ with a continuous derivative

$$x'(\mu) = \frac{1}{W_x + W_y y' + W_z z'}$$

on the interval $\mu_1\mu_2$ of values $\mu$ belonging to the arc (31·2), as one sees by the usual applications of implicit function theorems. The value of the integral

$$I = \int_{x_1}^{x_2} f(x, y, z, y', z')\, dx,$$

taken along the arc (31·2) from the point *1* to a variable point defined by $x_2 = x(\mu)$, is a function of $\mu$ which has the derivative

$$\frac{dI}{d\mu} = \frac{f}{W_x + W_y y' + W_z z'}. \tag{31·3}$$

At each fixed point $(x, y, z)$ this derivative is a function of $y'$ and $z'$, and the direction $1 : y' : z'$ in which it has its minimum value is called by Carathéodory the *direction of quickest descent.*

In accordance with the well-known rule for finding a minimum of a function of two variables $y'$ and $z'$, the direction of quickest descent at a point $(x, y, z)$ is determined by setting equal to zero the partial derivatives of the expression (31·3) with respect to $y'$ and $z'$. This gives the equations

$$(W_x + W_y y' + W_z z') f_{y'} - W_y f = 0,$$

$$(W_x + W_y y' + W_z z') f_{z'} - W_z f = 0,$$

which, after solving for the ratios of $W_x$, $W_y$, $W_z$, are found to be equivalent to the equations

$$f - y' f_{y'} - z' f_{z'} = \lambda W_x, \qquad f_{y'} = \lambda W_y, \qquad f_{z'} = \lambda W_z, \tag{31·4}$$

where $\lambda$ is a factor of proportionality. From the definition of transversality in Section 28 the truth of the following theorem is evident:

THEOREM 31·1. *A necessary and sufficient condition for an arc (31·2) to have the direction of quickest descent at its intersection point* (x, y, z) *with a surface of a family* W(x, y, z) = $\mu$ *is that the surface be transversal to the arc at that point.*

Let us suppose now that for a given family of surfaces $W(x, y, z) = \mu$ the equations (31·4) have a solution $(x_0, y_0, z_0, y_0', z_0', \lambda_0)$ for which the set $(x_0, y_0, z_0, y_0', z_0')$ is admissible and gives $f$ and the determinant $f_{y'y'}f_{z'z'} - (f_{y'z'})^2$ values different from zero. The functional determinant of the equations (31·4) with respect to $y', z', \lambda$, after transposing the second members, is readily found to be

$$-(W_x+W_y y'+W_z z')\,[f_{y'y'}f_{z'z'}-(f_{y'z'})^2].$$

This is different from zero at the initial set $(x_0, y_0, z_0, y_0', z_0')$, on account of the hypotheses just made, since with the help of equations (31·4) it is seen that

$$f = \lambda\,(W_x+W_y y'+W_z z')$$

at the initial set, and since $f$ is different from zero by hypothesis. From the usual implicit function theorems it follows that there exists a region $F$ of $xyz$-space in which the equations (31·4) have solutions

$$(31\cdot 5) \qquad y' = p(x, y, z), \qquad z' = q(x, y, z), \qquad \lambda = \lambda(x, y, z)$$

with continuous partial derivatives of the first order at least, and in which the sets $[x, y, z, p(x, y, z), q(x, y, z)]$ are all admissible and make $f$ different from zero. It will be supposed from now on that the family of surfaces (31·1) is a family simply covering a region $F$ in which equations (31·4) have solutions (31·5) as just described. The solutions of the first two equations (31·5) form a two-parameter family of curves in the region $F$, each cut transversally by the surfaces of the family $W = \mu$. They are called the *curves of quickest descent* of the family.

Two surfaces of the family (31·1) are said to be *geodesically equidistant* if the values of the integral $I$ on the segments of the curves of quickest descent bounded by the two surfaces are all the same. If every pair of surfaces in the family has this property, then equation (31·1) is said to define a *family of geodesically equidistant surfaces.* For such a family the following theorem can be proved:

THEOREM 31·2. *Every family of surfaces* W(x, y, z) $= \mu$ *with the properties described in the next to last paragraph in a region* F *of* xyz*-space is intersected by a two-parameter family of curves of quickest descent. A necessary and sufficient condition that the surfaces constitute a family of geodesically equidistant surfaces is that there be a representation* W(x, y, z) $= \mu$ *of the family for which* W *satisfies the Hamilton-Jacobi partial differential equation*

$$(31\cdot 6) \qquad W_x + H(x, y, z, W_y, W_z) = 0\,.$$

*In that case the curves of quickest descent are all extremals. The region* F *is a field with the slope functions of these extremals and with the family* W $= \mu$ *as its family of transversal surfaces.*

The first statement of the theorem has already been justified.

To prove the necessity of the condition in the second sentence of the theorem, it should first be noted that for a family of geodesically equidistant surfaces the values of the integral $I$, taken along curves of quickest descent from a fixed surface $W = \mu_1$ of the family to a second surface $W = \mu$, define a function $\varphi(\mu)$ with a non-vanishing derivative $\varphi'(\mu)$, since this derivative is equal at every point to the expression (31·3). Hence, if equation (31·1) is replaced by $\varphi(W) = \nu$, the value of the derivative $dI/d\nu$ is unity. Let us suppose that this change of representation for the family (31·1) has already been made, so that the value of $dI/d\mu$ in equation (31·3) is unity. By multiplying the last two equations (31·4) by $y'$ and $z'$, respectively, and adding to the first, it follows that $\lambda = 1$. If the solutions of the last two equations (31·4) for $y'$ and $z'$ are substituted in the first equation (31·4), it is found by the argument following equation (28·4) that $W$ satisfies the Hamilton-Jacobi equation (31·6).

Conversely, if $W$ satisfies equation (31·6), then the slope functions $p$ and $q$ defined by equations (28·5) will satisfy equations (28·4), which are equivalent to equations (31·4) with $y' = p$, $z' = q$, $\lambda = 1$. The solutions of the differential equations $y' = p$, $z' = q$ in (31·5) are therefore the curves of quickest descent of the family $W = \mu$. On one of these curves

$$\frac{dI}{dx} = f = W_x + W_y y' + W_z z' = \frac{dW}{dx},$$

as is seen with the help of equations (31·4) when $\lambda = 1$. It follows readily that the surfaces $W = \mu$ are geodesically equidistant. Theorem 28·1 now justifies the final statements of the theorem.

The theory of Carathéodory thus brings us back again to the theory of fields and their relationship to the partial differential equation of Hamilton and Jacobi, which was discussed in detail in Section 28.

# CHAPTER IV

## PROBLEMS IN THE PLANE AND IN HIGHER SPACES

**32. Introduction.** The preceding chapters of this book have been devoted to the simplest problems of the calculus of variations in three-dimensional space, the so-called "problems with fixed end-points." That part of the theory of the calculus of variations has been selected as an introduction because it has all the essential features of corresponding problems in higher spaces and because its results can be easily interpreted for the analogous problem in the plane. The theorems and proofs in the preceding chapters have been so formulated that they are applicable, with only slight changes in notation and wording, to problems in either two or higher dimensions.

Sections 33 and 34 of the present chapter are devoted to a summary of results for the theory of the problem in the plane. In Section 33 the theorems concerning necessary conditions and sufficient conditions for a minimum are discussed, while in Section 34 the more significant differences between problems in the plane and those in three-space are emphasized.

The remaining sections of the chapter, Sections 35–39, are devoted to the fixed end-point problem in spaces of higher dimensions. Instead of $(x, y, z)$ the coordinates used are $(x, y_1, \ldots, y_n)$, and repeated use is made of the summation convention of tensor analysis according to which a term containing a repeated literal subscript stands for a sum. Thus, the expression $y_i z_i$ is a symbol for the sum $y_1 z_1 + \ldots + y_n z_n$. The results described in Sections 35 and 36 are the analogues of those in Sections 33 and 34 and preceding chapters concerning necessary conditions and sufficient conditions for a minimum and concerning the determination of conjugate points. In Section 37 the criteria characterizing $n$-parameter families of extremals which simply cover fields, and in Section 38 the Hamilton-Jacobi theory, are summarized because of their rather marked notational variations from the corresponding parts of Chapters II and III for the three-dimensional case. In the last section of the chapter, Section 39, the theorems of Section 23 concerning the second variation are generalized, and a more comprehensive presentation of some parts of the theory of the second variation is given. This will be useful in the following chapters.

In perusing the present chapter the reader should bear in mind the fact that the results here described are in the nature of a summary. The details of proofs and theorems for the plane and higher spaces can easily be inferred from those in the preceding chapters, which should constantly be compared with the text here. The difficulties encountered in the process of making these inferences are only the notational ones involved in passing from three to two, or from three to more than three, dimensions.

**33. The problem in the plane.** The non-parametric problem of the calculus of variations in the plane is concerned with an integral of the form

$$I = \int_{x_1}^{x_2} f(x, y, y')\, dx \tag{33·1}$$

and with a class of admissible arcs

$$y(x) \qquad (x_1 \leqq x \leqq x_2),$$

on each of which the integral $I$ has a well-defined value. The problem which will be treated in this section is that of finding, in a class of admissible arcs joining two fixed points *1* and *2*, one which minimizes the integral $I$.

In order to define more explicitly a class of admissible arcs on each of which the integral $I$ has a well-defined value, it will be supposed, as in Section 3, that the integrand function $f(x, y, y')$ has continuous derivatives up to and including those of the fourth order in a region $R$ of $(x, y, y')$-space. Admissible sets $(x, y, y')$ are those interior to the region $R$, and admissible arcs for the problem here considered may be defined in a manner quite similar to the one adopted in Section 3. The analogues of the conditions discussed in Chapter I and their consequences, which may or may not hold on an admissible arc $E$, are described in the following paragraphs.

I. *An admissible arc* E *is said to satisfy the condition I if there exists a constant* c *such that the equation*

$$f_{y'} = \int_{x_1}^{x} f_y dx + c \tag{33·2}$$

*is an identity along* E.

It is evident that, when this property holds on an admissible arc $E$, the following consequences, analogous to those of the Corollaries 6·1, 6·2, and 6·3, are readily provable. On each sub-arc between corners of $E$ the function $f_{y'}$ has a derivative, and the Euler equation

$$\frac{d}{dx} f_{y'} = f_y$$

is satisfied. The right and left limits of the function $f_{y'}[x, y(x), y'(x)]$ are equal at each value of $x$ on the interval $x_1x_2$ belonging to $E$, including those values of $x$ which define corners of $E$. Furthermore, on every sub-arc of $E$ between corners on which the derivative $f_{y'y'}$ is different from zero the function $y(x)$ defining $E$ has a continuous derivative of the $n$th order, provided that the integrand function $f(x, y, y')$ has continuous partial derivatives of order $n$ near the set of values $(x, y, y')$ belonging to the sub-arc.

In accord with the notation of Section 9 we define the $E$-function of Weierstrass by the equation

$$E(x, y, y', Y') = f(x, y, Y') - f(x, y, y') - (Y' - y') f_{y'}(x, y, y').$$

Then we have the two further conditions:

II. *An admissible arc* E *is said to satisfy the condition of Weierstrass if at every element* (x, y, y′) *on* E *the condition* $E(x, y, y', Y') \geqq 0$ *is satisfied for every admissible element* $(x, y, Y') \neq (x, y, y')$.

III. *An admissible arc* E *is said to satisfy the condition of Legendre if at each element* (x, y, y′) *of* E *the derivative* $f_{y'y'}$ *is non-negative.*

To state the condition of Jacobi, we remark first that an extremal is an admissible arc defined by a function $y(x)$ having a continuous second derivative and satisfying the equation

$$f_{y'x} + f_{y'y}y' + f_{y'y'}y'' - f_y = \frac{d}{dx} f_{y'} - f_y = 0 . \tag{33·3}$$

Such an arc is said to be non-singular if the function $f_{y'y'}$ is different from zero on it. A point *3* on a non-singular extremal arc $E_{12}$ is then said to be conjugate to the initial point *1* of $E_{12}$ if *3* is a contact point of the arc $E_{12}$ with the envelope of a one-parameter family of extremals through the point *1*. This is the definition of Section 10 in terms of which the fourth condition has the following form:

IV. *A non-singular extremal arc* $E_{12}$ *is said to satisfy the condition of Jacobi if it has on it between* 1 *and* 2 *no point* 3 *conjugate to* 1.

By the methods of Chapter I it can be shown that every minimizing arc $E$ must satisfy conditions I, II, and III and that a non-singular minimizing arc $E_{12}$ without corners must further satisfy condition IV, since such an arc necessarily satisfies the condition I and is an extremal, by the proof in Section 16. Let us use again the notations $II_N$, III′, $III'_F$, IV′ for the conditions II, III, IV strengthened in the manner described in Section 16. Then the table of necessary and of sufficient conditions for a non-singular admissible arc without corners to be a minimizing arc, given at the beginning of Section 17, is applicable to the problem in the plane here considered. These results hold also for a maximizing arc, provided that the inequalities in the conditions II and III are changed in sense.

The proof of the necessity of Jacobi's condition by means of the envelope theorem, based on the geometric definition of a conjugate point given above, is subject again to the limitations described in Section 10. The analogue for the problem in the plane of the analytic definition of a conjugate point in Section 11 is given in Section 34 below.

**34. A comparison of the problems in the plane and in three-space.** While the problem in the plane described in the preceding section and the problem in three-space of Chapters I–III have many essential similarities, there are, nevertheless, some notable differences between them. In the next few paragraphs the divergences of the theorems for the two problems will be examined in some detail.

It was shown in Theorem 7·1 that every non-singular extremal arc $E$ for the problem in three-space is imbedded in a four-parameter family of extremals. An analogous discussion of equation (33·3) shows that for the plane problem a non-singular extremal arc $E$ is imbedded for values $x_1 \leqq x \leqq x_2$, $a_0$, $b_0$ in a two-parameter family of extremals

$$y(x, a, b) \tag{34·1}$$

with continuity properties analogous to those of the family of Theorem 7·1 and having the determinant

$$\begin{vmatrix} y_a & y_b \\ y_{ax} & y_{bx} \end{vmatrix}$$

different from zero along $E$.

It should also be noted that the Legendre condition III of Section 9, interpreted for the problem in the plane, is concerned with the sign of a quadratic form in a single variable, so that the condition as stated above for the plane case involves only the sign of the single coefficient $f_{y'y'}$ of the form.

One can easily verify the fact that for the problem in the plane the second variation $I_2(\eta)$ along an admissible arc $E_{12}$ has the form

$$I_2(\eta) = \int_{x_1}^{x_2} 2\omega(x, \eta, \eta')\, dx,$$

where the integrand is the quadratic form

$$2\omega(x, \eta, \eta') = f_{yy}\eta^2 + 2f_{yy'}\eta\eta' + f_{y'y'}\eta'^2. \tag{34·2}$$

The accessory minimum problem is that of finding in a class of admissible variations $\eta(x)$ vanishing at $x_1$ and $x_2$ one which minimizes $I_2(\eta)$. The Euler equation of this problem,

$$\frac{d}{dx}\omega_{\eta'} = \omega_\eta, \tag{34·3}$$

is called the "accessory differential equation." It was first used by Jacobi and is often called the "Jacobi equation."

One of the essential differences between problems in the plane and in three-space lies in the analytic method of determining conjugate points. By analogy with the definition of Section 11 we say that a point *3* on the extremal arc $E_{12}$ is conjugate to *1* if there is a solution $\eta(x)$ of equation (34·3) which vanishes at $x_1$ and $x_3$ but is not identically zero between these values. To establish the relationship between this analytic definition of a conjugate point and the geometric definition given in the preceding section, we may use arguments quite similar to those of Section 13. Consider a one-parameter family of extremals $y(x, a)$ all passing through the point *1*, containing the arc $E_{12}$ for values $x_1 \leqq x \leqq x_2$, $a = a_0$, and having the derivative $y_a(x, a_0)$ not identically zero on $E_{12}$. The function $y_a(x, a_0)$ is a solution of the accessory equation (34·3) belonging to $E_{12}$, by reasoning analogous to that of Section 12; and it vanishes at $x_1$ since all the extremals of the family pass through the point *1*. Its zeros, therefore, determine on $E_{12}$ the points conjugate to *1*. Moreover, in terms of the two-parameter family of extremals (34·1) the points *3* conjugate to *1* on $E_{12}$ are determined by the zeros of the function $\Delta(x, x_1, a_0, b_0)$, where

$$\Delta(x, x_1, a, b) = \begin{vmatrix} y_a(x, a, b) & y_b(x, a, b) \\ y_a(x_1, a, b) & y_b(x_1, a, b) \end{vmatrix}.$$

This can be readily seen by the use of the methods of Section 12.

In a manner analogous to that of Section 18 we say that a region $F$ of $xy$-space with a slope function $p(x, y)$ is a field if $p(x, y)$ has continuous first partial derivatives in $F$, if the elements $[x, y, p(x, y)]$ defined by points $(x, y)$ in $F$ are all admissible, and if in $F$ the Hilbert integral

$$I^* = \int [f\,dx + (dy - p\,dx)\,f_{y'}]$$

with the arguments $x, y, p(x, y)$ in place of $x, y, y'$ is independent of the path. It is readily seen, as in Section 18, that through every point of a field $F$ there passes one and but one solution of the differential equation of the field

$$\frac{dy}{dx} = p(x, y) \tag{34·4}$$

and that every solution of this equation is an extremal. The totality of extremals of a field may therefore be regarded as a one-parameter family.

Perhaps the most striking difference between the problem in the plane and in three-space lies in the method of constructing fields. This may be clearly seen by contrasting Theorem 20·1 with the following analogue of that theorem for the problem in the plane:

THEOREM 34·1. *If a one-parameter family of extremals*

$$y(x, a) \qquad [a_1 \leqq a \leqq a_2,\ x_1(a) \leqq x \leqq x_2(a)] \tag{34·5}$$

*is cut by a curve* C *defined on the family by a function* $x = \xi(a)$ $(a_1 \leqq a \leqq a_2)$ *and if the family and the intersecting curve have continuity properties like those described in Section 20, then every region* F *of the* xy*-plane which is simply covered by the extremals is a field with the slope function* $p(x, y)$ *of the family, provided that the derivative* $y_a(x, a)$ *is different from zero at each set of values* $(x, a)$ *corresponding to a point* $(x, y)$ *in* F.

The proof of this theorem need not be given here since it is similar to that of Theorem 20·1. In view of this result, it is important to note that, in order for a one-parameter family of extremals having suitable continuity properties to form a field in a plane region $F$, no properties of the family are required other than intersection by a curve $C$, the simple covering of the region, and the non-vanishing of the derivative $y_a(x, a)$. The reason for this is that on the intersecting curve $C$ in the plane there is only one arc joining two given points, and the Hilbert integral is necessarily independent of the path without further assumptions; whereas on an intersecting surface $(20 \cdot 3)$ in $xyz$-space there are infinitely many arcs joining two given points, and the independence property is not, in general, valid. Furthermore, a slope function $p(x, y)$ with suitable continuity properties in a simply connected region $F$ of the $xy$-plane will make the integral $I^*$ independent of the path in $F$ provided only that the solutions of the differential equation $(34 \cdot 4)$ are all extremals. In contrast to this, it has been seen in Theorem $22 \cdot 1$ that for the three-dimensional case the slope functions $p(x, y, z)$, $q(x, y, z)$ of a field must not only be the slope functions of a two-parameter family of extremals, as specified in the first two equations $(22 \cdot 1)$, but must also have the additional property required by the third equation $(22 \cdot 1)$. For the problem in the plane there is no condition analogous to that of Theorem $22 \cdot 2$, since the family $(34 \cdot 5)$ depends upon only one arbitrary constant. Every one-parameter family of extremals in the plane is a Mayer family. The reader should examine again the statements in the next to the last paragraph of Section 22.

In concluding this section the attention of the reader is also called to the very powerful and useful fundamental sufficiency theorem, Theorem $19 \cdot 2$, which with suitable simple modifications in its statement is also valid for the problem in the plane.

**35. The problem in a space of higher dimensions.** The last fixed end-point problem in non-parametric form which we shall consider in this chapter is a generalization from the problem in three-space to a problem in space of $(n + 1)$ dimensions whose points have coordinates $(x, y_1, \ldots, y_n)$. The problem to be considered involves an integral of the form

$$(35 \cdot 1) \qquad I = \int_{x_1}^{x_2} f(x, y_1, \ldots, y_n, v_1', \ldots, y_n') \, dx$$

and a class of so-called "admissible arcs"

$$y_i(x) \qquad (x_1 \leqq x \leqq x_2; \ i = 1, \ldots, n),$$

on each of which the integral has a well-defined value. The problem is then that of finding, in the subclass of admissible arcs joining two fixed points $1$ and $2$, one which minimizes the integral. A class of admissible arcs may be defined in a manner quite analogous to that of Sections 3 and 33. To simplify the theory we frequently use the notations

$$v = (y_1, \ldots, y_n), \qquad y' = (y_1', \ldots, y_n'),$$

and for the fixed end-points $1$ and $2$ the notations

$$y_1 = (y_{11}, \ldots, y_{n1}), \qquad y_2 = (y_{12}, \ldots, y_{n2}),$$

where no confusion will be caused thereby.

The first condition on an admissible arc $E$, analogous to that of Section 6, then takes the following form:

I. *An admissible arc* E *is said to satisfy the condition I if there exist constants* $c_i$ $(i = 1, \ldots, n)$ *such that along the arc* E *the equations*

$$f_{y'_i} = \int_{x_1}^{x} f_{y_i}\,dx + c_i \qquad (i = 1, \ldots, n) \tag{35·2}$$

*are identities in* x.

On an admissible arc $E$ satisfying condition I the right and left limits of the functions $f_{y'_i}[x, y(x), y'(x)]$ are equal even at corners, and on sub-arcs between corners they have derivatives such that

$$\frac{d}{dx} f_{y'_i} = f_{y_i}, \tag{35·3}$$

as we see by the methods of Section 6. In the notation now being used, the Hilbert differentiability condition, analogous to that of Corollary 6·3, asserts that, if an arc E satisfies the condition I, then on every sub-arc of $E$ on which the determinant

$$| f_{y'_i y'_k} | \tag{35·4}$$

is different from zero the functions $y_i(x)$ defining $E$ have continuous derivatives of order $m$, provided that the integrand function $f(x, y, y')$ has continuous partial derivatives of order $m$ near the set of values $(x, y, y')$ belonging to the sub-arc.

For the problem in $(n + 1)$-dimensional space here considered, the $E$-function of Weierstrass, analogous to that of Section 9, is defined by the equation

$$E(x, y, y', Y') = f(x, y, Y') - f(x, y, y') - (Y'_i - y'_i)\, f_{y'_i}(x, y, y'),$$

in which the last term represents a sum for $i = 1, \ldots, n$, as was stipulated in a preceding paragraph. The conditions of Weierstrass and Legendre have the following forms:

II. *An admissible arc* E *is said to satisfy the condition of Weierstrass if for every set of values* (x, y, y′) *belonging to* E *the condition* E(x, y, y′, Y′) ≧ 0 *is satisfied for every set* (x, y, Y′) *which is admissible and different from* (x, y, y′).

III. *An admissible arc* E *is said to satisfy the condition of Legendre if at each set of values* (x, y, y′) *belonging to* E *the condition*

$$f_{y'_i y'_k}(x, y, y')\,\pi_i \pi_k \geqq 0$$

*is valid for all sets of constants* $\pi = (\pi_1, \ldots, \pi_n)$ *such that* $\pi_i \pi_i = 1$.

A geometric definition of a conjugate point can be phrased, and the Jacobi condition formulated in terms of it, in a manner similar to that described above for the problems in the plane and in three-space. It should be remarked first that an extremal is an admissible arc defined by functions $y_i(x)$ having continuous second derivatives and satisfying the equations

$$(35\cdot 5) \qquad f_{y_i'x} + f_{y_i'y_k} y_k' + f_{y_i'y_k'} y_k'' - f_{y_i} = 0 \qquad (i = 1, \ldots, n).$$

Such an arc is said to be non-singular if the determinant (35·4) is different from zero along it. A point *3* on a non-singular extremal arc $E_{12}$ is then said to be conjugate to *1* if it is a contact point of $E_{12}$ with the envelope of a one-parameter family of extremals through the initial point *1*. It is evident that this definition is the natural generalization of those given in Sections 10 and 33 and that the fourth condition has the following form:

IV. *A non-singular extremal arc* $E_{12}$ *is said to satisfy the condition of Jacobi if it has on it between* 1 *and* 2 *no point* 3 *conjugate to* 1.

Every minimizing arc $E$ must satisfy the conditions I, II, III; and a non-singular minimizing arc $E$ without corners must further satisfy the condition IV. For a non-singular minimizing arc without corners the theorems implied in the table of Section 17 are again applicable, provided that we understand by $\mathrm{II}_N$, III′, $\mathrm{III}_F'$, IV′ the conditions II, III, IV strengthened in the manner described in Section 16 for the three-dimensional case. The theories of problems in the plane and in higher spaces are quite analogous at this stage. For a maximizing arc the inequalities in the conditions II and III must be changed in sense.

**36. The determination of conjugate points.** For the problem in $(n+1)$-dimensional space the application of the existence theorems for differential equations to equations (35·5), in analogy with the arguments of Section 7, shows that every non-singular extremal arc $E$ is imbedded for values $x_1 \leqq x \leqq x_2$, $a_i = a_{i0}$, $b_i = b_{i0}$ in a $2n$-parameter family of extremals

$$(36\cdot 1) \qquad y_i(x, a, b) = y_i(x, a_1, \ldots, a_n, b_1, \ldots, b_n)$$

with continuity properties like those in Theorem 7·1 and having the determinant

$$(36\cdot 2) \qquad \begin{vmatrix} y_{ia_k} & y_{ib_k} \\ y_{ixa_k} & y_{ixb_k} \end{vmatrix}$$

different from zero on the arc $E_{12}$. It will be seen later in this section that the family (36·1) plays an important role in the determination of conjugate points.

To define conjugate points on the arc $E_{12}$ analytically, it should first be noted that the second variation $I_2(\eta)$ along $E_{12}$, for the problem in $(n+1)$-space here considered, has the form

$$(36\cdot 3) \qquad I_2(\eta) = \int_{x_1}^{x_2} 2\omega(x, \eta, \eta')\, dx,$$

where $2\omega$ is the quadratic form

$$(36\cdot 4) \qquad 2\omega(x \quad \eta, \eta') = f_{y_iy_k}\eta_i\eta_k + 2f_{y_iy_k'}\eta_i\eta_k' + f_{y_i'y_k'}\eta_i'\eta_k'$$

with the arguments $x$, $y(x)$, $y'(x)$ belonging to $E_{12}$ substituted in the derivatives of $f$. The accessory minimum problem along $E_{12}$ is then that of finding in the class of admissible variations $\eta_i(x)$ joining the points $(x_1, 0)$ and $(x_2, 0)$ in $x\eta$-space one which makes the integral $I_2$ a minimum. The accessory equations for the arc $E_{12}$ are by definition the differential equations

$$(36\cdot 5) \qquad \frac{d}{dx}\omega_{\eta_i'} = \omega_{\eta_i} \qquad (i = 1, \ldots, n)$$

of the extremals of this accessory minimum problem.

A point $3$ on an extremal arc $E_{12}$ is conjugate to the initial point $1$ if there exists a solution $\eta_i(x)$ of the accessory equations (36·5) with elements vanishing at $x_1$ and $x_3$ but not all identically zero between these values. This analytic definition of a conjugate point is equivalent to the geometric definition in the last section above, by arguments similar to those of Section 13.

Let the functions

$$(36\cdot 6) \qquad y_i(x, a) = y_i(x, a_1, \ldots, a_n)$$

define an $n$-parameter family of extremals containing the arc $E_{12}$ for values $(x, a)$ satisfying conditions of the form $x_1 \leqq x \leqq x_2$, $a_i = a_{i0}$, having continuity properties analogous to those described in Theorem 7·2, and passing through the fixed end-point $1$ of $E_{12}$. Each of the $n$ sets of functions $y_{ia_k}(x, a_0)$ $(k = 1, \ldots, n)$ is a solution of the accessory equations (36·5). If the determinant $\Delta(x, a_0) = |y_{ia_k}(x, a_0)|$ of these solutions is not identically zero, its zeros determine the points $3$ conjugate to $1$ on $E_{12}$, in analogy with the result stated in Corollary 12·2. Furthermore, these conjugate points are also determined by the zeros of the function $D(x, x_1, a_0, b_0)$, where $D$ is the determinant

$$(36\cdot 7) \qquad D(x, x_1, a, b) = \begin{vmatrix} y_{ia_k}(x, a, b) & y_{ib_k}(x, a, b) \\ y_{ia_k}(x_1, a, b) & y_{ib_k}(x_1, a, b) \end{vmatrix}$$

formed for the family (36·1), as is stated for the three-dimensional case in Corollary 12·1.

**37. The construction of fields.** In $(n+1)$-dimensional space a field is a region $F$ of $(x, y)$-space with $n$ slope functions $p_i(x, y)$ $(i = 1, \ldots, n)$ having continuous first partial derivatives in $F$ and such that the integral

$$I^* = \int [f(x, y, p)\,dx + (dy_i - p_i dx)\, f_{y_i'}(x, y, p)]$$

is independent of the path in $F$ when the arguments $p_i$ in the integrand are the slope functions $p_i(x, y)$. The solutions of the differential equations of the field

$$\frac{dy_i}{dx} = p_i(x, y)$$

form an $n$-parameter family of extremals which simply cover $F$. These are the easily provable generalizations for $(n+1)$-space of the results in Section 18.

In Sections 20 and 22 criteria were given for determining when a region $F$ simply covered by a two-parameter family of extremals will be a field with the slope functions of the family. The analogous results for $(n+1)$-space are concerned with an $n$-parameter family of extremals defined by functions of the form

$$y_i(x, a) = y_i(x, a_1, \ldots, a_n) \tag{37·1}$$

with properties analogous to those of the family (20·1). Let us consider such a family with an intersecting $n$-space $S$ defined by equations

$$x = \xi(a_1, \ldots, a_n) = \xi(a), \quad y_i = y_i[\xi(a), a] = \eta_i(a) \tag{37·2}$$

analogous to (20·3). By an argument like that used in proving Theorem 20·1, it follows that every region $F$ in $(x, y)$-space simply covered by such a family of extremals will be a field with the slope functions of the family, provided that the determinant $|y_{ia_k}|$ is different from zero in $F$ and provided, further, that the integral $I^*$ belonging to the family is independent of the path on the intersecting space $S$. This latter property means that $I^*$ is independent of the path in the space of the parameters $(a_1, \ldots, a_n)$ when in the integrand of $I^*$ the variables $x, y$ are replaced by the functions (37·2) and the variables $p_i$ by the functions $y_{ix}[\xi(a), a]$.

If an $n$-space $S$ without singular points and with equations of the form

$$x = \xi(a_1, \ldots, a_n) = \xi(a), \quad y_i = \eta_i(a_1, \ldots, a_n) = \eta_i(a) \tag{37·3}$$

is given in advance, then an $n$-parameter family of extremals intersected by $S$ and having the integral $I^*$ of the family independent of the path on $S$ can, in general, be determined. To find such a family we may first solve for the variable $\eta_i'$ the $n$ equations

$$(f - y_i' f_{y_i'})\xi_{a_k} + f_{y_i'}\eta_{ia_k} = U_{a_k}, \tag{37·4}$$

in which the arguments $x, y, y'$ are to be replaced by $\xi(a), \eta(a), \eta'$, and in which $U(a)$ is an arbitrarily selected function of the variables $a_1, \ldots, a_n$. Implicit function theorems assure us that a solution $\eta'(a)$ of equations (37·4) will exist provided that these equations have an initial solution $(a, \eta')_0$ at which the functional determinant of their first members with respect to the variables $\eta'$ is different from zero. We suppose, then, that a solution $(a, \eta')_0$ exists such that the corresponding element $[\xi(a_0), \eta(a_0), \eta_0']$ is admissible, has its direction $1 : \eta_{10}' : \ldots : \eta_{n0}'$ not tangent to $S$, and makes the determinant $|f_{y_i'y_k'}|$ different from zero. The functional determinant of the equations (37·4) with respect to the variables $\eta_i'$ is the product of the two determinants

$$|f_{y_i'y_l'}|\,|\eta_{la_k} - \eta_l'\xi_{a_k}|$$

and is different from zero at $(a, \eta')_0$, as a result of the hypotheses just made above. The $n$-parameter family of extremals of the form (37·1), determined by the initial elements $\xi(a)$, $\eta(a)$, $\eta'(a)$, is then intersected by the $n$-space (37·3) for $x = \xi(a)$. Furthermore, the integral $I^*$ on this $n$-space is the integral of $dU$, as one sees with the help of equations (37·4), and is consequently independent of the path. Hence the slope functions of the family form a field in every region $F$ which is simply covered by the family and in which the determinant $|y_{ia_k}|$ is different from zero.

In Section 22 further criteria were deduced for slope functions and families of extremals forming fields in $xyz$-space. For the problem of the calculus of variations in $(n+1)$-space the invariant integral $I^*$ described in the preceding paragraphs has the form

$$I^* = \int [A(x, y)\,dx + B_i(x, y)\,dy_i],$$

where

$$A = f - y'_k f_{y'_k}, \qquad B_i = f_{y'_i}, \qquad y'_i = p_i(x, y).$$

By a generalization of the argument in Section 21 the conditions

$$(37\cdot5) \qquad \frac{\partial A}{\partial y_i} = \frac{\partial B_i}{\partial x}, \qquad \frac{\partial B_i}{\partial y_k} = \frac{\partial B_k}{\partial y_i}$$

are necessary for this integral to be independent of the path in a region $F$ and are sufficient if $F$ has the property of simple connectivity analogous to that defined in Section 21 for a three-dimensional region. The conditions (18·5) have as their analogues

$$(37\cdot6) \quad \frac{\partial}{\partial x}B_i - \frac{\partial}{\partial y_i}A = \frac{\partial}{\partial x}f_{y'_i} + p_k\frac{\partial}{\partial y_k}f_{y'_i} - f_{y_i} + p_k\left(\frac{\partial}{\partial y_i}B_k - \frac{\partial}{\partial y_k}B_i\right),$$

as one readily verifies. It follows then without difficulty, that the equations analogous to equations (22·1) and equivalent to (37·5) have the form

$$(37\cdot7) \qquad \begin{aligned} &f_{y_i} - f_{y'_i x} - f_{y'_i y_j} p_j - f_{y'_i y'_j}(p_{jx} + p_{jy_l} p_l) = 0, \\ &f_{y'_i y_k} + f_{y'_i y'_j} p_{jy_k} - f_{y'_k y_i} - f_{y'_k y'_j} p_{jy_i} = 0, \end{aligned}$$

in which the arguments of the derivatives of $f$ are $x, y, p$ in place of $x, y, y'$. For every field $F$ in $(x, y)$-space the slope functions $p_i(x, y)$ satisfy these partial differential equations. Conversely, a region $F$ with slope functions satisfying equations (37·7) is certainly a field if it is simply connected in the sense described above. These are the analogues of the results stated for $xyz$-space in Theorem 22·1.

For an $n$-parameter family of extremals (37·1) the analogues of the expressions (22·3) have the form

$$(37\cdot8) \qquad \frac{\partial y_j}{\partial a_i}\frac{\partial}{\partial a_k}(f_{y'_j}) - \frac{\partial y_j}{\partial a_k}\frac{\partial}{\partial a_i}(f_{y'_j})$$

in which the arguments $x, y, y'$ are the functions $x, y(x, a), y'(x, a)$ from (37·1) and the partial derivatives are taken with respect to the variables $x, a$. As in Theorem 22·2, the expressions (37·8) are constant on every extremal of the family for every pair of subscripts $i$ and $k$; and, if the family simply covers a field $F$, these constants are all zero. Conversely, if the values of the constants (37·8) on the extremals of a family (37·1) are all zero, then every simply connected region $F$ simply covered by the extremals, and having the determinant $|y_{ia_k}|$ of the family different from zero in $F$, is a field with the slope functions $p_i(x, y)$ of the family. An $n$-parameter family of extremals (37·1) whose constants (37·8) are all zero is called a *Mayer family*.

Evidently a family (37·1) whose extremals all pass through a fixed point $(x_1, y_1)$ is a Mayer family, since at the value $x_1$ the derivatives $\partial y_i/\partial a_k$ then all vanish and the constants (37·8) are all zero. It can also be proved that a family (37·1) intersected by a single space $S$ of the form (37·2) on which the integral $I^*$ of the family is independent of the path is a Mayer family. For on such an intersecting space $S$ the integrand of the integral $I^*$ has the form

$$f\,dx + f_{y'_j}(dy_j - y'_j dx) = (f\xi_{a_i} + f_{y'_j} y_{ja_i})\,da_i\,,$$

with the arguments $x, y, y'$ replaced by $\xi(a), y[\xi(a), a], y'[\xi(a), a]$. If the integral $I^*$ is independent of the path on $S$, the conditions

$$\frac{\partial}{\partial a_k}(f\xi_{a_i} + f_{y'_j} y_{ja_i}) - \frac{\partial}{\partial a_i}(f\xi_{a_k} + f_{y'_j} y_{ja_k}) = 0$$

must hold. After a rather careful computation it can be seen that the first member of this last equation reduces to (37·8). Thus we see that a region $F$ of $xy$-space simply covered by an $n$-parameter family of extremals will be a field with the slope functions of the family if the extremals of the family all pass through a single fixed point or if the family is intersected by a single space $S$ of the form (37·2) on which the integral $I^*$ of the family is independent of the path.

**38. The Hamilton-Jacobi theory.** The canonical variables $(x, y, z)$ of the problem of the calculus of variations in $(x, y_1, \ldots, y_n)$-space are defined in terms of the original variables $(x, y, y')$ by the equations

$$z_i = f_{y'_i}(x, y, y')\,. \tag{38·1}$$

We shall assume, in analogy with Section 26, that these equations establish a one-to-one correspondence between a region $R$ of interior points $(x, y, y')$, in which the function $f$ is assumed to have continuous partial derivatives of the third order, and a region $S$ of points $(x, y, z)$. We shall assume further throughout this section that the functional determinant $|f_{y'_i y'_k}|$ is different from zero in $R$. The equations (38·1) then have single-valued solutions

$$y'_i = P_i(x, y, z)\,, \tag{38·2}$$

which also define the one-to-one correspondence between the points of $S$ and $R$ and which have continuous derivatives of order $m-1$ in $S$ if $f$ has continuous derivatives of order $m$ in $R$.

A Hamiltonian function $H(x, y, z)$ may be defined by the equation

$$H=[y'_i f_{y'_i}-f]^{y'_i=P_i}=P_i z_i - f(x, y, P). \tag{38·3}$$

Its derivatives are found, by easy calculations, to be

$$H_x=-f_x(x, y, P), \quad H_{y_i}=-f_{y_i}(x, y, P), \quad H_{z_i}=P_i(x, y, z),$$

and $H$ has continuous derivatives of the third order when $f$ has that property. Every extremal arc $y_i(x)$ $(x_1 \leqq x \leqq x_2)$ in the region $R$ is transformed by equations (38·1) into an arc $y_i(x)$, $z_i(x)$ $(x_1 \leqq x \leqq x_2)$ in $S$ satisfying the canonical equations

$$\frac{dy_i}{dx}=H_{z_i}, \quad \frac{dz_i}{dx}=-H_{y_i}, \tag{38·4}$$

and conversely.

By the method of Section 27 we may prove the imbedding theorem for a non-singular extremal arc $E_{12}$ in $(x, y)$-space by means of the existence theorems for differential equations applied to the canonical equations (38·4). The results of the imbedding theorem described in Section 36 are obtained in this way even when the integrand function $f$ has derivatives only of order three, instead of four, in the region $R$ of admissible elements $(x, y, y')$. The family of extremals thus found is defined in the space of the canonical variables $x$, $y$, $z$ by functions of the form

$$y_i(x, a, b), \quad z_i(x, a, b), \tag{38·5}$$

which define the extremal arc $E_{12}$ for values

$$x_1 \leqq x \leqq x_2, \quad a_0=(a_{10}, \ldots, a_{n0}), \quad b_0=(b_{10}, \ldots, b_{n0}).$$

In a neighborhood of these values the functions $y_i$, $z_i$, $y_{ix}$, $z_{ix}$ have continuous second derivatives and have their determinant

$$\begin{vmatrix} y_{ia_k} & y_{ib_k} \\ z_{ia_k} & z_{ib_k} \end{vmatrix} \tag{38·6}$$

different from zero. It is easy to see that this determinant is the product of the determinant

$$\begin{vmatrix} \delta_{ik} & 0 \\ f_{y'_i y_k} & f_{y'_i y'_k} \end{vmatrix}$$

by the determinant (36·2), so that the non-vanishings of (36·2) and (38·6) are equivalent. The family may, in particular, be chosen so that the parameters $a$, $b$ are the initial values of $y$, $z$ at a value $x_0$, so that

$$a_i=y_i(x_0, a\ \ b), \quad b_i=z_i(x_0, a, b).$$

At the value $x_0$ the determinant (38·6) is then easily seen to be the identity determinant.

An $n$-space $W(x, y)$ = constant is transversal to a direction $1 : y'_1 : \ldots : y'_n$ at a point $(x, y)$ if the equation

$$(f - y'_i f_{y'_i})\, dx + f_{y'_i} dy_i = 0$$

is satisfied by every set of differentials $dx$, $dy_i$ for which

$$W_x dx + W_{y_i} dy_i = 0 .$$

Since in a field $F$ the integral

$$I^* = \int [(f - y'_i f_{y'_i})\, dx + f_{y'_i} dy_i]$$

formed with the slope functions $p_i(x, y)$ of the field is independent of the path, its value taken from a fixed point $(x, y)_0$ to a variable point $(x, y)$ of the field is a single-valued function $W(x, y)$ whose first derivatives are readily seen to have the values

$$(38{\cdot}7) \qquad W_x = f - p_i f_{y'_i} , \qquad W_{y_i} = f_{y'_i} ,$$

in which the arguments of $f$ and its derivatives are $x$, $y$, $p(x, y)$. Evidently the function $W$ has also continuous second derivatives in $F$. From the equations (38·7) it follows that the $n$-spaces $W(x, y)$ = constant all cut the extremals of the field transversally. They are called "transversal $n$-spaces of the field."

From equations (38·7), (38·2), and (38·1) it is evident that the slope functions of the field are the functions

$$(38{\cdot}8) \qquad p_i(x, y) = P_i(x, y, W_y) ,$$

and it follows from the definition (38·3) of the function $H$ that $W(x, y)$ satisfies the partial differential equation

$$(38{\cdot}9) \qquad W_x + H(x, y, W_y) = 0 .$$

This equation is called the "partial differential equation of Hamilton and Jacobi." From what has been said above, it is evident that every field $F$ has a one-parameter family of transversal $n$-spaces $W(x, y)$ = constant for which the function $W$ has continuous second derivatives in $F$ and satisfies the partial differential equation (38·9). One can prove, conversely, as in Section 28, that every solution $W(x, y)$ of the equation (38·9) with continuous second derivatives in a region $F$ of $(x, y)$-space defines a field in $F$ with the slope functions (38·8). These are results for fields analogous to those of Theorem 28·1. We may also easily generalize to $(n + 1)$-space the geometrical properties of a field described in Theorem 28·3.

The extremals of the problem of the calculus of variations which we are considering can be determined by a well-known method due to Jacobi if a solution

$W(x, y, \beta)$ of the equation (38·9) containing $n$ parameters $\beta = (\beta_1, \ldots, \beta_n)$ is known. By analogy with Section 29 let $W(x, y, \beta)$ be such a solution with continuous partial derivatives of the second order and with a determinant $|W_{\beta_i y_k}|$ different from zero in a region consisting of all sets $(x, y, \beta)$ for which $(x, y)$ is in a region $F$ and $\beta = (\beta_1, \ldots, \beta_n)$ in a region B. Then every admissible arc $E$ in the region $F$, defined by functions

$$y_i(x) \qquad (x_1 \leqq x \leqq x_2;\ i = 1, \ldots, n), \tag{38·10}$$

having no corners, and satisfying the equations

$$W_{\beta_i} = a_i \tag{38·11}$$

for particular constant values $(a, \beta)_0$, is an extremal. Furthermore, the equations (38·11) have a $2n$-parameter family of solutions

$$y_i(x, a, \beta) \tag{38·12}$$

containing $E$ for values $x, a, \beta$ satisfying conditions of the form

$$x_1 \leqq x \leqq x_2, \qquad a = a_0, \qquad \beta = \beta_0$$

and forming a $2n$-parameter family of extremals with properties analogous to those described in Theorem 7·1. The functions

$$z_i(x, a, \beta) = W_{y_i}[x, y(x, a, \beta), \beta]$$

with the functions (38·12) define the $2n$-parameter family of extremals in the space $S$ of the canonical variables $(x, y, z)$. These results are analogous to those of Section 29 for three-dimensional space. The attention of the reader is called to the final paragraphs of Section 29, in accordance with which the extremals are seen to be closely associated with the characteristic strips of the Hamilton-Jacobi equation (38·9).

In the preceding paragraph it was shown that, when a solution $W(x, y, \beta)$ of the Hamilton-Jacobi equation with $|W_{\beta_i y_k}| \neq 0$ is known, the extremals can be determined as solutions of the equations (38·11). Conversely, when the extremals are known, a solution $W(x, y, \beta)$ of the Hamilton-Jacobi equation (38·9) with the properties described above can be constructed. To show this we construct a family of fields in a region $F$ of $xy$-space with slope functions depending upon $n$ parameters $\beta = (\beta_1, \ldots, \beta_n)$. The invariant integral $I^*$, taken from a fixed point $(x_0, y_0)$ to a variable point $(x, y)$ in $F$, then defines a solution $W(x, y, \beta)$ of the Hamilton-Jacobi equation with the properties desired.

To justify this statement in full, consider an $n$-parameter family of extremals (37·1) cut by a space $S$, as in (37·2), on which the integral $I^*$ of the family is independent of the path, and simply covering a bounded and closed field $F$. The value of the integral $I^*$ on $S$ taken from a fixed point $a_0$ to a variable point $a$ is a function $U(a)$ with derivatives defined by equations (37·4). The equations

$$(f - y_i' f_{y_i'})\, \xi_{a_k} + f_{y_i'} \eta_{i a_k} = U_{a_k} + \beta_k, \tag{38·13}$$

which reduce to equations $(37 \cdot 4)$ for $\beta_k = 0$, have the initial solutions $(\alpha, \beta, \eta') = (\alpha_0, 0, \eta'_0)$ belonging also to equations $(37 \cdot 4)$. Consequently, at this solution the functional determinant of the first members of the equations $(38 \cdot 13)$ with respect to the variables $\eta'$ is the same as that of equations $(37 \cdot 4)$ and is therefore different from zero. Hence the equations $(38 \cdot 13)$ have solutions $\eta'(\alpha, \beta)$ such that $\eta'(\alpha_0, 0) = \eta'_0$. The extremals in $xy$-space determined by the initial values $(x, y, y') = [\xi(\alpha), \eta(\alpha), \eta'(\alpha, \beta)]$ form a $2n$-parameter family

$$(38 \cdot 14) \qquad\qquad Y_i(x, \alpha, \beta)$$

satisfying on the initial space $S$ the initial conditions

$$Y_i[\xi(\alpha), \alpha, \beta] = \eta_i(\alpha), \quad Y'_i[\xi(\alpha), \alpha, \beta] = \eta'_i(\alpha, \beta),$$

and their consequences

$$\eta'_i \xi_{\alpha_k} + Y_{i\alpha_k} = \eta_{i\alpha_k}, \qquad Y_{i\beta_k} = 0, \qquad Y'_{i\beta_k} = \eta'_{i\beta_k}.$$

From these equations it follows that the determinant analogous to $(36 \cdot 2)$ for the family $(38 \cdot 14)$ is equal on $S$ to the product

$$\left| \eta_{i\alpha_k} - \eta'_i \xi_{\alpha_k} \right| \left| \eta'_{i\beta_k} \right|.$$

The first factor is different from zero since $S$ is, by hypothesis, not tangent to the extremals. The second is also different from zero, since the functions $\eta'(\alpha, \beta)$ are solutions of equations $(38 \cdot 13)$; and the product of the determinant $|\eta'_{i\beta_k}|$ by the functional determinant of the first members of equations $(38 \cdot 13)$ with respect to the variables $\eta'$ is, therefore, the functional determinant of the second members of $(38 \cdot 13)$ with respect to the variables $\beta$, which is the identity determinant.

It is evident that the family $Y_i(x, \alpha, 0)$ is identical with the family $(37 \cdot 1)$ and that in the region $F$ the equations $y_i = Y_i(x, \alpha, 0)$ therefore have single-valued solutions $\alpha_i(x, y)$ on which the determinant $|Y_{i\alpha_k}(x, \alpha, 0)|$ is different from zero. From implicit function theorems it follows, then, that the equations

$$(38 \cdot 15) \qquad\qquad y_i = Y_i(x, \alpha, \beta)$$

have solutions $\alpha(x, y, \beta)$ with continuous second derivatives and $|Y_{i\alpha_k}| \neq 0$ for values $(x, y, \beta)$ sufficiently near to the values $(x, y, 0)$ belonging to $F$. The slope functions of the family $(38 \cdot 14)$ in $F$ have the values

$$(38 \cdot 16) \qquad p_i(x, y, \beta) = Y'_i[x, \alpha(x, y, \beta), \beta].$$

It follows readily from equations $(38 \cdot 13)$ that on $S$ the integral $I^*$ of the family $(38 \cdot 14)$ for fixed values $\beta$ is independent of the path, since its integrand is $dU + \beta_i d\alpha_i$. Hence the slope functions $p_i(x, y, \beta)$ form a field in $F$ for each fixed set of values $\beta$.

The value of the integral $I^*$ taken from a fixed point $(x_0, y_0)$ to a variable point $(x, y)$ in $F$ is a function $W(x, y, \beta)$ defined by the equation

$$W(x, y, \beta) = \int_{(x_0, y_0)}^{(x, y)} [(f - y_i' f_{y_i'})\, dx + f_{y_i'} dy_i],$$

with the arguments $x, y, y'$ in the integrand replaced by $x, y, p(x, y, \beta)$. Since the first derivatives of $W$ with respect to the variables $x, y$ have the values

$$(38 \cdot 17) \qquad W_x = f - y_i' f_{y_i'}, \qquad W_{y_i} = f_{y_i'},$$

it is clear that $W$ is a solution of the Hamilton-Jacobi equation (38·8).

To show that the determinant $|W_{y_i\beta_j}|$ is different from zero, we note first, from the second equation (38·17), that it is equal to the product $|f_{y_i'y_k'}|\ |p_{k\beta_j}|$, the first factor of which is different from zero by hypothesis. To prove the second factor different from zero, we differentiate with respect to $\beta_j$ the equations (38·15) and (38·16), with $a$ replaced by $a(x, y, \beta)$. The results are

$$0 = Y_{ia_k} a_{k\beta_j} + Y_{i\beta_j},$$
$$p_{i\beta_j} = Y'_{ia_k} a_{k\beta_j} + Y'_{i\beta_j}.$$

If there were constants $c_j$ not all zero such that $p_{i\beta_j} c_j = 0$, the last equations above would imply the equations

$$0 = Y_{ia_k} a_{k\beta_j} c_j + Y_{i\beta_j} c_j,$$
$$0 = Y'_{ia_k} a_{k\beta_j} c_j + Y'_{i\beta_j} c_j$$

which are impossible, since the determinant (36·2) for the family $Y_i(x, a, \beta)$ is different from zero. Hence we have proved the existence of a function $W(x, y, \beta)$ in terms of which the extremals are defined by equation (38·11).

It can be proved, by a method similar to the one described above, that, if a region $F$ of $xy$-space is simply covered by the extremals through a fixed point $(x_0, y_0)$ it will also be simply covered by the extremals through each neighboring point $(x_0, y_0 + \beta)$. The invariant integral in the $n$-parameter family of fields so determined over $F$ is also a function $W(x, y, \beta)$ effective for determining the extremals by means of equation (38·11).

**39. The theory of the second variation.** The theory of the second variation for the problem in $(n + 1)$-dimensional space differs from that for three-space in notation only. Let $E_{12}$ be a non-singular extremal arc for the problem in the space of points $(x, y_1, \ldots, y_n)$ formulated in Section 35.

The extremal arcs for the accessory minimum problem along $E_{12}$, formulated in Section 36, are solutions of the accessory differential equations (36·5). For two sets of variables $x, \eta, \eta'$ and $x, u, u'$ the integrand $2\omega$ of the second variation along $E_{12}$ satisfies the identity

$$\eta_i \omega_{\eta_i}(x, u, u') + \eta_i' \omega_{\eta_i'}(x, u, u') = u_i \omega_{\eta_i}(x, \eta, \eta') + u_i' \omega_{\eta_i'}(x, \eta, \eta')$$

because it is a homogeneous quadratic form in the variables $\eta, \eta'$. If we use the notation

$$J_i(\eta) = \frac{d}{dx}\omega_{\eta_i'} - \omega_{\eta_i},$$

we find easily the further relation, analogous to (23·2),

$$(39\cdot 1) \qquad \eta_i J_i(u) - u_i J_i(\eta) = \frac{d}{dx} L(\eta; u),$$

where

$$(39\cdot 2) \qquad L(\eta; u) = \eta_i \omega_{\eta_i'}(x, u, u') - u_i \omega_{\eta_i'}(x, \eta, \eta').$$

From the relation (39·1) it follows that for every pair of solutions $\eta, u$ of the accessory equations $J_i(\eta) = 0$ the expression $L(\eta; u)$ is a constant. If this constant is zero, the solutions $\eta, u$ are said to be conjugate.

Let $u_i(x)$, $u_{ik}(x)$ $(k = 1, \ldots, n)$ be $n + 1$ solutions of the accessory equations, the last $n$ of which are conjugate in pairs and have their determinant $\Delta = |u_{ik}(x)|$ different from zero on the interval $x_1 \leqq x \leqq x_2$. Then the $n$-parameter family of accessory extremals

$$(39\cdot 3) \qquad \eta_i = u_i + a_k u_{ik} \qquad (i = 1, \ldots, n)$$

forms a field for the accessory minimum problem in the portion of $(x, y)$-space bounded by the hyperplanes $x = x_1$ and $x = x_2$. This is a consequence of the fact that the expressions

$$\frac{\partial \eta_j}{\partial a_i}\frac{\partial \omega_{\eta_j'}}{\partial a_k} - \frac{\partial \eta_j}{\partial a_k}\frac{\partial \omega_{\eta_j'}}{\partial a_i},$$

analogous to (37·8), are the values of $L(u_i; u_k)$ formed for the conjugate pairs of solutions $u_{ji}$, $u_{jk}$ and are zero for every pair $i, k$. The slope functions $\pi_i(x, \eta)$ of the field are found by solving the equations (39·3) for the parameters $a_k$ and substituting in the expressions

$$\eta_{ix} = u_i' + a_k u_{ik}'.$$

They have the values

$$(39\cdot 4) \qquad \pi_i(x, \eta) = \frac{1}{\Delta}\begin{vmatrix} u_i' & u_{il}' \\ u_k - \eta_k & u_{kl} \end{vmatrix}.$$

From this result the differences $\eta_i' - \pi_i$ are seen to have the form

$$\eta_i' - \pi_i = \frac{1}{\Delta}\begin{vmatrix} \eta_i' - u_i' & u_{il}' \\ \eta_k - u_k & u_{kl} \end{vmatrix}.$$

We can now see, without difficulty, by the method used in proving Theorem 23·2, that for an arbitrary admissible arc $\eta(x)$ joining the end-points of the accessory extremal arc $u(x)$ the second variation has the value

$$(39\cdot 5) \qquad I_2(\eta) = I_2(u) + \int_{x_1}^{x_2} (\eta_i' - \pi_i)\, f_{y_i' y_k'}\, (\eta_k' - \pi_k)\, dx\,.$$

This result, analogous to that stated in Theorem 23·2, is a consequence of the remarks in the last paragraph above and of the analogue in $(x, \eta)$-space of the integral formula of Weierstrass of Theorem 19·1, since the $E$-function of Weierstrass for the integral $I_2(\eta)$ in (36·3) is

$$(39\cdot 6) \qquad E_{2\omega}(x, \eta, \eta', \pi) = (\eta_i' - \pi_i)\, f_{y_i' y_k'}\, (\eta_k' - \pi_k)\,.$$

To obtain the formula (39·5) it was supposed that there exist $n$ solutions $u_{ik}(x)$ $(k = 1, \ldots, n)$ of the accessory equations which are conjugate in pairs and have their determinant $|u_{ik}(x)|$ different from zero on the interval $x_1x_2$. If the non-singular extremal arc $E_{12}$ satisfies the condition IV′, so that the interval $x_1x_2$ has on it no value conjugate to $x_1$, then there is always such a set of $n$ solutions, as can be seen by an interpretation for $(n + 1)$-space of the proof of Theorem 23·3. Moreover, if $E_{12}$ also satisfies the condition III′, the quadratic form (39·6) for $E_{2\omega}$ is positive definite at every value $x$ on the interval $x_1x_2$, and it follows from formula (39·5) that the value $I_2(u)$ of the second variation on an accessory extremal $u$ is less than the value of $I_2$ on every other admissible arc $\eta_i(x)$ in $(x, \eta)$-space joining the ends of $u_i(x)$. If the value $x_2$ is conjugate to $x_1$ and there is no conjugate value between $x_1$ and $x_2$, then at least $I_2(u) \leqq I_2(\eta)$, provided that the condition III′ is satisfied. These sufficient conditions for the accessory minimum problem are analogues of those stated in Theorem 23·3 and Corollary 23·1 and are proved by methods quite like those of Section 23.

A very useful result in the theory of the second variation for the problem in three-space is the formula (23·10). The corresponding formula for the problem in $(n + 1)$-space is equally important. If the $n$ accessory extremals $u_{ik}(x)$ $(k = 1, \ldots, n)$ in equations (39·3) are conjugate in pairs and have their determinant $|u_{ik}(x)|$ different from zero on the interval $x_1x_2$, and if the functions $u_i(x)$ define another accessory extremal, then for every set of admissible variations $\eta_i(x)$ the formula

$$(39\cdot 7) \qquad \begin{aligned} 2\omega(x, \eta, \eta') - 2\omega(x, u, u') &= \frac{d}{dx}(\eta_i - u_i)\,[2\omega_{\eta_i'}(x, u, u') \\ &\quad + \omega_{\eta_i'}(x, \eta - u, \pi - u')] + 2\omega(x, 0, \eta' - \pi) \end{aligned}$$

is valid, where the functions $\pi_i$ are the slope functions (39·4) of the family (39·3) with the arguments $x, \eta_i(x)$. The proof of this formula is quite like that of the formula (23·10) for the three-dimensional case, though different in notation. When $u_i(x) \equiv 0$ ($i = 1, \ldots, n$), the formula takes the somewhat simpler form

$$(39\cdot 8) \qquad 2\omega(x, \eta, \eta') = \frac{d}{dx}\eta_i\omega_{\eta_i'}(x, \eta, \pi) + 2\omega(x, 0, \eta' - \pi).$$

It should be noted that the last terms in (39·7) and (39·8) have the values

$$2\omega(x, 0, \eta' - \pi) = (\eta_i' - \pi_i)\, f_{y_i'y_k'}(\eta_k' - \pi_k).$$

For the second variation the canonical variables $x, \eta_i, \zeta_i$ are defined by the equations

$$(39\cdot 9) \qquad \zeta_i = \omega_{\eta_i'}(x, \eta, \eta').$$

Since the determinant $|f_{y_i'y_k'}|$ is different from zero along the non-singular arc $E_{12}$, these linear equations in the variables $\eta_i$ and $\eta_i'$ have solutions

$$(39\cdot 10) \qquad \eta_i' = \Pi_i(x, \eta, \zeta)$$

which are linear and homogeneous in the canonical variables $\eta_i, \zeta_i$. The Hamiltonian function for the second variation is then

$$(39\cdot 11) \qquad \mathfrak{H}(x, \eta, \zeta) = [\eta_i'\omega_{\eta_i'} - \omega]^{\eta_i' = \Pi_i} = \Pi_i\zeta_i - \omega(x, \eta, \Pi).$$

It is quadratic and homogeneous in the variables $\eta_i, \zeta_i$. The canonical accessory equations, analogous to the equations (38·4) for the original problem, have the form

$$(39\cdot 12) \qquad \frac{d\eta_i}{dx} = \mathfrak{H}_{\zeta_i}, \qquad \frac{d\zeta_i}{dx} = -\mathfrak{H}_{\eta_i}$$

with second members which are linear and homogeneous in $\eta_i$ and $\zeta_i$. According to well-known theorems concerning linear differential equations, these equations have a unique solution $\eta_i(x), \zeta_i(x)$ determined by each set of initial solutions $\eta_i(x_0), \zeta_i(x_0)$. In particular, if $\eta_i(x_0) = \zeta_i(x_0) = 0$, the corresponding solution is $\eta_i(x) \equiv \zeta_i(x) \equiv 0$. For two such solutions $\eta_i, \zeta_i$ and $u_i, v_i$ the expression

$$(39\cdot 13) \qquad \zeta_i u_i - \eta_i v_i$$

is a constant, as one verifies readily directly from equations (39·12) or from the remark following equation (39·2). If this constant is zero, the two solutions are conjugate.

A system of $n$ linearly independent accessory extremals $u_{ik}(x), v_{ik}(x)$ ($k = 1, \ldots, n$) which are conjugate in pairs and have the determinant $|u_{ik}(x)|$ not identically zero is called a *coniugate system*. Such systems occur in many parts of the theory, some of which have already been noted above. We may represent by $U(x)$ and $V(x)$ the matrices of elements $u_{ik}(x)$ and $v_{ik}(x) = \omega_{\eta_i'}(x, u_k, u_k')$, where $u_k$ stands for the set $u_{ik}$ $(i = 1, \ldots, n)$. From what has been said in the preceding paragraph, it follows that to every pair of matrices of initial values $U(x_0)$, $V(x_0)$ there corresponds a pair of matrices $U(x)$, $V(x)$ whose columns $u_{ik}(x)$, $v_{ik}(x)$ $(k = 1, \ldots, n)$ form $n$ solutions of the canonical accessory equations (39·12). These $n$ solutions will form a conjugate system if, and only if, the product of the transposed matrix $\overline{U}(x_0)$ by $V(x_0)$ is symmetric. This follows because the elements of the matrix $\overline{V}U - \overline{U}V$ are the constants (39·13) belonging to the pairs of solutions $u_{ik}$, $v_{ik}$ $(k = 1, \ldots, n)$. In particular, we secure conjugate systems if we take $U(x_0) = I$, $V(x_0) = 0$, or $U(x_0) = 0$, $V(x_0) = I$, where $I$ is the identity matrix. In the former case the matrix $U(x)$ will certainly have its determinant $|U(x)| = |u_{ik}(x)|$ different from zero near $x = x_0$. We shall see in Chapter VI that the possibility of constructing a conjugate system with determinant different from zero on an interval including a given value $x_0$ has important consequences.

# CHAPTER V

## PROBLEMS IN PARAMETRIC FORM

**40. Introduction.** For the problems of the calculus of variations discussed in preceding chapters, the arcs considered have all been taken in non-parametric form. In the space of points $(x, y_1, \ldots, y_n)$, for example, they were defined by single-valued functions of the form $y_i(x)$ $(x_1 \leqq x \leqq x_2;\ i = 1, \ldots, n)$. This is in contrast to parametric arcs which have defining single-valued functions of the form $x(t)$, $y_i(t)$ $(t_1 \leqq t \leqq t_2;\ i = 1, \ldots, n)$. Evidently every non-parametric arc has a parametric representation which may be secured by setting $x = t$; but a parametric arc is representable non-parametrically only when the function $x(t)$ is properly monotonic. Since the coordinates $x, y_1, \ldots, y_n$ all play quite equivalent roles in the parametric representation of an arc, it is customary to formulate parametric problems of the calculus of variations in the space of points $(y_1, \ldots, y_n)$ in place of points $(x, y_1, \ldots, y_n)$. Frequently, when convenient, we shall, as before, use the notations $y$ and $y'$ for the sets

$$y = (y_1, \ \ldots, \ y_n), \qquad y' = (y_1', \ \ldots, \ y_n').$$

A function of parametric arcs $y_i(t)$ $(t_1 \leqq t \leqq t_2;\ i = 1, \ldots, n)$ can have geometric significance only if its value on each arc is the same for all parametric representations of the arc. The integrals to be minimized in parametric problems of the calculus of variations are therefore supposed to have values independent of the parametric representations of the arcs along which they are taken. It turns out, in Section **41** below, that their integrands are functions $f(y, y')$ which are positively homogeneous of order one in the derivatives $y_i' = dy_i/dt$. The presence of this homogeneity property complicates the theory considerably, and its consequences appear frequently. The more important formulas are listed for convenient reference in Section 43 below.

There are many problems of the calculus of variations for which a satisfactory discussion can be made only if they are taken in parametric form. A simple example of a problem of this sort is that of finding in the class of arcs joining two fixed points one which has a minimum length. It should not be inferred, however, that the theory of problems in parametric form is more important than the theory of non-parametric problems, or vice versa. Each has its applications in the places adapted to it. The variables for a problem in dynamics concerning $n$ bodies, for example, are the time $t$ and the $3n$ coordinates $(x_i, y_i, z_i)$ $(i = 1, \ldots, n)$ of the $n$ bodies of the system under consideration. The movement of the system is described by $3n$ functions $x_i(t)$, $y_i(t)$, $z_i(t)$ $(i = 1, \ldots, n)$ in which $t$ increases monotonically and which are extremals of a Hamiltonian integral analogous to that of Theorem 30·1 for the problem of one body. In the problem with $n$ bodies the roles of the variables $t$, $x_i$, $y_i$, $z_i$ are analogous to those of $x$, $y_1, \ldots, y_n$ in the preceding chapter, and the problem is evidently essentially non-parametric.

Many of the results desirable for parametric problems are deducible immediately from corresponding theorems for the non-parametric case. The places where new arguments seem to be necessary are in the discussions of the extremals, of the analogue of the Jacobi condition, and of the sufficiency theorems. The methods adopted here for the treatment of these and other parts of the theory are the ones which, at the time of writing, seemed most convenient. In the last section of this chapter, Section 54, a sketch of other possible theories is given with some comments on their applicability and relative convenience.

**41. Parametric representations of arcs.** The arcs to be considered will be defined in $(y_1, \ldots, y_n)$-space by functions of the form

$$y_i(t) \qquad (t_1 \leqq t \leqq t_2;\ i = 1, \ldots, n). \tag{41·1}$$

Such an arc will be called *regular* if the functions $y_i(t)$ have continuous derivatives $y_i'$ on the interval $t_1t_2$ and if the sum $y_i'y_i'$ is everywhere different from zero. Thus, a regular arc has no singular points. In the following pages derivatives with respect to the parameter $t$ will be designated sometimes by primes and sometimes by subscripts, and a repeated index will always indicate a sum, as is customary in tensor analysis.

The parameter may be changed by a substitution of the form $t = \varphi(\tau)$, where $\varphi(\tau)$ is continuous and has a continuous positive derivative on an interval $\tau_1 \leqq \tau \leqq \tau_2$ and takes the end-values $t_1 = \varphi(\tau_1)$, $t_2 = \varphi(\tau_2)$. The transformations of parameter used in the following sections of this chapter will all be of this sort. In particular, a transformation with a negative derivative $\varphi'(\tau)$ will not be permitted. Thus, all of the arcs considered are *directed arcs*, each with a positive sense determined by the direction in which the parameter increases along the arc.

In the $ty$-space the integral of the calculus of variations would normally have the form

$$\int_{t_1}^{t_2} f(t,\ y,\ y')\, dt. \tag{41·2}$$

But such an integral will, in general, change value when the parameter is changed; and the value of such an integral therefore cannot, in general, represent a number associated with an arc which has a purely geometric significance independent of the particular parameter chosen to represent the arc. The length of arc, for example, is a number quite independent of the parametric representation. Thus, if we are to have a theory effective for geometric problems, we must impose upon the integrand function $f(t, y, y')$ such properties as will make the value of the integral independent of the particular parameter used.

If we apply to the arc (41·1) the simple parametric transformation $t = \tau + c$ the values of the integral (41·2) in terms of the parameters $t$ and $\tau$ will be

$$(41\cdot 3) \qquad \int_{t_1}^{t} f(t,\ y,\ y_t)\,dt\,, \qquad \int_{\tau_1}^{\tau} f(\tau,\ y,\ y_\tau)\,d\tau\,,$$

where the derivatives of $y$ are represented by subscripts and the limits correspond by the transformation $t = \tau + c$. If these values are equal, then by differentiating with respect to $\tau$ we see that at each point of the arc

$$f(t,\ y,\ y_t) = f(\tau,\ y,\ y_\tau)\,.$$

But, since $y_t = y_\tau$, we have

$$f(t,\ y,\ y_t) = f(t-c,\ y,\ y_t)\,,$$

and this equation must be true for all values $c$. It follows readily that, if the integral (41·2) is to be independent of the parametric representation for all arcs (41·1), the integrand function must not contain the parameter $t$ explicitly.

A further property of the integrand function can be determined by the use of the transformation $t = \kappa\tau$ in which $\kappa$ is supposed to be a positive constant. In terms of the parameters $t$ and $\tau$ the integral (41·2) has again the values (41·3), in which $t$ and $\tau$ are now supposed not to occur explicitly in $f$. If the integrals are equal, differentiation with respect to $\tau$ and use of the relation $y_\tau = y_t\kappa$ gives the equation

$$f(y,\ y_t)\,\kappa = f(y,\ \kappa y_t) \qquad (\kappa > 0)\,.$$

THEOREM 41·1. *Necessary and sufficient conditions for an integral (41·2) to have values independent of the parametric representation on arcs of the type (41·1) are that the integrand function* f *is positively homogeneous in the variables* y′ *and does not contain the parameter* t *explicitly.*

The sufficiency of the conditions, for parametric transformations $t = \varphi(\tau)$ of the type described above, follows readily from the fact that the integrals (41·3) are equal at the initial value $\tau = \tau_1$ where $t = t_1$, and from the easily established equality of their derivatives with respect to $\tau$. In the following sections the integrals (41·2) to be considered are all independent of the parametric representation.

**42. Formulation of the parametric problem.** In view of the preliminary remarks made in the last section, we shall consider in this chapter an integral of the form

$$(42\cdot 1) \qquad I = \int_{t_1}^{t_2} f(y,\ y')\,dt\,,$$

taken along arcs defined parametrically in the $n$-dimensional space of points $y = (y_1, \ldots, y_n)$ by functions

$$(42\cdot 2) \qquad y_i(t) \qquad (t_1 \leqq t \leqq t_2;\ i = 1,\ \ldots,\ n)\,.$$

We shall suppose that there is an open region $R$ of $2n$-dimensional points $(y, y')$ with the properties:

*a*) $R$ contains only points $(y, y')$ for which $y_i'y_i' \neq 0$; and if a point $(y, y')$ is in $R$, so are the so-called ***related points*** $(y, \kappa y')$ for all values $\kappa > 0$;

*b*) $f(y, y')$ is continuous and has continuous partial derivatives up to and including those of order four in $R$;

*c*) $f(y, \kappa y') = \kappa f(y, y')$ for all points $(y, y')$ in $R$ and all values $\kappa > 0$.

An *admissible element* $(y, y')$ is one which is interior to the region $R$. An *admissible arc* (42·2) is one which is continuous and consists of a finite number of regular sub-arcs and which is, further, such that all of its elements $(y, y')$ are admissible.

The problem is then to find in the class of admissible arcs joining two given fixed points *1* and *2* in $y$-space one which minimizes the integral $I$.

For this chapter on problems of the calculus of variations in parametric form the following definitions will be found useful. *The set of points* (y, y′) *belonging to an admissible arc* E includes, by definition, not only the set of points $[y(t), y'(t)]$ $(t_1 \leqq t \leqq t_2)$ belonging to a particular parametric representation of the arc but also all of the related points $[y(t), \kappa y'(t)]$ $(\kappa > 0)$. It is evident that the set contains all of the points of every parametric representation of the arc.

The symbol $N$ will frequently be used to designate a *neighborhood* of the set of points $(y, y')$ on an admissible arc $E$. Such a neighborhood is defined to be a set of points $(y, y')$ which, if it contains a point $(y, y')$, contains all the related points $(y, \kappa y')$ $(\kappa > 0)$, and which, furthermore, contains in its interior all the points $(y, y')$ belonging to the arc $E$.

If a set $S$ of points $(y, y')$ contains all of its related points, then for every point interior to $S$ all of the related points are also interior to $S$. This follows because the $\delta$-neighborhood of $(y, \kappa y')$ is interior to $S$ whenever the $\epsilon$-neighborhood of $(y, y')$ is in $S$, provided that $\delta$ is less than $\epsilon$ and $\epsilon\kappa$. Hence, to construct a neighborhood $N$ of an arc $E$ one may take an $\epsilon$-neighborhood of a particular parametric representation of $E$ and extend it to contain all of its related points.

A *normed set* $(y, y')$ is, by definition, one for which $y_i'y_i' = 1$. When the length of arc

$$s = \int_{t_1}^{t_2} (y_i'y_i')^{1/2} dt$$

along an arc $E$ is taken as parameter, then every set $(y, y_s)$ belonging to that particular parametric representation of $E$ is normed.

**43. Consequences of the homogeneity relation.** There are a number of consequences of the homogeneity property of the integrand function $f(y, y')$ which are essential in the developments of the following pages and which can be deduced with little difficulty. It will simplify the theory if they are proved in advance. Typical properties of this sort are given in the list below. Others which will be needed are omitted because they can be derived from those in the list by very simple arguments. The functions $T_i$, $E$, $Q$, $2\omega$, $J_i$ are the analogues of others which have been used in the preceding chapters, and are defined by the first equations in which they occur. In particular, the equations $T_i = 0$ are the Euler equations of the problem, and their solutions are extremals. The tensor analysis notation for a sum is used freely here, as in the preceding chapter and in later sections. The list of homogeneity properties to be considered is as follows:

$$f(y,\ \kappa y') = \kappa f(y,\ y') \qquad (\kappa > 0). \tag{43·1}$$

$$y'_i f_{y'_i} = f, \qquad y'_i f_{y'_i y'_k} = 0. \tag{43·2}$$

$$f_{y_i}(y,\ \kappa y') = \kappa f_{y_i}(y,\ y'), \qquad f_{y'_i}(y,\ \kappa y') = f_{y'_i}(y,\ y') \tag{43·3}$$
$$f_{y'_i y'_k}(y,\ \kappa y') = \kappa^{-1} f_{y'_i y'_k}(y,\ y').$$

$$T_i = \frac{d}{dt} f_{y'_i} - f_{y_i}, \qquad y'_i T_i \equiv 0 \text{ in } y,\ y',\ y''. \tag{43·4}$$

$$\begin{aligned} E(y,\ y'\ \ Y') &= f(y,\ Y') - f(y,\ y') - (Y'_i - y'_i) f_{y'_i}(y,\ y') \\ &= f(y,\ Y') - Y'_i f_{y'_i}(y,\ y') \\ &= Y'_i [f_{y'_i}(y,\ Y') - f_{y'_i}(y,\ y')]. \end{aligned} \tag{43·5}$$

$$Q(y,\ y';\ \eta,\ \zeta) = f_{y'_i y'_k}(y,\ y') \eta_i \zeta_k \tag{43·6}$$

$$Q(y,\ y';\ \rho y',\ \zeta) = 0,$$

$$Q(y,\ y';\ \eta + \rho y',\ \zeta) = Q(y,\ y';\ \eta,\ \zeta).$$

$$2\omega(t,\ \eta,\ \eta') = f_{y_i y_k} \eta_i \eta_k + 2 f_{y_i y'_k} \eta_i \eta'_k + f_{y'_i y'_k} \eta'_i \eta'_k, \tag{43·7}$$

$$J_i(\eta) = \frac{d}{dt} \omega_{\eta'_i} - \omega_{\eta_i},$$

$$y'_i J_i(\eta) = -\eta'_i T_i = 0 \text{ along an extremal},$$

$$J_i(\rho y') = \frac{d}{dt}(\rho T_i) = 0 \text{ for all } \rho(t) \text{ along an extremal}.$$

The proofs of these relations are simple. The first equation (43·2) follows from the homogeneity property (43·1) by differentiating with respect to $\kappa$ and setting $\kappa = 1$. The second equation (43·2) follows from the first by differentiating with respect to $y'_k$. Equations (43·3) are deduced from (43·1) by differentiation with respect to the variables $y$, $y'$. To prove (43·4) we have

$$T_i = f_{y'_i y_k} y'_k + f_{y'_i y'_k} y''_k - f_{y_i},$$

from which the relation $y_i'T_i = 0$ follows with the help of the relations (43·2). The same relations justify the last two forms for the $E$-function and the formulas in (43·6) in which the symbol $\rho y'$ stands for the set $(\rho y_1', \ldots, \rho y_n')$. To prove the third equation in (43·7) we have

$$y_i'J_i(\eta) = \frac{d}{dt}(y_i'\omega_{\eta_i'}) - y_i''\omega_{\eta_i'} - y_i'\omega_{\eta_i},$$

$$\omega_{\eta_i} = f_{y_iy_k}\eta_k + f_{y_iy_k'}\eta_k', \qquad \omega_{\eta_i'} = f_{y_i'y_k}\eta_k + f_{y_i'y_k'}\eta_k';$$

and from equations easily deducible from (43·2) it follows that

$$y_i'\omega_{\eta_i'} = \eta_k f_{y_k'},$$

$$y_i'\omega_{\eta_i} + y_i''\omega_{\eta_i'} = \frac{d}{dt}(\eta_k f_{y_k'}) + \eta_k' T_k.$$

The desired equation follows at once from these results. The last equation in the set (43·7) is a consequence of the fact that when $\eta_i = \rho(t)y_i'$ we have

$$\omega_{\eta_i} = \frac{d\rho f_{y_i}}{dt}, \qquad \omega_{\eta_i'} = \frac{\rho d f_{y_i'}}{dt}.$$

It is evident from equations (43·2) that the determinant $|f_{y_i'y_k'}|$ of the bilinear form $Q$ is equal to zero. The determinant

(43·8) $$R = \begin{vmatrix} f_{y_i'y_k'} & y_i' \\ y_k' & 0 \end{vmatrix}$$

is, however, not always zero; and an admissible arc on which it remains different from zero is called a *non-singular arc* for our problem.

THEOREM 43·1. *At an admissible element* $(y, y')$ *the following three statements are equivalent: (1) the determinant (43·8) is different from zero; (2) the matrix* $\|f_{y_i'y_k'}\|$ *has rank* $n - 1$; *and (3) the matrix* $\|f_{y_i'y_k'} y_i'\|$ *has rank* $n$.

We may prove this by showing that (1) implies (2), (2) implies (3), and (3) implies (1). If the determinant (43·8) is different from zero, the matrix of its first $n$ rows must have rank $n$, and this cannot be true if the matrix in (2) has rank less than $n - 1$. Hence statement (1) implies statement (2). If the matrix in (2) has rank $n - 1$, then the equations whose coefficients are the first $n$ columns of the matrix in (3) have, from (43·2), the solutions $\rho y'$ and only these. But the set $\rho y'$ does not satisfy the linear equation whose coefficients are the last column of the matrix in (3) unless $\rho = 0$, and hence this last matrix must be of rank $n$. Consequently, statement (2) implies statement (3). Finally, suppose that the matrix in (3) is of rank $n$. The only solutions of the linear equations whose coefficients are its rows have the form $\rho y'$, 0; and these do not satisfy the linear equation whose coefficients are the last row of the determinant (43·8). Hence this determinant is different from zero. We see, therefore, that (3) implies (1), and the theorem is proved.

**44. First necessary conditions for a minimum.** The results which have been explained in preceding pages for non-parametric problems in the space of points $(x, y_1, \ldots, y_n)$ justify at once the formulation of the following conditions in the parametric case provided that we replace the independent variable $x$ by $t$. One can easily see, with the help of the formulas of Section 43 above, that these conditions are satisfied for all parametric representations of an arc $E$ if they are satisfied for one.

I. *An admissible arc* E *is said to satisfy the condition I if there exists a set of constants* $c_i$ *such that the equations*

$$f_{y'_i} = \int_{t_1}^{t} f_{y_i} dt + c_i$$

*hold along* E.

Corollary 44·1. *On every sub-arc of an admissible arc* E *without corners which satisfies condition I the functions* $f_{y'_i}$ *have derivatives and*

$$\frac{d}{dt} f_{y'_i} - f_{y_i} = 0 .$$

Corollary 44·2. *At every value* t *defining a corner of an admissible arc* E *which satisfies condition I the right and left limits of the function* $f_{y'_i}[y(t), y'(t)$ *are equal.*

The third corollary, analogous to that in Sections 6 and 35, with its proof, must be modified slightly for the parametric case, as follows:

Corollary 44·3. *If on a sub-arc without corners of an admissible arc* E *which satisfies the condition I the determinant (43·8) is different from zero, then the functions* $y_i(t)$ *defining* E *have continuous* m*th derivatives, provided that the integrand function* $f(y, y')$ *has continuous* m*th derivatives in a neighborhood of the elements* $(y, y')$ *on the sub-arc in question, and provided also that the parameter* t *is the length of arc.*

To prove this we may consider the $n + 1$ equations

$$(44\cdot1)\qquad \begin{gathered} f_{y'_i}[y(t), u] + lu_i - \int_{t_1}^{t} f_{y_i}[y(t), y'(t)]\, dt - c_i = 0 , \\ u_k u_k - 1 = 0 , \end{gathered}$$

which are satisfied, according to the condition I, by the functions $u_k = y'_k(t)$, $l = 0$, provided that $t$ is the length of arc on $E$. Along this solution the functional determinant of the first members of equations (44·1) with respect to the variables $u_k$, $l$ is twice the determinant (43·8) defined above. Furthermore, the first members of the equations (44·1) have continuous derivatives with respect to the variables $t$, $u_k$, $l$. Hence the usual theorems concerning implicit functions show that the solutions $u_k = y_k'(t)$, $l = 0$ have continuous derivatives near every value of $t$ defining a point between corners of the arc $E$ at which the determinant (43·8) is different from zero. The argument is similar to that of Section 6. Reapplying the implicit function theorems, we see, as in that section, that the functions $y_i(t)$ defining the minimizing arc in terms of its length of arc as parameter must have continuous $m$th derivatives near a value $t$ at which the determinant (43·8) is different from zero, when the function $f$ has continuous $m$th derivatives. An argument similar to that of Section 6 shows the existence of forward or backward derivatives of the $m$th order near a value $t$ defining a corner element $(y, y')$ of $E$ at which the determinant (43·8) is different from zero.

The conditions analogous to those of Weierstrass and Legendre are also immediate analogues of the conditions stated for the non-parametric case. If they are to be strengthened for the sufficiency proofs by leaving out equality signs, they must be modified slightly, however, as indicated in the following statements:

II. *An admissible arc* E *is said to satisfy the condition II of Weierstrass for the parametric problem if at every element* (y, y′) *of* E *the inequality*

$$E(y, y', Y') \geqq 0$$

*holds for every admissible element* (y, Y′) *with* $Y' \neq \kappa y'$ $(\kappa > 0)$.

III. *An admissible arc* E *is said to satisfy the condition III of Legendre for the parametric problem if at every element* (y, y′) *of* E *the condition*

$$Q(y, y'; \pi, \pi) = f_{y_i'y_k'}\pi_i\pi_k \geqq 0$$

*holds for every set* $\pi$ *with* $\pi \neq \rho y'$.

We can never exclude the equality sign in these conditions without the restrictions $Y' \neq \kappa y'$, $\pi \neq \rho y'$. For from the formulas (43·3) and (43·5) it follows that the value of the $E$-function in condition II vanishes when $Y' = \kappa y'$. Similarly, the formulas (43·6) show that the value of $Q$ in condition III vanishes when $\pi = \rho y'$, the factor $\rho$ being either positive or negative.

Theorem 44·1. *Every minimizing arc for the parametric problem with fixed end-points, formulated in Section 42, must satisfy the conditions I, II, III.*

The conclusion of this theorem is an immediate consequence of the proofs of the similar result for the problem in $(x, y_1, \ldots, y_n)$-space if we change the independent variable $x$ to $t$.

Lemma 44·1. *If an admissible arc* E *satisfies the condition III′, then there is a neighborhood* N *of the elements* (y, y′) *on* E *such that for every element* (y, y′) *in* N *the condition III′ is also satisfied.*

For the proof of the lemma we can see first that the condition III′ is equivalent to saying that the quadratic form

$$f_{y_i'y_k'}\zeta_i\zeta_k + \frac{(y_i'\zeta_i)^2}{(y_k'y_k')^{3/2}} \tag{44·2}$$

is positive definite at each element $(y, y')$ on $E$. This form is evidently positive when the variables $\zeta_i$ are not all zero and are proportional to the variables $y_i'$, as one sees with the help of the second formula (43·2). If III′ is satisfied, it is also positive for all other non-vanishing sets $\zeta_i$. Conversely, if the form (44·2) is positive definite, then the condition III′ must hold, since for each set $\pi \neq \rho y'$ there exists a non-vanishing set $\zeta_i = \pi_i - \rho y_i'$ such that $y_i'\zeta_i = 0$ and, furthermore, such that the form (44·2) is equal to $Q(y, y'; \pi, \pi)$, on account of the third formula (43·6).

If the form (44·2) is positive definite for all sets $(y, y')$ on the arc $E$, then it remains positive definite for all sets $(y, y')$ in a sufficiently small neighborhood of those on a particular parametric representation of $E$. The extension of that neighborhood to contain all its related sets is a neighborhood $N$ of the type described in Section 42. It has the property that the condition III′ is satisfied for all sets $(y, y')$ in $N$.

COROLLARY 44·4. *If at each element* (y, y′) *of an admissible arc* E *the condition III′ is satisfied, then the inequality*

$$E(y, y', Y') > 0$$

*holds for all* 3n-*dimensional sets* (y, y′, Y′) *having* $Y' \neq \kappa y'$ $(\kappa > 0)$ *and lying in a properly chosen neighborhood* $N_0$ *of the sets* $(y, y', Y') = [y(t), y'(t), y'(t)]$ *belonging to* E.

To prove this we use the formula

$$(44\cdot3)\quad \begin{aligned} &2E(y, y', Y') = \\ &(Y_i' - y_i')(Y_k' - y_k') f_{y_i'y_k'}[y, y' + \theta(Y' - y')] \quad (0 < \theta < 1), \end{aligned}$$

analogous to the expansion (9·3) for the non-parametric problem in three-space, and consider the set $S$ of points $[y(t), y'(t)]$ $(t_1 \leqq t \leqq t_2)$ belonging to a particular parametric representation of the arc $E$. There will be a $2\epsilon$-neighborhood of the set $S$ in the neighborhood $N$ of Lemma 44·1 where III′ holds. When a $3n$-dimensional point $(y, y', Y')$ is in the $\epsilon$-neighborhood of the points $[y(t), y'(t), y'(t)]$ belonging to $E$, the corresponding $2n$-dimensional point $[y', y' + \theta(Y' - y')]$ will lie in the $2\epsilon$-neighborhood of $S$ and will therefore also lie in $N$ as can easily be verified. The differences $Y_i' - y_i'$ can not be proportional to the values $y_i' + \theta(Y_i' - y_i')$ when $\epsilon$ is sufficiently small, as will be shown in the following paragraph; and the expression (44·3) is therefore positive. Hence the $\epsilon$-neighborhood described above, extended to contain all of its related sets $(y, \kappa y', \lambda Y')$ $(\kappa > 0, \lambda > 0)$, has the properties demanded in the corollary for the neighborhood $N_0$.

If the differences $Y_i' - y_i'$ were proportional to the values $y_i' + \theta(Y_i' - y_i')$, we should also have $Y_i' = \rho y_i'$ for some $\rho$. For the points $(y, y', Y')$ in the

$\epsilon$-neighborhood described above the sums $y_i'y_i'$ all have a positive minimum $m$, and absolute value $|Y_i' - y_i'| < \epsilon$. Hence we should have

$$|\rho - 1|\,|y_i'| < \epsilon, \qquad |\rho - 1| < \epsilon\left(\frac{n}{m}\right)^{1/2},$$

which would imply that $\rho > 0$ when $\epsilon$ is sufficiently small. But this would contradict the hypothesis $Y' \neq \kappa y'$ $(\kappa > 0)$ of the lemma.

LEMMA 44·2. *If the condition III holds at an admissible element* (y, y′), *then a necessary and sufficient condition that III′ holds is that the determinant*

$$\begin{vmatrix} f_{y_i'y_k'} & y_i' \\ y_k' & 0 \end{vmatrix}$$

*shall be different from zero, or, in other words, that the element* (y, y′) *be non-singular.*

The condition is necessary since, if the determinant were equal to zero, there would be constants $\pi_i$, $l$ not all zero satisfying the linear equations

$$f_{y_i'y_k'}\pi_k + y_i'l = 0\,, \qquad y_k'\pi_k = 0\,. \tag{44·4}$$

On account of the second relation (43·2) it would follow that $l = 0$, so that the values $\pi_k$ would not all be zero. Furthermore, the set $\pi$ would not be proportional to the set $y'$ because of the last equation (44·4). But from the first of these equations it would then follow that $f_{y_i'y_k'}\pi_i\pi_k = 0$, which shows that the condition III′ cannot hold when the determinant is zero.

The condition is sufficient, since if the determinant (44·4) is different from zero it follows, by arguments like those used in proving Theorem 43·1, that the same is true of the determinant of the quadratic form (44·2). This non-negative form cannot, therefore, take its minimum value zero at a set of values $\zeta \neq 0$ and must be positive definite.

**45. The extremals.** In this section we shall consider the definition of an extremal and the analogue for parametric problems of the imbedding theorems of Sections 7 and 36. An *extremal arc* is an admissible arc without corners for which there are defining functions $y_i(t)$ which have continuous second derivatives and which satisfy the Euler differential equations

$$\frac{d}{dt}f_{y_i'} - f_{y_i} = f_{y_i'y_k}y_k' + f_{y_i'y_k'}y_k'' - f_{y_i} = 0\,. \tag{45·1}$$

A non-singular extremal arc is one along which the determinant $R$ in (43·8) is different from zero. Such an arc is imbedded in a $(2n - 2)$-parameter family of extremals, as indicated in the following theorem:

THEOREM 45·1. THE IMBEDDING THEOREM. *Through a given non-singular admissible element* $(y, y') = (\eta, \eta')$ *there passes one and but one extremal arc. Furthermore, every non-singular extremal arc* $E_0$ *is a member for parameter values*

$$t_{10} \leqq t \leqq t_{20}, \qquad a_r = a_{r0}, \qquad b_r = b_{r0} \qquad (r = 1, 2, \ldots, n-1)$$

*of a* $(2n-2)$*-parameter family of extremals*

$$(45\cdot 2) \qquad y_i(t, a_1, \ldots, a_{n-1}, b_1, \ldots b_{n-1}) = y_i(t, a, b)$$

*for which the functions* $y_i$, $y_{it}$ *have continuous partial derivatives of at least the second order in a neighborhood of the values* $(t, a, b)$ *belonging to* $E_0$ *and for which the determinant*

$$(45\cdot 3) \qquad \begin{vmatrix} y_{ia_r} & y_{ib_r} & y'_i & 0 \\ y'_{ia_r} & y'_{ib_r} & y''_i & y'_i \end{vmatrix}$$

*is different from zero along* E.

To prove this theorem we may use a device which seems artificial. It is suggested by, but is somewhat different from, the procedure followed in the study of the parametric problem as a problem of Lagrange, a type of problem which will be considered in some detail in a later chapter. Let us consider the equations

$$(45\cdot 4) \qquad \frac{d}{dt} f_{y'_i} - f_{y_i} + l y'_i = 0, \qquad y'_k y''_k = 0,$$

the last of which insures a parametric representation for which the sum $y'_k y'_k$ is a constant. These equations are linear in the variables $y''$, $l$; and the determinant of coefficients of these variables is the determinant $R$ in (43·8), which is, by definition, different from zero at every non-singular element $(y, y')$. Hence the equations (45·4) have solutions

$$(45\cdot 5) \qquad y''_k = A_k(y, y'), \qquad l = L(y, y'),$$

whose second members have continuous partial derivatives of at least the second order in a neighborhood of a non-singular admissible element $(y, y') = (\eta, \eta')$ or in an $\epsilon$-neighborhood of the set of elements $(y, y')$ belonging to a particular parametric representation of a non-singular extremal arc $E$, since the integrand $f$ has continuous derivatives of the fourth order. The function $L$ is identically zero, since from the equations (43·4) and the first equation (45·4) it follows that $y'_i T_i + L y'_i y'_i = L y'_i y'_i = 0$. Consequently, every solution of the first $n$ equations (45·5) will satisfy the equations (45·4) with $l \equiv 0$ and will be an extremal arc with $y'_i y'_i =$ constant along it.

There is one and but one extremal arc through a non-singular admissible initial element $(\eta, \eta')$. This follows because the equations (45·5) have one and but one solution $y_i(t)$ through a given non-singular element $(t, y, y') = (0, \eta, \eta')$ and because every extremal arc $y_i(\tau)$ through the initial element $(\eta, \eta')$ is representable, after a change of parameter, by the unique functions $y_i(t)$ which satisfy the equations (45·5) and pass through the element $(t, y, y') = (0, \eta, \eta')$. If $\tau_1$ is the value defining the element $(\eta, \eta')$ on the extremal $y_i(\tau)$, the parametric transformation needed to justify this statement is

$$(\eta_i'\eta_i')^{1/2}t = \int_{\tau_1}^{\tau} (y_{i\tau}y_{i\tau})^{1/2}d\tau .$$

Let us suppose now that the length of arc is the parameter $t$ in terms of which the non-singular extremal arc $E_0$ of the theorem is expressed, so that the equations $y_i'y_i' = 1$ and $y_i'y_i'' = 0$ are identities along $E_0$. The existence theorems for differential equations tell us that through each element $(t, y, y') = (\tau, \eta, \eta')$ in a neighborhood of the elements of this type belonging to $E_0$ there passes a solution of the first $n$ equations (45·5) defined by equations of the form

$$y_i = \varphi_i(t, \tau, \eta, \eta'). \tag{45·6}$$

According to the existence theorems, the functions $\varphi_i$, $\varphi_{it}$ have continuous partial derivatives of at least the second order in a neighborhood of the sets $(t, \tau, \eta, \eta')$ belonging to $E_0$, since the functions $A_k(y, y')$ in equations (45·5) have such derivatives.

The curves of the family (45·6) depend upon $2n + 1$ parameters $\tau, \eta, \eta'$ but their projections in $y$-space form a $(2n - 2)$-parameter family, as we shall see in a later paragraph. To define this $(2n - 2)$-parameter family (45·2) with the properties described in the theorem, let $(\tau_0, \eta_0, \eta_0')$ be a particular fixed element on $E_0$, with $\eta_0$ standing for the set $(\eta_{10}, \ldots, \eta_{n0})$ and with a similar interpretation for $\eta_0'$. Let $\eta_i(a_1, \ldots, a_{n-1})$ $(i = 1, \ldots, n)$ be $n$ functions of $n - 1$ parameters $a_r$ $(r = 1, \ldots, n - 1)$ having continuous derivatives of at least the second order near a set $a_0 = (a_{10}, \ldots, a_{n-1,0})$ at which $\eta_i(a_0) = \eta_{i0}$, and such that the determinant

$$| \eta_{ia_r}(a_0) \quad \eta_{i0}' | \tag{45·7}$$

is different from zero. Furthermore, let $\eta_i'(b_1, \ldots, b_{n-1})$ be $n$ functions of $n - 1$ parameters $b_r$ $(r = 1, \ldots, n - 1)$ having continuous derivatives of the second order near a set $b_0 = (b_{10}, \ldots, b_{n-1,0})$ at which $\eta_i'(b_0) = \eta_{i0}'$, satisfying the equations $\eta_i'\eta_i' = 1$ and having their matrix $\|\eta_{ib_r}'(b_0)\|$ of rank $n - 1$. We shall prove that the family

$$y_i = \varphi_i[t, \tau_0, \eta(a), \eta'(b)] = y_i(t, a, b) \tag{45·8}$$

has the properties of the theorem.

To prove this we see, first of all, that the family (45·8) contains the arc $E_0$ for values $(t, a, b)$ satisfying the conditions $t_{10} \leqq t \leqq t_{20}$, $a = a_0$, $b = b_0$, where $t_{10}$ and $t_{20}$ are the parameter values defining the ends of $E_0$. Furthermore, it follows readily from the preceding paragraph that the functions $y_i(t, a, b)$ and their derivatives have the continuity properties described in the theorem. Because of the identities

$$\eta_i = \varphi_i(\tau, \tau, \eta, \eta'), \qquad \eta_i' = \varphi_{it}(\tau, \tau, \eta, \eta')$$

and their easily deduced consequences

$$\delta_{ik} = \varphi_{i\eta_k}(\tau, \tau, \eta, \eta'), \qquad 0 = \varphi_{it\eta_k}(\tau, \tau, \eta, \eta'),$$

$$0 = \varphi_{i\eta_k'}(\tau, \tau, \eta, \eta'), \qquad \delta_{ik} = \varphi_{it\eta_k'}(\tau, \tau, \eta, \eta'),$$

one sees that at the values $(t, a, b) = (\tau_0, a_0, b_0)$ the determinant $(45\cdot3)$ has the value

$$\begin{vmatrix} \eta_{ia_r}(a_0) & 0 & \eta_{i0}' & 0 \\ 0 & \eta_{ib_r}'(b_0) & y_{itt} & \eta_{i0}' \end{vmatrix}.$$

By moving the next to last column over the $n-1$ preceding ones, it follows that, except for sign, this determinant is the product of $(45\cdot7)$ by

$$|\eta_{ib_r}'(b_0) \quad \eta_{i0}'|.$$

This last determinant is also different from zero. Otherwise there would be a set of constants $c_r$, $d$, not all zero, such that

$$c_r \eta_{ib_r}'(b_0) + d\eta_{i0}' = 0.$$

If these equations are multiplied by $\eta_{i0}'$ and added, we find $d = 0$, since differentiation of the identity $\eta_i'(b)\eta_i'(b) = 1$ implies that $\eta_i'\eta_{ib_r}' = 0$. But this would imply also $c_r = 0$ $(r = 1, \ldots, n-1)$, since the matrix $\|\eta_{ib_r}'(b_0)\|$ is, by hypothesis, of rank $n-1$. Hence the determinant $(45\cdot3)$ for the family $(45\cdot8)$ is different from zero at the point defined by $t = \tau_0$ on the arc $E$. We shall see in connection with the proof of a later corollary (Corol. $48\cdot1$) that this determinant is either everywhere equal to zero or everywhere different from zero on the arc $E$. Thus the theorem is proved.

When the functions $(45\cdot2)$ are substituted in equations $(45\cdot5)$, it is evident that the second derivatives $y_{itt}$ also have continuous partial derivatives of the second order. Furthermore, if the integrand function has continuous $m$th derivatives, then the functions $A_k(y, y')$ in equations $(45\cdot5)$ have continuous partial derivatives of order $m-2$, and the same is true of the functions $y_i$, $y_{it}$, $y_{itt}$.

On a preceding page it was stated that in $y$-space the family of curves $(45\cdot8)$ contains all the arcs of the family $(45\cdot6)$. This can be seen, at least for values $(\tau, \eta, \eta')$ sufficiently near to $(\tau_0, \eta_0, \eta_0')$, by changing the parameter $t$ in $(45\cdot8)$ to $p + qt$ and noting that the $2n$ constants $a, b, p, q$ can then be determined by implicit function theory so that the initial values at $t = \tau$ of the functions $(45\cdot8)$ and their derivatives with respect to $t$ are $\eta$ and $\eta'$.

THEOREM 45·2. *The extremals through a fixed point* 0 *on a non-singular extremal arc* $E_0$ *constitute an* (n − 1)*-parameter family which may be represented by functions of the form*

$$(45\cdot 9) \qquad y_i(t, \alpha_1, \ldots, \alpha_{n-1}) = y_i(t, \alpha).$$

*The family contains* $E_0$ *for values* (t, α) *satisfying conditions of the form*

$$t_{10} \leqq t \leqq t_{20}, \qquad \alpha_r = \alpha_{r0} \qquad (r = 1, \ldots, n-1),$$

*and the extremals of the family pass through the point* 0 *for a fixed parameter value* $t = \tau_0$ *on the interval* $t_{10}t_{20}$. *The functions* $y_i$, $y_{it}$, $y_{itt}$ *have continuous partial derivatives of at least the second order in a neighborhood of the values* (t, α) *belonging to* $E_0$, *and the matrix*

$$(45\cdot 10) \qquad \begin{Vmatrix} y_{i\alpha_r} & 0 & y_i' \\ y_{i\alpha_r}' & y_i' & y_i'' \end{Vmatrix}$$

*is of rank* n + 1 *at every point of* $E_0$.

The extremals of the theorem are those of the family (45·8) for which $a_r = a_{r0}$ and with the notations $\alpha_r = b_r$. The matrix (45·10) consists of the last $n + 1$ columns of the determinant (45·3) for the family (45·8) and hence must be of rank $n + 1$ along $E_0$, by the preceding theorem.

We may determine an $(n - 1)$-parameter family of extremals through a point *0* on $E_0$ by a second method. Let us suppose that a $(2n - 2)$-parameter family of extremals (45·2) with the properties described in Theorem 45·1 has been found by any method of integrating the Euler differential equations. The equations

$$(45\cdot 11) \qquad y_{i0} = y_i(t_0, a, b)$$

have as a particular solution the values $(t_0, a, b) = (\tau_0, a_0, b_0)$, where $\tau_0$ is the value of $t$ determining the point *0* on $E_0$. At this solution one determinant, at least, of the matrix

$$\| y_{ia_r} \quad y_{ib_r} \quad y_{it} \|$$

is different from zero, since the determinant (45·3) is different from zero. This determinant can be chosen among those including the last column, since the elements of that column cannot all be zero. Hence the $n$ equations (45·11) have solutions for $t_0$ and $n - 1$ of the variables $a, b$ in terms of $n - 1$ others of the variables $a, b$, which may be denoted by $\alpha_1, \ldots, \alpha_{n-1}$. These equations therefore determine solutions $t_0(\alpha)$, $a_r(\alpha)$, $b_r(\alpha)$ reducing to $\tau_0$, $a_{r0}$, $b_{r0}$ for $\alpha_r = \alpha_{r0}$ $(r = 1, \ldots, n-1)$ and having continuous partial derivatives of at least the second order near $\alpha = \alpha_0$. The matrix of derivatives of the functions $a_r(\alpha)$, $b_r(\alpha)$ is of rank $n - 1$, since $n - 1$ of these functions are identical with the variables $\alpha_r$. The arcs defined by the functions

$$y_i[t, a(\alpha), b(\alpha)] = y_i(t, \alpha)$$

pass through the point *0* for the parameter values $t = t_0(a)$ and have the continuity properties described in the theorem, except that the constant $\tau_0$ is replaced by the function $t_0(a)$. The matrix (45·10) for the family so determined is the product of the matrices

$$\begin{Vmatrix} y_{ia_s} & y_{ib_s} & 0 & y_i' \\ y_{ia_s}' & y_{ib_s}' & y_i' & y_i'' \end{Vmatrix} \begin{Vmatrix} a_{sa_r} & 0 & 0 \\ b_{sa_r} & 0 & 0 \\ 0 & 1 & 0 \\ 0 & 0 & 1 \end{Vmatrix}$$

in which $r$ and $s$ both have the range $1, \ldots, n-1$. The product matrix is of rank $n+1$, since the last two matrices have, respectively, the ranks $2n$ and $n+1$.

A final remark concerning the matrix (45·3) of Theorem 45·1 may be of interest. The family of extremals

$$y_i(p+qt,\ a,\ b) = Y_i(t,\ a,\ b,\ p,\ q)$$

obtained from the family (45·2) by replacing $t$ by $p+qt$ contains $2n$ constants. The determinant

$$\begin{vmatrix} Y_{ia_r} & Y_{ib_r} & Y_{ip} & Y_{iq} \\ Y_{ia_r}' & Y_{ib_r}' & Y_{ip}' & Y_{iq}' \end{vmatrix} \tag{45·12}$$

is the analogue for this family of the determinants (7·6) and (36·2), which are different from zero along extremal arcs of the families (7·5) and (36·1), respectively, in the non-parametric cases. By very simple calculations it can be shown that the last determinant is equal to the determinant (45·3) multiplied by $q^{n-1}$.

**46. The envelope theorem and Jacobi's condition.** In the space of $n$-dimensional points $y$ a one-parameter family of extremals through a point *1* can be represented by functions of the form

$$y_i(t,\ \beta) \qquad [t_1(\beta) \leqq t \leqq t_4(\beta),\ \beta_1 \leqq \beta \leqq \beta_0], \tag{46·1}$$

in which $\beta$ is a single parameter and $t_1(\beta)$, $t_4(\beta)$ are functions having continuous derivatives on an interval $\beta_1 \leqq \beta \leqq \beta_0$. We assume that the functions $y_i$, $y_{it}$, $y_{itt}$ have continuous partial derivatives of at least the second order in a neighborhood of the set of values $(t, \beta)$ satisfying the conditions in the square brackets and that, at least along the arc of the family corresponding to the parameter value $\beta_0$, the derivatives $y_{i\beta}$ are not everywhere zero or proportional to the derivatives $y_i'$. This last assumption is made in order to be sure that the arcs of the family for values $\beta$ near $\beta_0$ are not identical with the arc corresponding to $\beta_0$.

For the parameter values $t_1(\beta)$ the arcs (46·1) are all supposed to pass through the point *1* with coordinates $(y_{11}, \ldots, y_{n1})$, so that the equations

$$y_{i1} = y_i[t_1(\beta),\ \beta] \qquad (\beta_1 \leqq \beta \leqq \beta_0) \tag{46·2}$$

are identities in $\beta$. The arc $D$ defined by the equations

$$y_i = y_i\,[t_4(\beta)\,,\ \beta] = Y_i(\beta) \qquad (\beta_1 \leqq \beta \leqq \beta_0) \tag{46·3}$$

will be an envelope of the extremals of the family (46·1), provided that equations of the form

$$Y_i'(\beta) = \kappa(\beta)\, y_i'\,[t_4(\beta)\,,\ \beta] \tag{46·4}$$

hold, where $\kappa(\beta)$ is positive on the interval $\beta_1 \leqq \beta < \beta_0$. On that interval the arc $D$ has no singular point, since the derivatives $y_i'$ never vanish simultaneously, but it may have a singularity at $\beta = \beta_0$ if $\kappa(\beta_0) = 0$.

It is easy to see that the auxiliary theorems of Section 8, extended to the problem in $(x, y_1, \ldots, y_n)$-space, are applicable to one-parameter families of extremals for the parametric problem when we change the name of the independent variable from $x$ to $t$. If in Figure 10·1 we change the number 6 to 3 and designate the arc of the family (46·1) which corresponds to $\beta_0$ by $E_{13}$, then, since the arc $C$ of Corollary 8·1 is now the point *1*, we have the equation

$$I(E_{13}) - I(E_{14}) = I^*(D_{43})\,.$$

In the invariant integral $I^*$ for the parametric case the coefficient $f - y_i'f_{y_i'}$ of $dt$ is zero on account of the first formula (43·2). With the help of the homogeneity property (43·3) of the derivatives $f_{y_i'}$ and (43·2) again, we find $f_{y_i'}(Y, y') = f_{y_i'}(Y, Y')$ and

$$I^*(D_{43}) = \int_{\beta_4}^{\beta_3} f_{y_i'}(Y,\ Y')\, Y_i'(\beta)\, d\beta$$

$$= \int_{\beta_4}^{\beta_3} f(Y,\ Y')\, d\beta = I(D_{43})\,.$$

Hence we have the following theorem:

THEOREM 46·1. THE ENVELOPE THEOREM. *For a one-parameter family of extremals (46·1) through a fixed point* 1, *having an envelope* D *as shown in Figure 10·1 with* 6 *replaced by* 3, *the equation*

$$I(E_{13}) = I(E_{14}) + I(D_{43})$$

*holds for every point* 4 *sufficiently near to* 3 *on* D.

If we define a *point conjugate to the point 1* on an extremal arc $E_{12}$ as a point of contact *3* of $E_{12}$ with an envelope $D$ of a one-parameter family of extremals through the point *1*, such as is described above, then we may formulate a property for non-singular extremals as follows:

IV. *A non-singular extremal arc* $E_{12}$ *is said to satisfy the condition IV of Jacobi if it has on it between* 1 *and* 2 *no point* 3 *conjugate to* 1.

By a method similar to that of Section 10 for the non-parametric case we can now prove the following theorem:

THEOREM 46·2. *Every non-singular minimizing arc* E *without corners must satisfy the condition IV of Jacobi.*

A non-singular minimizing arc without corners is always an extremal, by Theorem 44·1 and Corollary 44·3 to the condition I. By the envelope theorem the value of the integral $I$ along the composite arc $E_{14} + D_{43} + E_{32}$, in Figure 10·1 with *6* replaced by *3*, is the same as that along $E_{12}$. This composite arc is not an extremal, since by our hypothesis it is not identical with $E_{12}$ for small values of $\beta$ and since $E_{12}$ itself is the only extremal arc through the element $(y, y')$ belonging to $E_{12}$ at the point *3*. Hence, in every neighborhood of the composite arc there are other arcs with the same end-points giving the integral $I$ a smaller value than that given by the composite arc, and the same is clearly true of $E_{12}$ itself.

**47. Analytic proof of the condition of Jacobi.** A non-singular minimizing arc $E_{12}$ without corners for the parametric problem is necessarily an extremal, as was stated in the last paragraph. The second variation along such an arc has the form

$$I_2(\eta) = \int_{t_1}^{t_2} 2\omega(\eta, \eta')\, dt, \tag{47·1}$$

where $2\omega$ is the quadratic form (43·7). It can be proved, as in Section 4 for the non-parametric case, that for a minimizing arc the second variation $I_2(\eta)$ must be non-negative in the class of admissible sets $\eta_i(t)$ for which $\eta_i(t_1) = \eta_i(t_2) = 0$.

The accessory minimum problem is that of minimizing $I_2(\eta)$ in the class of admissible variations with elements vanishing at $t_1$ and $t_2$. The differential equations of the accessory extremals are the accessory equations

$$J_i(\eta) = \frac{d}{dt}\omega_{\eta'_i} - \omega_{\eta_i} = 0\,. \tag{47·2}$$

In the discussion of the Jacobi condition for parametric problems it turns out that the solutions $\eta_i(t)$ of these equations which satisfy the relation $y'_i\eta_i = 0$ play an important auxiliary role. Such solutions are called *normal solutions* of the accessory equations.

Definition of a Conjugate Point. *On a non-singular extremal arc* $E_{12}$ *a point* 3 *is said to be conjugate to the initial point* 1 *if there exist constants* $\rho_1, \rho_2$ *and a solution of the accessory equations with functions* $\eta_i(t)$ *not everywhere proportional to the functions* $y'_i(t)$ *on the interval* $t_1t_2$ *but such that*

$$\eta_i(t_1) = \rho_1 y'_i(t_1)\,, \qquad \eta_i(t_3) = \rho_3 y'_i(t_3)\,.$$

This definition is entirely equivalent to saying that there exists a normal solution $u_i(t)$ of the accessory equations vanishing at $t_1$ and $t_3$ but not identically zero on the interval $t_1t_3$. The functions $u_i(t) = \eta_i(t) - \rho(t)y'_i(t)$ with $\rho = y'_k\eta_k/y'_ky'_k$ are, in fact, such a normal solution, since the equations (47·2) are linear, and the fourth equation (43·7) shows that the set $\rho y'_i$ is also a solution.

If we use this definition in place of the geometric definition of a conjugate point in Section 46, we can again prove Theorem 46·2, which says that on a non-singular minimizing arc $E_{12}$ without corners there can be no point *3* conjugate to *1* between *1* and *2*. To establish this result, suppose that there were a conjugate point *3* between *1* and *2*, and consider the variations $\eta_i(t)$ defined by the conditions

$$\eta_i(t) = u_i(t) \qquad (t_1 \leqq t \leqq t_3)$$

$$\eta_i(t) = 0 \qquad (t_3 \leqq t \leqq t_2),$$

where $u_i(t)$ is a normal solution not identically zero on the interval $t_1t_2$ but vanishing at $t_1$ and $t_3$. The functions $\eta_i$ so defined would give to the second variation the value zero but would not minimize it, as one sees by an argument like that of Section 11, supplemented by the following additional remark. The corner condition $\omega_{\eta_i'}(t_3 - 0) = \omega_{\eta_i'}(t_3 + 0)$ and the relations $y_i'u_i \equiv 0$, $u_i(t_3) = 0$ would imply in the present case that at $t = t_3$

$$f_{y_i'y_k'}u_k' = 0, \qquad \frac{d}{dt}(y_k'u_k) = y_k'u_k' = 0.$$

These equations, however, could not be satisfied, since by Theorem 43·1 they would require the derivatives $u_k'$ to vanish at $t = t_3$, as well as the functions $u_k$. This is not possible if the functions $u_i$ defining the normal solution are not all identically zero, as will be seen in the first paragraph of Section 48 below.

**48. The determination of conjugate points.** Every normal solution of the accessory equations for a non-singular extremal arc $E_{12}$ satisfies with $\lambda = 0$ the equations

$$J_i(\eta) + \lambda y_i' = 0, \qquad (y_i'\eta_i)'' = 0, \tag{48·1}$$

which are linear and homogeneous in the variables $\eta_i$, $\eta_i'$, $\eta_i''$, $\lambda$. These equations can be solved for the variables $\eta_i''$, $\lambda$, since the determinant of the coefficients of the $\eta_i''$ and $\lambda$ is the determinant (43·8). On account of the identity $y_i'J_i(\eta) = 0$, from (43·7), the solution $\lambda$ is identically zero. The solutions for $\eta_i''$ have the form

$$\eta_i'' = A_i(t, \eta, \eta'), \tag{48·2}$$

in which the functions $A_i$ are linear and homogeneous in $\eta_i$ and $\eta_i'$ with coefficients functions of $t$ having continuous derivatives of at least the first order on the interval $t_1t_2$. Every solution $\eta_i(t)$ of equations (48·2) is a solution with $\lambda = 0$ of equations (48·1), and conversely. From well-known theorems concerning linear differential equations a solution of equations (48·2) is identically zero if it vanishes with its first derivatives at a single point $t_0$. This is in particular true of a normal solution of the accessory equations (47·2).

LEMMA 48·1. *For every set* $\eta_{i\sigma}(t)$ $(\sigma = 1, \ldots, 2n - 2)$ *consisting of* $2n - 2$ *solutions of the accessory equations the determinant*

$$d(t) = \begin{vmatrix} \eta_{i\sigma} & y_i' & 0 \\ \eta_{i\sigma}' & y_i'' & y_i' \end{vmatrix} \tag{48·3}$$

*is either identically zero or everywhere different from zero.* When $d(t) \neq 0$ the system $\eta_{i\sigma}$ is called a *fundamental* system of solutions of the accessory equations.

To justify the lemma we note first, with the help of the fourth equation (43·7), that when $\varphi(t) = 1/(y_i' y_i')$ the sets $\varphi y_i'$ and $t\varphi y_i'$ form two independent solutions of the equations (48·1) and therefore also of (48·2). For $\sigma = 1, \ldots,$ $2n - 2$ the functions $u_{i\sigma} = \eta_{i\sigma} - \rho_\sigma y_i'$ with $\rho_\sigma = y_k'\eta_{k\sigma}/y_i'y_i'$ form $2n - 2$ normal solutions of the accessory equations, and all the columns of the determinant

$$(48\cdot4) \qquad \begin{vmatrix} u_{i\sigma} & \varphi y_i' & t\varphi y_i' \\ u_{i\sigma}' & (\varphi y_i')' & (t\varphi y_i')' \end{vmatrix}$$

are therefore the elements and their derivatives of solutions of the equations (48·2). From well-known theorems concerning linear differential equations such a determinant is either identically zero or nowhere zero. By easy reductions the determinant (48·4) is seen to have the value $\varphi^2 d(t)$, which proves the lemma.

LEMMA 48·2. *If the set* $\eta_{i\sigma}(\sigma = 1, \ldots, 2n - 2)$ *of solutions of the accessory equations is a fundamental system, then the determinant*

$$D(t, t_1) = \begin{vmatrix} \eta_{i\sigma}(t) & y_i'(t) & 0 \\ \eta_{i\sigma}(t_1) & 0 & y_i'(t_1) \end{vmatrix}$$

*has the form*

$$D(t, t_1) = (t - t_1)^{n-1}\lambda(t, t_1),$$

*with* $\lambda(t_1, t_1) = \pm d(t_1)$, *and hence is different from zero near the value* $t_1$. *If the set* $\eta_{i\sigma}$ *is not a fundamental system, then* $D(t, t_1)$ *vanishes identically.*

The determinant $D(t, t_1)$ may be written in the form

$$D(t, t_1) = \begin{vmatrix} \eta_{i\sigma}(t) - \eta_{i\sigma}(t_1) & y_i'(t) - y_i'(t_1) & -y_i'(t_1) \\ \eta_{i\sigma}(t_1) & y_i'(t_1) & y_i'(t_1) \end{vmatrix}.$$

After applying Taylor's formula with integral form of remainder and removing a factor $(t - t_1)^{n-1}$, the remaining factor $\lambda(t, t_1)$ has the properties described in the lemma.

If the set $\eta_{i\sigma}$ is not a fundamental system, the determinants (48·3) and (48·4) vanish identically. There is then a set of constants $c_\sigma$, $d$, $e$, not all zero, satisfying the $2n$ linear equations whose coefficients are the rows of (48·4) at $t = t_1$. The $n$ functions

$$c_\sigma u_{i\sigma}(t) + d\varphi(t)\, y_i'(t) + et\varphi(t)\, y_i'(t) \qquad (i = 1, \ldots, n)$$

vanish identically, since they vanish with their derivatives at $t = t_1$ and form a solution of equations (48·2). The determinant

$$48\cdot5) \qquad \begin{vmatrix} u_{i\sigma}(t) & \varphi(t)\, y_i'(t) & t\varphi(t)\, y_i'(t) \\ u_{i\sigma}(t_1) & \varphi(t_1)\, y'(t_1) & t_1\varphi(t_1)\, y_i'(t_1) \end{vmatrix}$$

therefore vanishes identically, and so does $D(t, t_1)$, since (48·5) has the value $(t_1 - t)\,\varphi(t)\,\varphi(t_1)\,D(t, t_1)$.

THEOREM 48·1. *If* $2n - 2$ *solutions* $\eta_{i\sigma}(t)$ $(\sigma = 1, \ldots, 2n-2)$ *of the accessory equations for a non-singular extremal arc* $E_{12}$ *have a determinant* $D(t, t_1)$ *not identically zero, then each root* $t_3$ *of the equation* $D(t_3, t_1) = 0$ *on the interval* $t_1 < t \leqq t_2$ *determines a point* 3 *conjugate to* 1 *on* $E_{12}$, *and conversely.*

If $t_3$ is a root of the equation $D(t_3, t_1) = 0$, the linear equations

$$u_{i\sigma}(t_3)\,c_\sigma + \varphi(t_3)\,y_i'(t_3)\,d + t_3\varphi(t_3)\,y_i'(t_3)\,e = 0\,,$$

$$u_{i\sigma}(t_1)\,c_\sigma + \varphi(t_1)\,y_i'(t_1)\,d + t_1\varphi(t_1)\,y_i'(t_1)\,e = 0$$

have solutions $c_\sigma$, $d$, $e$, with $d = e = 0$, since $y_i'u_{i\sigma} = 0$ for every $\sigma$, and with constants $c_\sigma$ not all zero. The solution $u_i = u_{i\sigma}c_\sigma$ of equations (48·2) is then normal and vanishes at $t_1$ and $t_3$ and cannot be identically zero on the interval $t_1t_3$ since $D(t, t_1) \not\equiv 0$ near $t_1$, by Lemma 48·2. Hence the point *3* on $E_{12}$ is conjugate to *1*.

Conversely, if $u_i(t)$ is a normal solution of the accessory equations determining a point *3* conjugate to *1* on $E_{12}$, then there are constants $c_\sigma$, $d$, $e$, not all zero such that

$$u_i \equiv u_{i\sigma}c_\sigma + \varphi y_i' d + t\varphi y_i' e\,,$$

since every solution of the equations (48·2) is linearly expressible in terms of the $2n$ solutions $u_{i\sigma}$, $\varphi y_i'$, $t\varphi y_i'$, which are linearly independent because the determinant $D(t, t_1)$ is, by hypothesis, not identically zero. From $u_i(t_1) = u_i(t_3) = 0$ it follows that the determinant (48·5) and hence $D(t, t_1)$ are zero at $t = t_3$.

THEOREM 48·2. *If the solutions* $\eta_{i\tau}(t)$ $(\tau = 1, \ldots, n-1)$ *of the accessory equations along a non-singular extremal arc* $E_{12}$ *have a determinant*

$$\Delta(t) = |\,\eta_{i\tau}(t)\;\; y_i'(t)\,|$$

*not identically zero and with rank one at* $t = t_1$, *then each root* $t_3$ *of* $\Delta(t)$ *on the interval* $t_1 < t \leqq t_2$ *determines a point* 3 *conjugate to* 1 *on* $E_{12}$, *and conversely.*

The determinant

$$(48\cdot 6) \qquad |\,u_{i\tau}\;\;(t - t_1)\,\varphi y_i'\,|$$

is easily seen to be equal to $(t - t_1)\varphi\Delta(t)$. Its columns are $n$ solutions of the equations (48·2), all of whose elements vanish at $t = t_1$ since the solutions $u_{i\tau}$ are normal and have elements proportional to those of the set $y_i'$ at $t = t_1$. If the determinant of the derivatives of these $n$ solutions is different from zero at $t = t_1$, then by applications of Taylor's formula with integral remainder term it follows that the determinant (48·6) is the product of $(t - t_1)^n$ by a factor different from zero at $t = t_1$. On the other hand, if the determinant of derivatives vanishes at $t = t_1$, there will be a linear combination of the columns of (48·6) with constant coefficients not all zero which vanishes with its derivatives at $t = t_1$

and is therefore identically zero. Thus we see that $\Delta(t)$ either has the form $(t - t_1)^{n-1}\mu(t)$ with $\mu(t_1) \neq 0$ or else is identically zero.

Suppose, now, that $\Delta(t)$ is not identically zero and that $t_3$ is one of its roots. The equations

$$u_{i\tau}(t_3)\, c_\tau + y_i'(t_3)\, d = 0$$

have solutions $c_\tau$, $d$ not all zero, but with $d = 0$ since the solutions $u_{i\tau}$ are normal. The normal solution $u_i = u_{i\tau}c_\tau$ then vanishes at $t_1$ and $t_3$ and is not identically zero, since $\Delta(t) \not\equiv 0$. Hence $t_3$ determines a point conjugate to *1*.

Conversely, let $u_i(t)$ be a normal solution defining a point *3* conjugate to *1* on $E_{12}$. It is a solution of equations (48·2) with elements vanishing at $t_1$ and therefore expressible in terms of the columns of (48·6) in the form

$$u_i(t) = u_{i\tau}(t)\, c_\tau + (t - t_1)\, \varphi(t)\, y_i'(t)\, d\ ,$$

as one sees by an argument like that used in the proof of Theorem 12·3. The constant $d$ is zero, since the solutions $u_i$ and $u_{i\tau}$ are all normal. The constants $c_\tau$ are not all zero, since the normal solution $u_i$ is not identically zero. Since the values $u_i(t_3)$ are all zero, it follows readily that $t_3$ is a root of $\Delta(t)$.

Corollary 48·1. *Let* $E_{12}$ *be a non-singular extremal arc contained for*

$$t_{10} \leqq t \leqq t_{20}\ , \qquad a_r = a_{r0}\ , \qquad b_r = b_{r0} \qquad (r = 1, \ldots, n-1)$$

*in a* $(2n - 2)$*-parameter family of extremals*

$$y_i(t, a, b) \tag{48·7}$$

*with continuity properties as described in Theorem 45·1 and such that the determinant*

$$D(t, t_1, a, b) = \begin{vmatrix} y_{ia_r}(t) & y_{ib_r}(t) & y_i'(t) & 0 \\ y_{ia_r}(t_1) & y_{ib_r}(t_1) & 0 & y_i'(t_1) \end{vmatrix}$$

*is not identically zero along* $E_{12}$. *Then the points* 3 *conjugate to* 1 *on* $E_{12}$ *are determined by the zeros* $t_3 \neq t_{10}$ *of* $D(t, t_{10}, a_0, b_0)$.

This follows from Theorem 48·1, since by the argument of Section 12, the $2n - 2$ sets $y_{ia_r}$, $y_{ib_r}$ are solutions of the accessory equations.

In the proof of Theorem 45·1 it was stated that the determinant (45·3) is either identically zero or everywhere different from zero. This is a consequence of the statement in the preceding paragraph and of Lemma 48·1.

It is interesting to note that except for a factor $(t_1 - t)^{-1}$ the determinant $D$ of Corollary 48·1 is the determinant of the derivatives of the functions $y_i(p + qt, a, b)$, $y_i(p + qt_1, a, b)$ with respect to the $2n$ constants $a_r$, $b_r$, $p$, $q$, as one can see by simple transformations. This fact emphasizes the analogy between the determinant of Corollary 48·1 and the corresponding determinants of Corollary 12·1 and (36·7) for the non-parametric theory. This remark supplements the comment concerning the determinant (45·3) made in the last paragraph of Section 45.

The determinant $D$ of the corollary is certainly not identically zero when the family (48·7) has its determinant (45·3) different from zero along $E_{12}$, since then the solutions $y_{ia_r}$, $y_{ib_r}$ of the accessory equations are linearly independent and we have seen in Lemma 48·2 that $D$ is not identically zero near $t = t_1$.

COROLLARY 48·2. *Let* $E_{12}$ *be a non-singular extremal arc contained for*

$$t_{10} \leqq t \leqq t_{20}\,, \qquad a_r = a_{r0} \qquad (r = 1, \ldots, n-1)$$

*in an* (n − 1)*-parameter family of extremals*

$$y_i(t,\ a) \tag{48·8}$$

*all passing through the point* 1, *with continuity properties as described in Theorem 45·2 and such that the determinant*

$$\Delta(t,\ a) = |\, y_{ia_r}\ \ y'_i \,|$$

*is not identically zero along* $E_{12}$. *Then the points* 3 *conjugate to* 1 *on* $E_{12}$ *are determined by the zeros* $t_3 \neq t_{10}$ *of* $\Delta(t, a_0)$.

If the extremals of the family (48·8) all pass through the point *1* for the parameter values $t_1(a)$, where $t_1(a)$ has a continuous first derivative near $a = a_0$, then from the equations

$$y_{i1} = y_i\,[t_1(a)\,,\ a]$$

it is found by differentiation that the rank of $\Delta(t, a)$ is unity at $t = t_1$. Hence the corollary follows from Theorem 48·2.

LEMMA 48·3. *If* $E_{12}$ *is a non-singular extremal arc having on it no point* 3 *conjugate to* 1, *then there is always a point* 0 *on the extension of* $E_{12}$ *in the order* 0 1 2 *which also has no conjugate on* $E_{12}$.

We have $\lambda(t, t_1) \neq 0$ on $t_1 < t \leqq t_2$ in the formula of Lemma 48·2, since $E_{12}$ contains no point conjugate to *1* and since $\lambda(t_1, t_1) \neq 0$. It follows that $\lambda(t, t_0)$ remains different from zero for $t_1 \leqq t \leqq t_2$ if $t_0$ is taken less than $t_1$ and sufficiently near to $t_1$. For such values of $t_0$ the determinant $D(t, t_0)$ is different from zero on $t_1t_2$. The lemma now follows from Theorem 48·1.

The following theorem shows that the conjugate points defined in Section 46 are also conjugate points as defined in Section 47:

THEOREM 48·3. *On a non-singular extremal arc* $E_{12}$ *every contact point* 3 *of an envelope of a one-parameter family of extremals through the point* 1, *as described in Section 46, is a point conjugate to* 1 *on* $E_{12}$ *in the sense defined in Section 47.*

To prove this, consider the one-parameter family of extremal arcs (46·1). The derivatives $y_{i\beta}(t, \beta_0)$ of this family define a solution of the accessory equations along the arc $E_{12}$. From equations (46·2), (46·3), and (46·4) it is seen that this solution satisfies the conditions

$$y'_i\,[t_1(\beta_0)\,,\ \beta_0]\,t'_1(\beta_0) + y_{i\beta}\,[t_1(\beta_0)\,,\ \beta_0] = 0,$$

$$y'_i\,[t_4(\beta_0)\,,\ \beta_0]\,[t'_4(\beta_0) - \kappa(\beta_0)] + y_{i\beta}\,[t_4(\beta_0)\,,\ \beta_0] = 0$$

and hence has elements proportional to those of the set $y_i'$ at $t_1(\beta_0)$ and $t_3 = t_4(\beta_0)$. Its elements are not everywhere proportional to those of the set $y_i'$, however, as one sees by reference to the hypothesis in the first paragraph of Section 46. Thus the contact point *3* of the arc $E_{12}$ with the envelope $D_{43}$, as shown in Figure 10·1 with *6* replaced by *3*, is a conjugate point of the kind defined in Section 47.

**49. Fields and a fundamental sufficiency theorem.** For parametric problems the notion of a field is analogous to that described for the non-parametric problem in Section 18, but the homogeneity of the integrand function $f$ is the cause of some modifications in the theory which will appear in the following paragraphs.

Definition of a Field. A field is a region $F$ of $y$-space containing only interior points and having a set of slope functions $p_i(y_1, \ldots, y_n)$ with the following properties:

*a*) The functions $p_i(y)$ have continuous partial derivatives of at least the first order in $F$ and are normed so that $p_i p_i = 1$;

*b*) The sets $[y, p(y)]$ corresponding to $F$ are all admissible;

*c*) The integral

$$I^* = \int f_{y_i'}[y, p(y)]\,dy_i \tag{49·1}$$

is independent of the path in $F$ in the sense that it has the same value on all continuous arcs in $F$ consisting of a finite number of regular sub-arcs and having the same two end-points.

The assumption that the functions $p_i(y)$ are normed is convenient for the sequel but not necessary. On account of the second homogeneity property (43·3), the functions $p_i(y)$ in the integrand of $I^*$ could be replaced by any set $\kappa p_i$ ($\kappa > 0$) without changing the value of the integrand.

In the definition (49·1) of the invariant integral no term in $dt$ occurs. This is because, by analogy with the non-parametric problem, the coefficient of $dt$ would be $f - y_i' f_{y_i'}$, which vanishes identically by (43·2).

For the functions

$$A_i(y) = f_{y_i'}[y, p(y)]$$

we find, with the help of the homogeneity properties of the derivatives of $f$, the relations

$$p_k\left(\frac{\partial A_i}{\partial y_k} - \frac{\partial A_k}{\partial y_i}\right) = f_{y_i' y_k} p_k + f_{y_i' y_j'} p_{j y_k} p_k - f_{y_i},$$

analogous to the relations (18·5) and (37·6).

When $I^*$ is independent of the path, the differences $\partial A_i/\partial y_k - \partial A_k/\partial y_i$ all vanish, and the last equation shows that the solutions of the differential equations

$$\frac{dy_i}{dt} = p_i(y) \tag{49·2}$$

are all extremals. They are called the *extremals of the field.* They form an $(n-1)$-parameter family, since one and but one of them passes through each point of $F$. Furthermore, on every extremal arc $E_{12}$ of the field $I^*(E_{12}) = I(E_{12})$, from the definition (49·1) of $I^*$ and the property (43·2) of $f$.

If a continuous arc $y_i(\tau)$ in $F$ consists of a finite number of regular sub-arcs and is a solution of the equations

$$\frac{dy_i}{d\tau} = \kappa p_i(y) \qquad (\kappa > 0), \tag{49·3}$$

it will necessarily be an extremal arc of the field. For in terms of the new parameter

$$t = \int_{\tau_0}^{\tau} \kappa(\tau)\, d\tau,$$

the arc will satisfy the equation (49·2), as one readily verifies.

THEOREM 49·1. THE FORMULA OF WEIERSTRASS. *If* $E_{12}$ *is an extremal arc of a field* $F$ *and if* $C_{12}$ *is an admissible arc in* $F$ *joining the ends of* $E_{12}$, *then*

$$I(C_{12}) - I(E_{12}) = \int_{t_1}^{t_2} E[y,\ p(y),\ y']\, dt,$$

*where the variables* $y$ *in the integrand are to be replaced by the functions* $y_i(t)$ *defining* $C_{12}$.

The proof of this theorem is the same as that of the analogous Theorem 19·1 for non-parametric problems.

THEOREM 49·2. A FUNDAMENTAL SUFFICIENCY THEOREM. *If* $E_{12}$ *is an extremal of a field* $F$ *in which the condition*

$$E[y,\ p(y),\ y'] > 0$$

*holds for every admissible set* $(y, y')$ *with* $y_i$ *in* $F$ *and* $y_i' \neq \kappa p_i$ $(\kappa > 0)$, *then the inequality* $I(C_{12}) > I(E_{12})$ *is true for every admissible arc* $C_{12}$ *in* $F$ *which is not coincident with* $E_{12}$.

To prove the theorem we may suppose that the parameter $t$ on $C_{12}$ is the length of arc. From Theorem 49·1 it follows that $I(C_{12}) > I(E_{12})$ unless $y_i' = \kappa p_i$ $(\kappa > 0)$ at every point of $C_{12}$. But in that case we would have $\kappa = 1$, since $y_i'y_i' = 1$ and $p_ip_i = 1$, and hence $C_{12}$ would be an extremal of the field. This is impossible unless $C_{12}$ coincides with $E_{12}$, since $E_{12}$ is the only extremal of $F$ through the point *1*.

As in the non-parametric case, there are a number of methods for the construction of the so-called *Mayer families of extremals* whose slope functions form fields in every region $F$ of $y$-space which they simply cover. Such families are defined by equations

$$y_i = y_i(t,\ a_1,\ \ldots,\ a_{n-1}) = y_i(t,\ a) \qquad [(t,\ a) \text{ in } T] \tag{49·4}$$

containing $n-1$ parameters. The functions $y_i$, $y_{it}$ are supposed to have continuous partial derivatives of at least the second order for values $(t, a)$ in the region $T$. A family of this sort is said to simply cover a region $F$ of $y$-space if the equations (49·4) have a unique solution $[t(y), \alpha(y)]$ in $T$ for each point $y$ in $F$. The functions

$$p_i(y) = y_i'[t(y),\ \alpha(y)] \tag{49·5}$$

are called the slope functions of the family in $F$. If the determinant $\Delta(t, \alpha) = |y_{i\alpha_r}\ y_i'|$ is different from zero at the values $(t, \alpha)$ corresponding to points in $F$, then by the usual implicit function theorems it follows that the functions $t(y)$, $\alpha(y)$ have continuous derivatives of at least the second order in $F$.

The slope functions of a family (49·4) will not always form a field in a region $F$ which is simply covered by the family. By methods analogous to those of Sections 20 and 37 it can be shown that a family (49·4) will be a Mayer family and form a field in every region which it simply covers if it is intersected by a single $(n-1)$-space $\Sigma$ on which the integral $I^*$ of the family, from (49·1), is independent of the path. The $(n-1)$-space $\Sigma$ is supposed to be defined by a function $t = T(\alpha)$ substituted in the equations (49·4). Special cases are again those for which $\Sigma$ is a fixed point, or an $(n-1)$-space which cuts the extremals of the family transversally so that $I^*$ has the value zero on every arc on $\Sigma$.

To construct a Mayer family in most general fashion, let us start from a $(2n-2)$-parameter family of extremals containing a particular extremal arc $E$, as described in the imbedding theorem, Theorem 45·1. Let us intersect $E$ by an arbitrarily selected $(n-1)$-space $\Sigma$ not tangent to $E$, defined by functions $Y_i(\alpha_1, \ldots, \alpha_{n-1})$. The point of intersection of $\Sigma$ and $E$ is supposed to be defined on $\Sigma$ by values $\alpha_{r0}$ near which the functions $Y_i(\alpha)$ have continuous second derivatives, and on $E$ by a parameter value $t_0$. At those values the non-tangency of $\Sigma$ and $E$ is expressed by the fact that the determinant $|Y_{i\alpha_r}\ y_i'|$ is different from zero.

To determine an $(n-1)$-parameter family of extremals intersected by $\Sigma$ and having an integral $I^*$ independent of the path on $\Sigma$, we determine $a_r$, $b_r$, $T$ as functions of the parameters $\alpha$ by means of the equations

$$y_i(T,\ a,\ b) = Y_i(\alpha),\quad f_{y_i'}[Y,\ y'(T,\ a,\ b)]\,Y_{i\alpha_r} = U_{\alpha_r}. \tag{49·6}$$

Here $U(\alpha)$ is an arbitrarily selected function having continuous third derivatives near the values $\alpha_{r0}$ and having first derivatives which satisfy the second set of equations (49·6) at the special values $(\alpha, a, b, T) = (\alpha_0, a_0, b_0, t_0)$ defining the intersection of $\Sigma$ and $E$. The functional determinant of the first members of equations (49·6) with respect to the variables $a_r$, $b_r$, $T$ is not zero at this initial solution. It is, in fact, the product of

$$\begin{vmatrix} \delta_{ik} & 0 \\ 0 & f_{y_i'y_k'}Y_{i\alpha_r} \\ 0 & y_k' \end{vmatrix} = -\begin{vmatrix} Y_{i\alpha_r} & 0 \\ y_i' & 0 \\ 0 & 1 \end{vmatrix}\begin{vmatrix} f_{y_i'y_k'} & y_i' \\ y_k' & 0 \end{vmatrix}$$

by the non-vanishing determinant (45·3), divided by $(y_i' y_i')^2$. The product displayed above is not zero, since $\Sigma$ is not tangent to $E$ and since $E$ is non-singular. Hence the equations (49·6) have solutions $a_r(\alpha)$, $b_r(\alpha)$, $T(\alpha)$ with continuous derivatives of at least the second order near the values $\alpha_{r0}$ and such that $a_r(\alpha_0) = a_{r0}$, $b_r(\alpha_0) = b_{r0}$, $T(\alpha_0) = t_0$. If we substitute the functions $a_r(\alpha)$, $b_r(\alpha)$ in the functions (45·2), a family of the form (49·4) is obtained which is intersected by the surface $\Sigma$ for $t = T(\alpha)$. The integral $I^*$ of the family is independent of the path on $\Sigma$, since from the second set of equations (49·6) its integrand has on the space $\Sigma$ the value

$$f_{y_i'} dy_i = f_{y_i'} Y_{i\alpha_r} d\alpha_r = dU \; .$$

Hence the family of the form (49·4) so constructed is a Mayer family and has slope functions defining a field in every region $F$ which it simply covers.

**50. Sufficient conditions for relative minima.** The conditions I–IV which appear in the sufficiency theorems below for relative minima were described in Sections 44 and 46. As in preceding chapters, we shall use the symbols II′ and III′ to denote the conditions II and III strengthened to exclude the equality signs, and $\mathrm{II}_N$ to denote the condition II extended to hold in a neighborhood $N$ of the elements $(y, y')$ on an admissible arc $E$. The symbol IV′ will denote the condition IV of Section 46 with the added restriction that the point *2* is not conjugate to the point *1* on $E_{12}$. The definition of conjugate point to be used is that of Section 47. With these definitions agreed upon, we may state the following lemma:

LEMMA 50·1. *If a non-singular extremal arc* $E_{12}$ *not intersecting itself has on it no point conjugate to its initial point* 1, *then there exists a field* F *of which* $E_{12}$ *is an extremal.*

To prove this, we note first that by Lemma 48·3 there is a point *0* on the extension of $E_{12}$ in the order *0 1 2* such that *0* has no conjugate on $E_{12}$. According to Corollary 48·2, this insures the non-vanishing on $E_{12}$ of the determinant

$$\Delta(t, \alpha) = | \, y_{i\alpha_r} \quad y_i' \, |$$

belonging to the $(n - 1)$-parameter family of extremals (48·8) passing through the point *0* and containing $E_{12}$. Without loss of generality we may assume that the parameter $t$ in the equations of this family is the length of arc measured from the point *0*. The equations

$$y_i = y_i(t, \alpha) \tag{50·1}$$

have as initial solutions the points $(y, t, \alpha)$ belonging to $E_{12}$. This set of points contains no two distinct points with the same projection $y$, since $E_{12}$, by hypothesis, does not intersect itself; and, furthermore, $\Delta(t, \alpha) \neq 0$ on this set, as we have just seen. Hence, from a well-known implicit function theorem, the equations (50·1) have solutions $t(y)$, $a_r(y)$ with continuous partial derivatives of at least the second order in a neighborhood $F$ of the points $y$ on $E_{12}$ and such that $a_r(y) = a_{r0}$ on $E_{12}$. The functions

$$p_i(y) = y_{it}[t(y), a(y)]$$

are a normed set of slope functions of the family (50·1) in $F$. For every continuous arc $D_{34}$ in $F$ consisting of a finite number of regular sub-arcs and for the extremals $E_{03}, E_{04}$ joining the point *0* to the ends of $D_{34}$, we have the relation

$$I(E_{04}) - I(E_{03}) = I^*(D_{34}).$$

This is a consequence of the extension of Corollary 8·1 to parametric problems, as explained and used in the third paragraph of Section 46. Hence $I^*$ has the same value on all arcs $D$ in $F$ joining the same two points *3* and *4* and is inde-

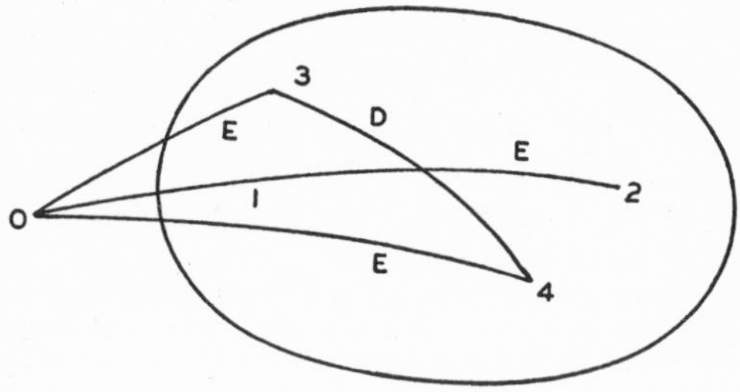


FIG. 50·1

pendent of the path in the sense described in the definition of a field in Section 49. The region $F$ with the slope functions $p_i(y)$ is, therefore, a field whose extremals are the extremals (50·1).

THEOREM 50·1. SUFFICIENT CONDITIONS FOR A WEAK RELATIVE MINIMUM. *If an admissible arc* $E_{12}$ *without corners and not intersecting itself satisfies the conditions I, III′, IV′, then there is a neighborhood* N *of the elements* (y, y′) *on* $E_{12}$ *such that the relation* $I(C_{12}) > I(E_{12})$ *holds for every admissible arc* $C_{12}$ *in* N *which is not coincident with* $E_{12}$.

To prove this we note first that the arc $E_{12}$ is a non-singular extremal, by Lemma 44·2 and Corollary 44·3. Hence by Lemma 50·1 it is an extremal of a field $F$ in $y$-space with slope functions $p_i(y)$. The hypothesis of Corollary 44·4 is satisfied by $E_{12}$ because of the property III′ of $E_{12}$.

To select a neighborhood $N$ with the properties of the theorem, we may consider the set $S$ of points $[y(t), y'(t)]$ $(t_1 \leqq t \leqq t_2)$ on the arc $E_{12}$ with the parameter $t$ as length of arc. An $\epsilon$-neighborhood $S_\epsilon$ of the set $S$ can be selected with $\epsilon$ so small that all of the points $[y, p(y), y']$ corresponding to points of $S_\epsilon$ are in the neighborhood $N_0$ of Corollary 44·4 in which the $E$-function remains non-negative. The set $S_\epsilon$ extended to contain all of its related points is then a neighborhood $N$ with the properties specified in Theorem 50·1, as one may see with the help of the fundamental sufficiency theorem, Theorem 49·2, if it is agreed that the admissible arcs of this latter theorem shall be those whose elements $(y, y')$ lie in the neighborhood $N$.

In order to prove for parametric problems a sufficiency theorem for a strong relative minimum analogous to Theorem 16·1, we may make use of Lemma 16·1, which says that on a non-singular extremal arc $E_{12}$ the condition $II_N$ implies $II'_N$. The proof of this lemma needs the following emendations in order to be effective for the parametric case. As in the non-parametric case, we consider a neighborhood $N$ of the arc $E_{12}$ in which $II_N$ holds and the determinant (43·8) is different from zero. We further infer that, if $E(y, y', Y')$ were zero for a normed set $(y, y', Y')$ with $(y, y')$ in $N$ and $Y' \neq y'$, then for these values $y$, $Y'$ considered as fixed, the function $E(y, y', Y')$ would be minimized by the values $y'$. Hence with the help of Theorem 43·1 and the second formula (43·2) we should have $Y' = -\kappa y'$ $(\kappa > 0)$, since

$$E_{y'_k} = -Y'_i f_{y'_i y'_k} = 0 ,$$

and also, with the help of the homogeneity properties of $f$ and the second order conditions for a minimum of $E$ at $y'$,

$$E_{y'_k y'_l}\pi_k\pi_l = y'_i f_{y'_i y'_k y'_l}\pi_k\pi_l = -f_{y'_k y'_l}\pi_k\pi_l \geqq 0$$

for all sets $\pi$. But this last inequality is impossible if $N$ is suitably chosen, since II implies III as in the non-parametric case, since the non-singularity of $E_{12}$ and III imply III′ by Lemma 44·2, and since III′ along $E_{12}$ implies III′ at each element of a neighborhood $N$ of $E_{12}$ by Lemma 44·1.

We may now prove for the parametric case the following analogue of Theorem 16·2:

THEOREM 50·2. SUFFICIENT CONDITIONS FOR A STRONG RELATIVE MINIMUM. *If an admissible arc* $E_{12}$ *without corners and not intersecting itself is non-singular and satisfies the conditions I,* $II_N$*, IV′, then there is a neighborhood* F *of the points* y *on* $E_{12}$ *such that the inequality* $I(C_{12}) > I(E_{12})$ *holds for every admissible arc* $C_{12}$ *in* F *which is not coincident with* $E_{12}$.

The proof is like that of Theorem 50·1 provided that we select the neighborhood $F$ so small that for points $y$ in $F$ the sets $[y, p(y)]$ are all in a neighborhood $N$ where the condition $II'_N$ holds.

It is evident that these theorems establish for the parametric problem in $n$-space, and for admissible arcs without corners and not intersecting themselves, the results implied in the first two rows of the table in Section 17. In the next section below we shall see that the third row, and a quite different sufficiency theorem for a strong relative minimum, can be justified for parametric problems for which the region $R$ of admissible elements $(y, y')$ has suitable properties.

**51. Further sufficient conditions for strong relative minima.** The first theorem to be proved in this section is effective for a parametric problem for which the region $R$ of admissible elements consists of all sets $(y, y')$ for which $y$ is in a region $R_y$ of $y$-space containing only interior points with $y'_i y'_i \neq 0$. For such problems it turns out that the conditions I, II′, III′, IV′ are sufficient for a strong relative minimum.

In order to deduce this result, we shall need some further properties of the $E$-function. Let $p_i$, $q_i$ be two directions normed and orthogonal to each other, and let $a_i(\theta)$, $\alpha_i(\theta)$ represent the directions

$$a_i(\theta) = p_i \cos\theta + q_i \sin\theta\,, \quad \alpha_i(\theta) = -p_i \sin\theta + q_i \cos\theta \quad (0 \leqq \theta \leqq \pi)\,,$$

which are also normed and orthogonal. In the following paragraphs we shall denote these directions frequently simply by $a$ and $\alpha$. We have, first of all, the following lemma:

LEMMA 51·1. *If at a particular point* $y$ *the sets* $(y, y') = [y, a(\theta)]$ $(0 \leqq \theta \leqq \pi)$ *are all admissible, then for every* $\omega$ *on the interval* $0 \leqq \omega \leqq \pi$

$$(51\cdot1) \qquad \begin{aligned} E[y, p, a(\omega)] &= \int_0^\omega \sin(\omega-\theta)\, Q[y, a; \alpha, \alpha]\, d\theta \\ &= (1-\cos\omega)\, Q[y, a(\theta^*); \alpha(\theta^*), \alpha(\theta^*)] \end{aligned}$$

*where* $\theta^*$ *is a suitably selected intermediate value between* $0$ *and* $\omega$.

By a simple differentiation we find that

$$a_i(\omega) \frac{d}{d\theta} f_{y'_i}(y, a) = Q[y, a; \alpha, a(\omega)]\,.$$

The second property (43·6) and the equation

$$a_i(\omega) = a_i \cos(\omega-\theta) + \alpha_i \sin(\omega-\theta)$$

then show that

$$a_i(\omega) \frac{d}{d\theta} f_{y'_i}(y, a) = \sin(\omega-\theta)\, Q(y, a; \alpha, \alpha)\,.$$

The first formula of the lemma then follows from the third formula (43·5) and an integration of the last equation. The second formula of the lemma is then easily deducible by means of the mean-value theorem for a definite integral.

COROLLARY 51·1. *The function* $W(y, p, q, \omega)$ *defined by the equations*

$$\begin{aligned} W &= \frac{E[y, p, a(\omega)]}{1-\cos\omega} && \text{for} \quad 0 < \omega \leqq \pi\,. \\ &= Q[y, p; q, q] && \text{for} \quad \omega = 0 \end{aligned}$$

*is continuous for all sets* $(y, p, q, \omega)$ *such that* $y$ *is in* $R_y$,

$$p_i p_i - 1 = q_i q_i - 1 = p_i q_i = 0, \quad 0 \leqq \omega \leqq \pi\,.$$

This follows readily from the definition of $W$ and the second formula of Lemma 51·1.

LEMMA 51·2. *If an admissible arc* E *satisfies the conditions II′ and III′, it also satisfies the condition* $II'_N$.

To prove this we note, first, that except when $Y' = \pm\kappa y'$ ($\kappa > 0$) a particular set $(y, y', Y')$ will determine uniquely a set $(y, p, q, \omega)$ by the equations

$$(51\cdot 2)\qquad \begin{aligned} p_i &= \frac{y'_i}{(y'_k y'_k)^{1/2}}, \qquad q_i = \frac{Y'_i - \rho y'_i}{[(Y'_k - \rho y'_k)(Y'_k - \rho y'_k)]^{1/2}}, \\ a_i(\omega) &= p_i \cos\omega + q_i \sin\omega = \frac{Y'_i}{(Y'_k Y'_k)^{1/2}}, \end{aligned}$$

in which $\rho$ is to be determined by the condition $p_i q_i = 0$. When $Y' = -\kappa y'$ or $Y' = \kappa y'$, the last equation is satisfied by arbitrary normed values $q$ defining a direction orthogonal to $p$, and $\omega = \pi$ or $\omega = 0$, respectively. We have, then, for every set $(y, y', Y')$ for which $y$ is in the region $R_y$ a set $(y, p, q, \omega)$ for which the equation

$$\begin{aligned} E(y, y', Y') &= (Y'_k Y'_k)^{1/2} E[y, p, a(\omega)] \\ &= (Y'_k Y'_k)^{1/2} (1 - \cos\omega) W(y, p, q, \omega) \end{aligned}$$

holds. The conditions II′ and III′ imply that the function $W(y, p, q, \omega)$ is positive on the bounded closed set of points $(y, p, q, \omega)$ determined by the conditions

$$(y, p) \text{ is on } E, \quad p_i p_i - 1 = q_i q_i - 1 = p_i q_i = 0, \quad 0 \leqq \omega \leqq \pi .$$

From the continuity of $W$ it follows that there is a neighborhood $N$ of the elements $(y, y')$ on $E$ such that $W$ remains positive at points $(y, p, q, \omega)$ for which

$$(y, p) \text{ is in } N, \quad p_i p_i - 1 = q_i q_i - 1 = p_i q_i = 0, \quad 0 \leqq \omega \leqq \pi .$$

The conclusion of the lemma follows readily.

THEOREM 51·1. A SECOND SUFFICIENCY THEOREM FOR A STRONG RELATIVE MINIMUM. *If an admissible arc* $E_{12}$ *without corners and not intersecting itself satisfies the conditions I, II′, III′, IV′, then* $I(E_{12})$ *is a strong relative minimum, as described in Theorem 50·2, provided that the region* R *of admissible elements* (y, y′) *consists of all sets* (y, y′) *with* $y'_i y'_i \neq 0$ *and* y *interior to a given region* $R_y$ *of* y-*space.*

This theorem is an immediate consequence of Lemmas 44·2 and 51·2 and Theorem 50·2. The former of the lemmas says that an arc $E_{12}$ which satisfies condition III′ is non-singular, and the latter states that conditions II′ and III′ imply $II'_N$. Thus an arc $E_{12}$ which satisfies the hypotheses of Theorem 51·1 also satisfies those of Theorem 50·2.

Let us say that arc $E_{12}$ satisfies *the condition III″* if the condition III′ holds at every element $(y, y')$ with $y$ on $E_{12}$. The formula (51·1) shows that the property III″ implies the property II′ along $E_{12}$. Hence we have the following corollary:

COROLLARY 51·2. *If an admissible arc* $E_{12}$ *without corners and not intersecting itself satisfies the conditions I, III″, IV′, then* $I(E_{12})$ *is a strong relative minimum.*

A corollary similar to this holds when the region $R$ has a suitable convexity property, even if it is not of the form described in the first paragraph of this section. We shall say that $R$ is *convex relative to the variables* $y'$ when it contains all of the sets $[y, a(\theta)]$ $(0 \leqq \theta \leqq \omega)$ defined by equations (51·2) whenever it contains $(y, y')$ and $(y, Y')$. An admissible arc $E_{12}$ is said to satisfy the condition $III'_F$ if there is a neighborhood $F$ of $E_{12}$ in $y$-space such that the condition III′ is satisfied at every admissible set $(y, y')$ with $y$ in $F$.

COROLLARY 51·3. *If the region* R *has the property of convexity just described, then an admissible arc* $E_{12}$ *without corners, not intersecting itself, and satisfying the conditions I,* $III'_F$*, IV′ will make* $I(E_{12})$ *a strong relative minimum.*

This is a consequence of Theorem 50·2, since the condition $III'_F$ implies that $E_{12}$ is non-singular, by Lemma 44·2, and the formula (51·1) with $III'_F$ shows that the condition $II_N$ holds when $N$ consists of all elements $(y, y')$ with $y$ in $F$.

For parametric problems a table analogous to that of Section 17 for non-parametric problems is given here. The theorem implied in the third row of

TABLE OF NECESSARY AND OF SUFFICIENT CONDITIONS

| Type of Minimum | Necessary Conditions | Sufficient Conditions |
|---|---|---|
| Weak relative | I, III, IV | I, III′, IV′ |
| Strong relative | I, II, III, IV | I, $II_N$, IV′, $E$ non-singular |
| Strong relative | ........... | I, $III'_F$, IV′ |
| Strong relative | ........... | I, II′, III′, IV′ |
| Strong relative | ........... | I, III″, IV′ |

the table holds when the region $R$ of admissible elements $(y, y')$ is convex relative to the variables $y'$ in the manner described above. The last two rows of the table are applicable when $R$ is of the form presupposed in the first paragraph of this section.

**52. Canonical variables and equations.** On account of the homogeneity properties of the integrand function $f(y, y')$, it is not possible to define canonical variables $(y, z)$ for the parametric problem by equations as simple as the equations (26·1) and (38·1) used in the non-parametric cases, the reason being that for the parametric case the determinant $|f_{y'_i y'_k}|$ is identically zero, as follows from the second equation (43·2). We may, however, define canonical variables by means of similar equations whose form is suggested by the theory of the parametric problem when formulated as a problem of Lagrange,[1] equations whose effectiveness can be readily understood without reference to the Lagrange theory.

[1] See Teach, "The Hamilton-Jacobi Theory for the Problem of Lagrange in Parametric Form" (diss., University of Chicago), *Contributions 1933–1937*, pp. 165–206.

Let us define a function $G$ by the equation

$$G(y,\ y',\ l) = f + l(\varphi - 1)\ ,$$

where $\varphi(y, y')$ is a function with the same homogeneity and continuity properties as those of $f$. Then relations connecting the variables $y$, $y'$, $l$ with a set of canonical variables $y$, $z$ may be written in the form

$$z_i = G_{y'_i} = f_{y'_i} + l\varphi_{y'_i},\quad \varphi - 1 = 0\ . \tag{52·1}$$

Near a particular solution $(y, y', l, z)$ at which their functional determinant with respect to the variables $y'$, $l$ is different from zero, these equations have solutions

$$y'_i = P_i(y,\ z)\ ,\quad l = L(y,\ z)\ , \tag{52·2}$$

as we know from the usual implicit function theorems.

As a basis for the Hamilton-Jacobi theory, we shall assume that there is a region $R'$ of points $(y, y', l)$ defined by conditions of the form

$$(y,\ y')\ \text{in}\ R,\quad 0 < |l| < \epsilon$$

and such that the equations (52·1) transform $R'$ in a one-to-one way into a region $S$ of points $(y, z)$. Furthermore, we assume that the value of the function $\varphi$ is different from zero everywhere in $R'$ and that the functional determinant of equations (52·1) with respect to the variables $y'$, $l$ is everywhere different from zero. Then the equations (52·1) have unique solutions (52·2) corresponding to each point $(y, z)$ in $S$, and by well-known properties of implicit functions the functions $P_i$, $L$ defining them have continuous partial derivatives of at least the order $m - 1$ when the function $f$ has continuous derivatives of the $m$th order ($m \geqq 1$). An *admissible set of values* $(y, z)$ is, by definition, one belonging to the set $S$.

A Hamiltonian function $H(y, z)$ may be defined, in analogy with the definitions in equations (26·3) and (38·3), by the equation

$$H(y,\ z) = [y'_i G_{y'_i} - G]^{y'=P,\ l=L} = P_i z_i - f(y,\ P) = L(y,\ z)\ . \tag{52·3}$$

The last value for $H$ is found by multiplying the first equation (52·1) by $P_i$ and summing with respect to $i$. With the help of equations (52·1) the derivatives of $H$ are found to have the values

$$H_{y_i} = -G_{y_i}(y,\ P)\ ,\quad H_{z_i} = P_i\ . \tag{52·4}$$

These have continuous derivatives of order $m - 1$ when $f$ has continuous derivatives of order $m$, so that $H$ also has continuous derivatives of order $m$.

The *canonical equations* of the parametric problem are, by definition, the equations

$$(52\cdot 5)\qquad \frac{dy_i}{dt}=P_i=H_{z_i}, \qquad \frac{dz_i}{dt}=G_{y_i}(y,\ P)\ =-H_{y_i}.$$

Along every solution $y(t)$, $z(t)$ of these equations the value of $H = L$ is a constant, as one may readily verify by differentiation of $H[y(t), z(t)]$ with respect to $t$. By means of equations (52·1) with $l = 0$ every extremal $y_i(t)$ $(t_1 \leqq t \leqq t_2)$, with parameter $t$ so chosen that $\varphi \equiv 1$ along it, defines a solution $y_i(t)$, $z_i(t)$ of equations (52·5) on which $H = L = 0$. Conversely, for every solution $y_i(t)$, $z_i(t)$ of equations (52·5) on which $H = L = 0$ the functions $y_i(t)$ define an extremal with parameter such that $\varphi \equiv 1$. The proofs of these statements are simple consequences of the equations (52·4), (52·2), and (52·1).

For the definition of canonical accessory variables $(t, \eta, \zeta)$ the difficulty mentioned above in the first paragraph of this section again arises and may be avoided in a similar manner. We define a function $\Omega$ by the equation

$$\Omega(t,\ \eta,\ \eta',\ \lambda)\ =\omega(t,\ \eta,\ \eta')\ +\lambda\Phi,$$

where $2\omega$ is the quadratic form in the first equation (43·7) and

$$\Phi(t,\ \eta,\ \eta')\ =\varphi_{y_i}\eta_i+\varphi_{y_i'}\eta_i'$$

is the first variation of $\varphi$. The arguments $y(t)$, $y'(t)$ $(t_1 \leqq t \leqq t_2)$ in the coefficients of $\omega$ are supposed to be those belonging to an extremal arc $E$ whose corresponding functions $y(t)$, $z(t)$ satisfy equations (52·5) and make $L \equiv 0$. *Accessory canonical variables* $(t, \eta, \zeta)$ may then be defined in terms of $(t, \eta, \eta', \lambda)$ by means of the equations

$$(52\cdot 6)\qquad \zeta_i=\Omega_{\eta_i'}=f_{y_i'y_k}\eta_k+f_{y_i'y_k'}\eta_k'+\lambda\varphi_{y_i'},\quad \Phi=0.$$

The properties of these canonical variables are summarized in this paragraph. They will be proved in the next paragraph below. The equations (52·6) have the solutions

$$(52\cdot 7)\qquad \eta_i'=H_{z_iy_k}\eta_k+H_{z_iz_k}\zeta_k, \qquad \lambda=H_{y_i}\eta_i+H_{z_i}\zeta_i,$$

in which the arguments of the derivatives of $H$ are the functions $y(t)$, $z(t)$ belonging to the extremal arc $E$. We shall use the notations $\Pi_i(t, \eta, \zeta)$ and $\Lambda(t, \eta, \zeta)$ for the second members of these equations, respectively. The accessory Hamiltonian function $\mathfrak{H}$ is defined by the first equation (52·8), and its derivatives have the values in (52·9):

$$(52\cdot 8)\qquad \mathfrak{H}(t,\ \eta,\ \zeta)\ =\ [\eta_i'\Omega_{\eta_i'}-\Omega]^{\eta'=\Pi,\ \lambda=\Lambda}$$

$$=\Pi_i\zeta_i-\Omega(t,\ \eta;\ \Pi,\ \Lambda),$$

$$2\mathfrak{H}=H_{y_iy_k}\eta_i\eta_k+2H_{y_iz_k}\eta_i\zeta_k+H_{z_iz_k}\zeta_i\zeta_k$$

$$(52\cdot 9)\qquad \mathfrak{H}_t=-\Omega_t,\ \mathfrak{H}_{\eta_i}=-\Omega_{\eta_i}, \qquad \mathfrak{H}_{\zeta_i}=\Pi_i.$$

In these equations the arguments $t, \eta, \eta', \lambda$ of the derivatives of $\Omega$ are $t, \eta, \Pi, \Lambda$. The *canonical accessory equations* are defined to be the equations

$$(52\cdot 10) \qquad \frac{d\eta_i}{dt} = \mathfrak{H}_{\zeta_i}, \qquad \frac{d\zeta_i}{dt} = -\mathfrak{H}_{\eta_i}.$$

In order to justify the statements hitherto unproved in the last paragraph above, we first differentiate with respect to $y_k$ and $z_k$ the equations (52·1) with their solutions (52·2) substituted. From the relations $H = L$, $y_i' = H_{z_i} = P_i$ and the fact that $L = 0$ along an extremal we thus find

$$f_{y_i'y_k} + f_{y_i'y_j'} H_{z_jy_k} + H_{y_k}\varphi_{y_i'} = 0, \qquad f_{y_i'y_j'} H_{z_jz_k} + H_{z_k}\varphi_{y_i'} = \delta_{ik},$$
$$0 = \varphi_{y_k} + \varphi_{y_j'} H_{z_jy_k}, \qquad 0 = \varphi_{y_j'} H_{z_jz_k}.$$

With the help of these equations and by direct substitution it follows that the functions (52·7) are the solutions of equations (52·6). Next the values (52·9) for the derivatives of $\mathfrak{H}$ can be calculated without difficulty from the second expression (52·8). To deduce the third formula in (52·8) we differentiate the first equation (52·4) and find

$$H_{y_iy_k} = -f_{y_iy_k} - f_{y_iy_j'} H_{z_jy_k} - H_{y_k}\varphi_{y_i}, \qquad H_{y_iz_k} = -f_{y_iy_j'} H_{z_jz_k} - H_{z_k}\varphi_{y_i'}.$$

Hence from equations (52·9) and (52·7) we see that

$$\mathfrak{H}_{\eta_i} = -\Omega_{\eta_i} = H_{y_iy_k}\, \eta_k + H_{y_iz_k}\, \zeta_k,$$
$$\mathfrak{H}_{\zeta_i} = \quad \Pi_i \quad = H_{z_iy_k}\, \eta_k + H_{z_iz_k}\, \zeta_k;$$

and the desired formula follows at once, since $\mathfrak{H}$ is a homogeneous quadratic form and therefore

$$2\mathfrak{H} = \eta_i \mathfrak{H}_{\eta_i} + \zeta_i \mathfrak{H}_{\zeta_i}.$$

The canonical accessory equations (52·10) have a number of important special properties. There is one and but one solution $\eta_i(t)$, $\zeta_i(t)$ of these equations which at a given value $t$ takes given initial values $\eta_{i0}$, $\zeta_{i0}$. In particular, the unique solution determined by the values $\eta_{i0} = \zeta_{i0} = 0$ is identically zero. Along each solution $\eta(t)$, $\zeta(t)$ the value of $\lambda = \Lambda[t, \eta(t), \zeta(t)]$ is a constant, as one can see by differentiation of the second formula (52·7) with respect to $t$ and the use of (52·10), (52·5), (52·8). By differentiation of $H(y, z)$ and the equations (52·5) with respect to $t$ we see that the functions $y'$, $z'$ belonging to a solution of equations (52·5) are a solution of the accessory canonical equations (52·10) along which $\lambda = 0$. The *accessory equations* for the parametric problem are, by definition, the equations

$$\frac{d}{dt}\omega_{\eta_i'} - \omega_{\eta_i} = 0,$$

and an *accessory extremal* is a solution $\eta(t)$ of these equations. Every accessory extremal $\eta(t)$ defines by means of equations (52·6) a solution $\eta(t)$, $\zeta(t)$ of the accessory canonical equations (52·10) along which $\lambda = 0$, and conversely. For every family of solutions $y_i(t, \alpha)$, $z_i(t, \alpha)$ of the canonical equations (52·5), depending on a parameter $\alpha$, the derivatives $y_{i\alpha}$, $z_{i\alpha}$ are solutions of the canonical accessory equations (52·10); and if $H \equiv 0$ on the original family, then $\lambda \equiv 0$ on the corresponding accessory extremals. Since the equations (52·10) are linear and homogeneous in the variables $\eta$, $\zeta$ and their derivatives, it follows from a well-known theorem that a determinant whose columns are $2n$ solutions of these equations is either identically zero or everywhere different from zero.

LEMMA 52·1. *If* $\eta_{i\sigma}$, $\zeta_{i\sigma}$ $(\sigma = 1, \dots, 2n - 2)$ *are* $2n - 2$ *solutions of the canonical accessory equations with* $\lambda = 0$, *and if* $\eta$, $\zeta$ *is a solution with* $\lambda = 1$, *then the determinant*

$$\begin{vmatrix} \eta_{i\sigma} & y'_i & \eta_i \\ \zeta_{i\sigma} & z'_i & \zeta_i \end{vmatrix} \tag{52·11}$$

*is either identically zero or everywhere different from zero and is equal to the determinant* d(t) *of Lemma 48·1 multiplied by a non-vanishing factor.*

This follows at once from the fact that the product

$$\begin{vmatrix} \delta_{ij} & 0 & 0 \\ f_{y'_i y_j} & f_{y'_i y'_j} & y'_i \\ 0 & y'_j & 0 \end{vmatrix} \begin{vmatrix} \eta_{j\sigma} & y'_j & 0 & \eta_j \\ \eta'_{j\sigma} & y''_j & y'_j & \eta'_j \\ 0 & 0 & 0 & 1 \end{vmatrix}$$

is equal to the determinant (52·11) except for a non-vanishing factor.

A solution $\eta$, $\zeta$ with the properties described in the lemma may be determined by initial values at a particular value $t_0$ satisfying the equations $\eta_i = 0$, $H_{z_i}\zeta_i = 1$. The $2n - 2$ solutions $\eta_{i\sigma}$, $\zeta_{i\sigma}$ may be determined by any set of initial values which satisfies $\lambda = H_{y_k}\eta_k + H_{z_k}\zeta_k = 0$ at $t = t_0$ and makes the initial value of the determinant (52·11) different from zero. These are accessory extremals which determine conjugate points such as described in Lemma 48·2 and Theorem 48·1. A set of $n - 1$ solutions $\eta_{i\tau}$ effective for the determination of conjugate points as in Theorem 48·2 may be determined by a matrix of initial values $\eta_{i\tau} = 0$, $\zeta_{i\tau}$ with the columns of the matrix $\|\zeta_{i\tau}\|$ linearly independent and making $\lambda = 0$ at $t = t_0$.

**53. The imbedding theorem and the Hamilton-Jacobi theory.** The imbedding theorem for a non-singular extremal arc $E$ can be established anew by the use of canonical variables and equations. As in Section 27 for the non-parametric case, the same continuity properties for the family of imbedding extremals can be obtained by this method with the weaker hypothesis that the integrand function $f(y, y')$ has continuous derivatives of only the third order, instead of the fourth, in a neighborhood $R$ of the values $(y, y')$ belonging to $E$. We make the further restrictive hypotheses that the arc $E$ does not intersect itself in $y$-space and that the function $\varphi(y, y')$ is positive, so that the parameter $t$ can be so chosen that $\varphi \equiv 1$ along $E$.

The equations (52·1) defining canonical variables have as solutions the set of values $[y(t), z(t), y'(t), l = 0]$ belonging to the extremal arc $E$ which we are seeking to imbed. No two of these solutions have the same projection $(y, z)$, since the arc $E$ does not intersect itself. Furthermore, the functional determinant of the equations (52·1) with respect to the variables $y'$, $l$ is different from zero along the arc $E$, since $E$ is non-singular, as one may show by the methods used in proving Theorem 43·1. It now follows, with the help of well-known implicit function theorems, that there is a neighborhood $R$ of the sets $[y(t), y'(t), l = 0]$ belonging to $E$ which is transformed in one-to-one fashion into a neighborhood $S$ of the points $(y, z)$ belonging to $E$, and the functions (52·2) so defined in $S$ have continuous partial derivatives of at least the second order, since the same is true of the second members of equations (52·1) when $f(y, y')$ and $\varphi(y, y')$ have continuous third derivatives.

The second members of the canonical differential equations (52·5) are thus well defined and have continuous second derivatives in the neighborhood $S$ of the arc $E$. By the usual existence theorems for differential equations the unique solution of equations (52·5) through an initial point $(t^0, y^0, z^0)$ is defined by functions of the form

$$y_i(t-t^0,\ y^0,\ z^0)\ , \qquad z_i(t-t^0,\ y^0,\ z^0)\ , \tag{53·1}$$

which with their derivatives $y_{it}$, $z_{it}$ have continuous second partial derivatives in a neighborhood of the values $(t, t^0, y^0, z^0)$ belonging to the arc $E$. The argument $t^0$ occurs only in the difference $t - t^0$, since the second members of equations (52·5) do not contain $t$ explicitly. Let $t^0$, $y^{00}$, $z^{00}$ be a fixed set of values belonging to the arc $E$. Since from the homogeneity property of $\varphi$

$$\varphi(y,\ P) = P_i \varphi_{y'_i}(y,\ p) = 1\ ,$$

the values $P_i = H_{z_i}$ cannot vanish simultaneously; and we may assume, without loss of generality, that the notation is so chosen that $H_{z_n}(y^{00}, z^{00}) \neq 0$. Let $\eta_{i\sigma}$, $\zeta_{i\sigma}$ $(\sigma = 1, \ldots, 2n-2)$ be solutions of the canonical accessory equations (52·10) along $E$ with the properties described in Lemma 52·1. We define functions $y_i^0(a)$, $z_r^0(a)$ by the equations

$$\begin{aligned} y_i^0(a) &= y_i^{00} + \eta_{i\sigma}(t^0)\, a_\sigma\ , \\ z_r^0(a) &= z_r^{00} + \zeta_{i\sigma}(t^0)\, a_\sigma \end{aligned}$$

$$(i = 1, \ldots, n\ ; \qquad r = 1, \ldots, n-1\ ; \qquad \sigma = 1, \ldots, 2n-2)\ ,$$

and a final function $z_n^0(a)$ by the equation

$$H[y^0(a),\ z^0(a)] = 0\ ,$$

which has the initial solution $a = 0$, $z_n = z_n^{00}$ at which $H_{z_n} \neq 0$. The function $z_n^0(a)$ so determined has continuous derivatives of the third order, since $H(y, z)$ has such derivatives. Since for each column $\eta_{i\sigma}$, $\zeta_{i\sigma}$ of the determinant (52·11)

$$\lambda = H_{y_i}\eta_{i\sigma} + H_{z_i}\zeta_{i\sigma} = 0 ,$$

it follows without difficulty that $z_n^0(a)$ has the derivative $\zeta_{n\sigma}(t^0)$ at $a = 0$.

The $(2n - 2)$-parameter family of solutions of the canonical equations

$$y_i = Y_i(t, a) = y_i[t - t^0, y^0(a), z^0(a)] ,$$
$$z_i = Z_i(t, a) = z_i[t - t^0, y^0(a), z^0(a)] ,$$

obtained from (53·1) by substituting the functions $y^0(a)$, $z^0(a)$, is a family of extremals with the properties described in the imbedding theorem, Theorem 45·1. It contains the arc $E$ for the values $t_1 \leqq t \leqq t_2$, $a_\sigma = 0$. Its variations relative to the parameter $a_\sigma$ have the initial values $\eta_{i\sigma}(t^0)$, $\zeta_{i\sigma}(t^0)$ and satisfy the canonical accessory equations, and hence are identical with $\eta_{i\sigma}(t)$, $\zeta_{i\sigma}(t)$. The determinant of the family analogous to (45·3) is different from zero because the determinant (52·11) has that property. Thus the conclusions of the imbedding theorem are proved.

The imbedding theorem has to do with extremals and regions $R'$ and $S$ which are near to a given extremal arc $E$. Let us return to the somewhat more general regions described at the beginning of Section 52. The slope functions $p_i(y)$ of a field can be modified by a positive factor $\kappa(y)$ so that they satisfy the conditions $\varphi[y, p(y)] \equiv 1$. We have then the following theorem, which is fundamental for the Hamilton-Jacobi theory:

THEOREM 53·1. *For every field* F *the invariant integral taken from a fixed point* $y^0$ *to a variable point* y *defines a function* W(y) *having continuous second derivatives in* F *and satisfying the partial differential equation*

$$H(y, W_y) = 0 . \tag{53·2}$$

*Conversely, if in a region* F *a function* W(y) *with continuous second derivatives defines points* (y, z) = (y, $W_y$) *in* S *for every* y *in* F, *and satisfies the equation (53·2), then* F *is a field with the slope functions*

$$p_i(y) = P_i[y, W_y] \tag{53·3}$$

*which satisfy the condition* $\varphi[y, p(y)] \equiv 1$.

To prove this, one should note, first of all, that the condition $H(y, z) = 0$ is a necessary and sufficient condition for the equations

$$z_i = f_{y_i}(y, y') , \qquad \varphi(y, y') = 1$$

to have a solution $y'$ when $y$ and $z$ are given. This is a consequence of the equivalence of the systems (52·1) and (52·2). Furthermore, the condition is necessary and sufficient for the equations

$$z_i = f_{y'_i}(y, y')$$

by themselves to have a solution $y'$ when $y$ and $z$ are given, since a set $y$, $y'$ which satisfies these equations can always be made into a set which satisfies $\varphi = 1$ by multiplying the variables $y'$ by a suitable factor $\kappa > 0$. All of the equations $H(y, z) = 0$ obtained by using different functions $\varphi(y, y')$ in the equations (52·1) are equivalent because of the property which has just been proved.

The first part of the theorem is now an easy consequence of the definition

$$W(y) = \int_{y^0}^{y} f_{y'_i}[y, p(y)]\, dy_i \tag{53·4}$$

of $W(y)$, since it follows from this equation that

$$W_{y_i} = f_{y'_i}[y, p(y)] \tag{53·5}$$

and hence that the equation (53·2) is satisfied. Conversely, suppose that $W(y)$ has the properties described in the last part of the theorem. Then the functions $p_i(y)$ defined by equations (53·3) satisfy the equations (53·5). Consequently, the integral (53·4) is independent of the path in $F$, and $F$ is a field.

The equation (53·2) is called the *partial differential equation of Hamilton and Jacobi*. The surfaces $W(y) =$ constant, where $W$ is the function defined for a field $F$ as in Theorem 53·1, are the transversal surfaces of the field. These surfaces have properties like those described in Theorem 28·3 and provable in the same way.

There is a theorem for the parametric problem which describes the determination of extremals by means of a so-called *complete integral* $W(y, b_1, \ldots, b_{n-1}) + c$ of the Hamilton-Jacobi equation. In this theorem, whose results are analogous to those of Theorem 29·1 and Section 38 for non-parametric problems in $(n + 1)$-space, the function $W$ involved is supposed to have continuous partial derivatives of at least the third order and to have its matrix $\|W_{b_r y_k}\|$ of rank $n - 1$ at all sets $(y, b)$ such that $y$ is in a region $F$ of $y$-space and $b$ is in an $(n - 1)$-dimensional region $B$. Furthermore, the sets $(y, z) = (y, W_y)$ corresponding to such points $(y, b)$ are all supposed to be admissible.

THEOREM 53·2. *If for points* y *and* b *in regions* F *and* B *the complete integral* W(y, b) + c *of the Hamilton-Jacobi equation (53·2) has the properties described above, then every admissible arc* $E_{12}$ *interior to* F, *having no corners and satisfying the equations*

$$W_{b_r}(y, b) = a_r \qquad (r = 1, \ldots, n-1) \tag{53·6}$$

*for particular values* $a_{r0}$, $b_{r0}$, *is either already an extremal or else becomes one when its parameter* t *is changed in sign. It follows from this, also, that the equations (53·6) have as solutions a* (2n − 2)*-parameter family of extremals* $y_i(t, a, b)$ *which contains* $E_{12}$ *and has the properties described in the imbedding theorem, Theorem 45·1.*

To prove the theorem we note first that the equations

$$(53\cdot 7) \qquad H_{z_i} W_{y_i b_r} = 0\,, \qquad H_{y_i} + H_{z_k} W_{y_k y_i} = 0$$

are consequences of the equation (53·2). Furthermore, along the arc $E_{12}$ the functions $y_i$, $z_i = W_{y_i}$ satisfy the relations

$$(53\cdot 8) \qquad W_{b_r y_i} y_i' = 0\,, \qquad z_i' = W_{y_i y_k} y_k'\,.$$

These, with equations (53·7), show that the derivatives $y_i'$, $z_i'$ along $E_{12}$ are proportional to $H_{z_i'}$, $-H_{y_i'}$. If the paramater $t$ is properly transformed, and changed in sign if necessary, the proportionality becomes equality. The arc $E_{12}$ then satisfies the canonical equations (52·5) and has $H = 0$ along it from (53·2), and hence is an extremal.

To establish the second part of the theorem we first prove that the equations (53·6) are satisfied by a family of extremals $y_i(t, a, b)$ with the continuity properties described in the theorem. These equations have as an initial solution the set of values $y_{i0}$, $a_{r0}$, $b_{r0}$ belonging to an arbitrarily selected parameter value $t_0$ on $E_{12}$, and at least one determinant of the matrix $\|W_{b_r y_i}\|$ is different from zero at this solution. Hence by the usual implicit function theorems the equations (53·6) have a set of solutions $y_i = \eta_i(a, b)$ with continuous second derivatives near $(a_0, b_0)$ and such that $\eta_i(a_0, b_0) = y_{i0}$. The existence theorems for differential equations then tell us that for the equations

$$(53\cdot 9) \qquad y_i' = H_{z_i}[y,\ W_y(y,\ b)]$$

there exist unique solutions $y_i(t, a, b)$ determined by the initial values $\eta_i(a, b)$ at $t = t_0$ and having the desired continuity properties. On account of the first equation (53·7) and (53·9) the derivative $W_{b_r}$ is constant along these solutions, and the value of the constant is $a_r$, since the equation (53·6) is satisfied at $t = t_0$.

With the help of Lemma 52·1 we can further prove that the determinant (45·3) is different from zero along the arc $E_{12}$. For, if we define functions $z_i(t, a, b)$ in terms of $y_i(t, a, b)$ by the equations $z_i = W_{y_i}$, then the resulting curves are extremals and the sets $y_{ia_r}$, $z_{ia_r}$ and $y_{ib_r}$, $z_{ib_r}$ form $2n - 2$ solutions of the accessory canonical equations (52·10) on which $\lambda = 0$, according to the remarks in the paragraph preceding Lemma 52·1. For these solutions we form the determinant

$$\begin{vmatrix} y_{ia_r} & y_{ib_r} & y_i' & \eta_i \\ z_{ia_r} & z_{ib_r} & z_i' & \zeta_i \end{vmatrix}$$

described in Lemma 52·1. When we substitute the values

$$z_{ia_r} = W_{y_i y_k} y_{ka_r}\,, \qquad z_{ib_r} = W_{y_i y_k} y_{kb_r} + W_{y_i b_r}\,,$$

it follows, after a simple reduction, that the value of the determinant is a power of $-1$ times the product

$$\begin{vmatrix} W_{b_r y_k} \\ \zeta_k - W_{y_k y_i}\eta_i \end{vmatrix} \begin{vmatrix} y_{ka_s} & y'_k \end{vmatrix} .$$

But this product is equal to unity, as one sees with the help of the easy consequence $W_{b_r y_k} y_{ka_s} = \delta_{rs}$ of equation (53·6), the second equation (53·8), the canonical equations (52·5), and the fact that $H_{y_i}\eta_i + H_{z_i}\zeta_i = 1$ in Lemma 52·1.

**54. The construction of a complete integral of the Hamilton-Jacobi equation.** In the preceding paragraphs it has been shown that, when a complete integral $W(y, b) + c$ of the Hamilton-Jacobi equation (53·2) is known, a $(2n - 2)$-parameter family (45·2) of extremals can be determined by solving the equations $W_{b_r} = a_r$. Conversely it is true that, when the extremal family of the imbedding theorem is known, a complete integral can be constructed. These results are described in the following theorem:

THEOREM 54·1. *Every non-singular extremal arc* $E_{12}$ *can be imbedded in a* $(2n - 2)$*-parameter family of extremals* $y_i(t, a, b)$ *with the properties described in the imbedding theorem, Theorem 45·1, and with the further property that for every fixed set of values* $b_r$ $(r = 1, \ldots, n - 1)$ *the family is a Mayer family with the variable parameters* $a_r$*. Every region* F *of* y*-space which is simply covered with determinant* $|y_{ia_r}\ y'_i|$ *different from zero by such a Mayer family is a field with the slope functions* $p_i(y, b)$ *of the family. The value* $W(y, b)$ *of the invariant integral* $I^*$ *taken from a fixed point* $y_0$ *to a variable point* y *in the field defines a complete integral* $W(y, b) + c$ *of the Hamilton-Jacobi equation with the properties described in Theorem 53·2. Every complete integral is definable in this way.*

To prove this theorem let us consider the equations (49·6) with the function $U$ replaced by $U + a_r\beta_r$. The resulting equations have solutions $a_r(\alpha, \beta)$, $b_r(\alpha, \beta)$, $T(\alpha, \beta)$ having continuous second derivatives near the values $(\alpha, \beta) = (\alpha_0, 0)$ and such that $a_r(\alpha_0, 0) = a_{r0}$, $b_r(\alpha_0, 0) = b_{r0}$, $T(\alpha_0, 0) = t_0$, according to the argument in the last paragraph of Section 49. When the functions $a_r(\alpha, \beta)$, $b_r(\alpha, \beta)$ are substituted, the family (45·2) has functions of the form

$$y_i(t, \alpha, \beta) . \tag{54·1}$$

They define the arc $E$ for values $t_1 \leqq t \leqq t_2$, $\alpha_r = \alpha_{r0}$, $\beta_r = 0$ and have continuity properties like those of the functions (45·2).

The determinant analogous to (45·3) for the functions (54·1) is the product of (45·3) by the determinant

$$\begin{vmatrix} a_{r\alpha_s} & a_{r\beta_s} & 0 & 0 \\ b_{r\alpha_s} & b_{r\beta_s} & 0 & 0 \\ 0 & 0 & 1 & 0 \\ 0 & 0 & 0 & 1 \end{vmatrix} \tag{54·2}$$

and is different from zero if this last determinant does not vanish. If the determinant (54·2) were zero at the initial values $(\alpha, \beta) = (\alpha_0, 0)$, we should have constants $c_s$, $d_s$, not all zero, such that

$$a_{r\alpha_s} c_s + a_{r\beta_s} d_s = 0 \ , \qquad b_{r\alpha_s} c_s + b_{r\beta_s} d_s = 0 \ .$$

But from equations (49·6), with $U_{\alpha_r} + \beta_r$ in place of $U_{\alpha_r}$,

$$y_{ia_r} a_{r\alpha_s} + y_{ib_r} b_{r\alpha_s} + y_i' T_{\alpha_s} = Y_{i\alpha_s} \ ,$$

$$y_{ia_r} a_{r\beta_s} + y_{ib_r} b_{r\beta_s} + y_i' T_{\beta_s} = 0 \ .$$

$$Y_{i\alpha_r} f_{y_i' y_k'} (y_{ka_r}' a_{r\beta_s} + y_{kb_r}' b_{r\beta_s} + y_k'' T_{\beta_s}) = \delta_{rs} \ .$$

Multiplying the first of these equations by $c_s$, the second by $d_s$, and adding, we see that we should then have $c_s = T_{\beta_s} d_s = 0$ because the $(n-1)$-space $\Sigma$ and the extremal $E$ are not tangent and the determinant $|Y_{i\alpha_r} \ y_i'|$ is therefore not zero. Multiplying the last equations by $d_s$ and adding shows that we should also have $d_r = 0$, which with $c_s = 0$ is a contradiction.

Thus the family (54·1) contains the arc $E$ and has all the properties of the family (45·2) of the imbedding theorem with parameters $\alpha$, $\beta$ in place of $a$, $b$. Furthermore, we can see that for every fixed set of sufficiently small values $\beta$ this family is a Mayer family with the variable parameters $\alpha$, because of the arguments in Section 49. In every region $F$ of $y$-space simply covered by the family with determinant $|y_{i\alpha_r} \ y_i'|$ different from zero, the equations

(54·3) $$y_i(t, \alpha, \beta) = y_i$$

have solutions $t(y, \beta)$, $\alpha_r(y, \beta)$ with continuous second derivatives for $y$ in $F$ and for $\beta$ sufficiently small. The slope functions

(54·4) $$p_i(y, \beta) = y_i' [t(y, \beta), \alpha(y, \beta), \beta]$$

have their determinant $|p_{i\beta_r} \ p_i|$ different from zero. Otherwise there would be multipliers $c_r$, $c$, not all zero, such that

$$c_r p_{i\beta_r} + c p_i = 0 \ .$$

But from equations (54·3) and (54·4) we have

$$0 = y_{i\alpha_r} \alpha_{r\beta_s} + y_{i\beta_s} + y_i' t_{\beta_s} \ ,$$

$$p_{i\beta_s} = y_{i\alpha_r}' \alpha_{r\beta_s} + y_{i\beta_s}' + y_i'' t_{\beta_s}$$

from which it would follow that the constants

$$c_s \alpha_{r\beta_s} \ , \qquad c_s \ , \qquad c_s t_{\beta_s} \ , \qquad c$$

would satisfy the linear equations whose coefficients are the rows of the determinant analogous to (45·3) for the family (54·3). This would require $c_s = c = 0$, which is a contradiction.

The value of the integral $I^*$ taken from a fixed point $y_0$ to a variable point $y$ in the field $F$ is now a function $W(y, \beta)$ with the properties described in Theorem 53·2. It has the derivatives

$$W_{y_i} = f_{y'_i}[y, p(y, \beta)], \qquad W_{y_i\beta_r} = f_{y'_iy'_k}p_{k\beta_r}.$$

The matrix of derivatives $W_{y_i\beta_r}$ is of rank $n - 1$. Otherwise there would be multipliers $c_r$, not all zero, satisfying the equations

$$c_rW_{y_i\beta_r} = c_rf_{y'_iy'_k}p_{k\beta_r} = 0;$$

and the linear combinations $c_rp_{k\beta_r}$ would necessarily be proportional to the values $y'_k = p_k$, which is impossible since the determinant $|p_{i\beta_r}\ p_i|$ is different from zero.

The last statement of the Theorem 54·1 is easily proved. For every fixed set of values $b$ a complete integral $W(y, b) + c$ defines a field in the region $F$ with slope functions $p(y, b) = W_y(y, b)$, according to Theorem 53·1. The extremals of these fields form a $(2n - 2)$-parameter family defined by functions $y_i(t, a, b)$ with the properties described in Theorem 54·1. Thus the theorem is completely proved.

**55. Other theories of parametric problems.** There are a number of methods for the discussion of parametric problems of the calculus of variations other than that presented in the preceding sections. In the present section a brief description of some of these will be given, with comments on their relative convenience.

Since the choice of a parameter on a parametric arc can be made quite arbitrarily, it turns out to be reasonable to formulate the parametric problem as that of finding, in a class of arcs $y_i(t)$ $(0 \leqq t \leqq t_2)$ joining two given points *1* and *2* in $y$-space and satisfying an equation of the form

$$\varphi(y, y') = 1, \tag{55·1}$$

one which minimizes the parametric integral $I$ in equation (42·1). The function $\varphi$ is supposed to be positive in the region $R$ of points $(y, y')$ under consideration and, like the integrand function $f$, is assumed to be positively homogeneous with order one in the variables $y'$.

The equation (55·1) is really only equivalent to a specification of the parameter to be used on a particular arc $y(\tau)$ $(\tau_1 \leqq \tau \leqq \tau_2)$. For, if on this arc the function $\varphi[y(\tau), y'(\tau)]$ is represented by $\psi(\tau)$, then in terms of the new parameter

$$t = \int_{\tau_1}^{\tau} \psi(\tau)\, d\tau$$

the arc will be defined on an interval $0 \leqq t \leqq t_2$ and will satisfy the equation (55·1).

Formulated in the manner described in the next to the last paragraph above, the parametric problem becomes, in the space of points $(t, y)$, a non-parametric problem of the type usually designated by the name of Lagrange. It is a special case of the problem of Bolza, which will be discussed in a later chapter of this book. The theory of such problems is not so simple as that of problems having no differential equations, such as (55·1), as side conditions. It is complicated further in the problem formulated above because in $(t, y)$-space the second end-value $t_2$ is not fixed. At the initial point the values $t = 0$, $y_i(0) = y_{i1}$ are all prescribed; but at the second end-point we require only $y_i(t_2) = y_{i2}$, leaving the coordinate $t_2$ variable.

In spite of these complexities, the theory of the problem as a problem of Lagrange has been very suggestive for the developments of the preceding pages. If we use the notation $G = f + l\varphi$, the equations for the extremals and canonical variables of the Lagrange problem are, respectively,

$$\frac{d}{dt} G_{y'_i} - G_{y_i} = 0 \ ,$$

$$z_i = G_{y'_i} = f_{y'_i} + l\varphi_{y'_i} \, , \quad \varphi = 1 \ .$$

For the special case when $\varphi = (y'_i \, y'_i)^{1/2}$, these suggested the treatment of the equations of the extremals in Section 45 and the equations (52·1) defining canonical variables.

For the case when the integrand function $f$ is positive in the region $R$ of points $(y, y')$ in which the continuity properties of $f$ are prescribed, Wren has devised a quite different method. The function $g(y, y')$ defined by the equation $2g = f^2$ is positively homogeneous of order two in the variables $y'$; and from a well-known property of homogeneous functions

$$2g = g_{ij}(y, y') \, y'_i y'_j \ ,$$

where $g_{ij}$ is a notation for the derivative $\partial^2 g / \partial y'_i \, \partial y'_j$. The integral (42·1) is then expressible in the form

$$I = \int_{t_1}^{t_2} (2g)^{1/2} dt = \int_{t_1}^{t_2} (g_{ij} y'_i y'_j)^{1/2} dt \ .$$

The length integrals in the theory of Riemannian geometries and the integrals which play a fundamental role in the theory of relativity are of the form last given with coefficients $g_{ij}$ which do not contain the variables $y'$. Analogous theories have been studied for the more general integrals $I$ for which the coefficients $g_{ij}$ contain the variables $y'$. A space in which the length of an arc is defined to be the value of such an integral is called a "Finsler space." In all of these theories tensor analysis plays an important role. The formulation of Wren seems especially well adapted to the use of this mechanism. It is interesting to note that the defining equations for canonical variables and the form of the Hamilton-Jacobi theory, presented by Wren, were suggested by the formulation of the problem as a Lagrange problem with the function $\varphi$ in equation (55·1) equal to the integrand function $f$ itself.

In the discussion of the accessory equations (47·2) and their solutions frequent use was made of the so-called "normal solutions" $\eta_i$, which satisfy the equation $y'_i\eta_i = 0$. In the theory of the parametric problem as a Lagrange problem it turns out that a role equivalent to that of this last equation is played by the equation

$$\varphi_{y_i}\eta_i + \varphi_{y'_i}\eta'_i = 0 \; . \tag{55·2}$$

The use of either one of them is compatible with the fact that the accessory equations are not independent, as indicated by the third equation (43·7). Hestenes has used the equation $y'_i\,\eta'_i$ = constant, which is closely related to the equation (55·2) for the special case when $\varphi = (y'_i\, y'_i)^{1/2}$. He has also called attention to the fact that a large class of equations other than (55·2) can be used in the same way.

There is one final method of reducing a parametric problem to a non-parametric problem in a neighborhood of an arc $E$ not intersecting itself whose minimizing properties are to be studied. If the functions defining $E$ are $y_i(t)(t_1 \leqq t \leqq t_2;\ i = 1, \ldots, n)$, let us select $n-1$ vectors $\xi_{ir}(t)(r = 1, \ldots, n-1)$ such that for each value of $t$ on the interval $t_1 \leqq t \leqq t_2$ the determinant

$$| \, y'_i(t) \qquad \xi_{ir}(t) \, | \tag{55·3}$$

is different from zero. The equations

$$y_i = y_i(t) + u_r \xi_{ir}(t) \tag{55·4}$$

then have as initial solutions the values $(y, t, u) = [y(t), t, 0]$ belonging to the arc $E$, and at these solutions the functional determinant of the second members is the determinant (55·3), which is different from zero. From the usual implicit function theorems it follows that the equations (55·4) define a one-to-one correspondence between the points $y$ of a neighborhood $F$ of the arc $E$ and the points $(t, u)$ of a neighborhood $T$ of the values $(t, u)$ belonging to $E$. The solutions $t(y)$, $u_r(y)$ of the equations (55·4) defined over $F$ will have continuous derivatives of as many orders as are possessed by the functions $y_i(t)$, provided that the vectors $\xi_{ir}(t)$ are chosen to have continuous derivatives of the same orders.

After the transformation (55·4) the equations of the arc $E$ take the simple non-parametric form $u_r = 0$ $(r = 1, \ldots, n-1)$ in $(t, u)$-space, and the integrand $f(y, y')$ becomes a function $g(t, u, u')$. All of the necessary and the sufficient conditions for an arc to minimize the transformed integral $I$ in non-parametric form are applicable to $E$ in $(t, u)$-space. For a complete theory of the original parametric problem it is necessary to extend the condition of Weierstrass and the sufficiency proofs to include all parametrically admissible directions and curves and, further, to interpret the results for the non-parametric problem in terms of the original coordinates $y$ and integrand function $f(y, y')$.

This method of transformation of coordinates is an interesting and sometimes very useful method, which has, however, features which make it not always desirable. In the first place, the determination of a transformation (55·4) with the desired properties is difficult and sometimes quite impractical if the arc $E$ has corners. To preserve for the transformed integrand $g(t, u, u')$ the continuity properties originally assumed for the integrand function $f(y, y')$, it is necessary that the functions $y_i(t)$ defining the arc $E$ should have continuous derivatives of at least the fifth order. The interpretation for the parametric problem in $y$-space of the results for the non-parametric problem in $(t, u)$-space and the extension of the condition of Weierstrass and the sufficiency theorems mentioned above involve labor comparable with that required in making the proofs directly, as in the preceding sections of this chapter.

# CHAPTER VI

## PROBLEMS WITH VARIABLE END-POINTS

**56. Introduction.** The problem of the calculus of variations considered in the preceding chapters is concerned with the determination of a minimizing arc for an integral

$$I = \int_{x_1}^{x_2} f(x, y, z, y', z')\, dx \qquad (56\cdot 1)$$

of the form $(1\cdot 6)$ in a class of arcs joining two fixed points, *1* and *2*, in *xyz*-space. Such a problem is said to have fixed end-points. A natural modification would be to seek a minimizing arc in a class of arcs joining a fixed surface to a fixed point, or a fixed surface to a fixed curve. Other similar problems suggest themselves at once. They are called "problems with variable end-points," for reasons which are evident.

The brothers James and John Bernoulli were apparently the first to consider a problem with variable end-points. About the year 1697 they sought to determine in a vertical plane an arc down which a particle will fall from a fixed point *1* to a fixed curve $L$ in the shortest time, when started at *1* with a given initial velocity. Euler, in his famous book of 1744 on the calculus of variations, studied much more general problems with variable end-points but did not formulate his end-conditions clearly. About ten years later Lagrange and Borda found that the problem of the Bernoullis described above, with first end-point variable instead of the second, or both end-points variable on fixed curves, had quite new characteristics. As a result of his study of these special problems, Lagrange devised others with variable end-points of great generality, including those before described by Euler, and found first necessary conditions for a minimum. Not much further progress was made until about the year 1898, when Kneser defined what is called a "focal point" and proved a sufficiency theorem for a general problem in the plane with one end-point variable. His focal point is the analogue, for a problem with one variable end-point, of the conjugate point for a fixed end-point problem. In 1902 and 1904 the author of these pages discussed the dependence of the focal point upon the curvature of the initial end-curve and treated in detail problems in the plane for which both end-points are allowed to vary on curves. Within the past few years a similar discussion of a very general problem, formulated by Bolza in 1913, has been given by Graves, Hestenes, Bliss, and others. Among the most general problems of the calculus of variations so far formulated, the problem of Bolza is in many ways the most convenient in form. Its theory is presented in Part II of this book.

The purpose of the present chapter is to present, in the most general form yet devised, the theory of the problems of the calculus of variations with variable end-points associated with the problems with fixed end-points which have been studied in preceding chapters. In Sections 57 and 58 the problems in $xyz$-space with second end-point fixed and first end-point variable on a surface or a curve are studied in a preliminary way by relatively geometrical methods closely related to those of the preceding chapters. In Sections 59–64 a very general problem with variable end-points in $(x, y_1, \ldots, y_n)$-space is formulated, and the theory of necessary and of sufficient conditions for a minimum is developed. The fourth necessary condition which appears in the theory, developed in Section 64, is a modification by Goldstine of an earlier one given for the problem of Bolza by Hestenes. Sufficiency theorems are proved in Sections 60 and 63 with the help of an important theorem due to Hahn and with the aid, further, of the theory of the so-called "extremal integral." When only one end-point is variable, the condition which is usually called the "fourth necessary condition" can be stated in terms of the focal point of the manifold on which the initial end-point is allowed to vary. The theory of these focal points and the dependence of the focal point of a curve on the first curvature of the curve are studied in Sections 65 and 66. Finally, in Section 67, some interesting theorems concerning problems in the $(x, y)$-plane with variable end-points are deduced.

**57. Problems in three-space with one end-point variable on a surface.** The problem to be studied in this section is that of finding in the class of admissible arcs joining a fixed surface $S$ to a fixed point *2* one which minimizes the integral $I$ in equation (56·1). The properties which characterize a minimizing arc can readily be deduced by methods similar to those applied in the preceding chapters for problems in three-space with fixed end-points.

Let $E_{12}$ represent, as before, a particular admissible arc whose minimizing properties are to be studied. It will be supposed that the fixed surface $S$ is defined by functions

$$\xi(\alpha, \beta), \quad \eta(\alpha, \beta), \quad \zeta(\alpha, \beta), \tag{57·1}$$

which have continuous derivatives of the third order near the values $(\alpha_1, \beta_1)$ which define the intersection point *1* of $S$ and $E_{12}$.

Since every admissible arc joining the end-points *1* and *2* of $E_{12}$ also joins the surface $S$ with *2*, it is evident that $E_{12}$ must satisfy all the necessary conditions for a minimizing arc in the class of arcs joining its end-points—in particular, the necessary condition I of Section 6 and the necessary conditions II and III of Weierstrass and Legendre of Section 9. It will be seen presently that a further necessary condition, called the "transversality condition," must be satisfied at the intersection point *1* of $S$ and $E_{12}$ and that the condition of Jacobi for the fixed end-point case can be replaced by a stronger condition of a similar character.

In order to deduce the so-called "tranversality condition," let $\Gamma$ be an arbitrary curve on $S$ through the point *1*, defined by functions $\alpha(a)$, $\beta(a)$ which have continuous second derivatives near the parameter value $a_1$ defining the point *1*. The curve $\Gamma$ can be joined to the point *2* by a one-parameter family of admissible arcs containing $E_{12}$ as a member, and Theorem 8·1 of Chapter I is applicable to the family. For example, when the arc $E_{12}$ is defined by functions $y(x)$, $z(x)$ ($x_1 \leqq x \leqq x_2$), such a family is defined by functions

$$y(x) + \{\eta[\alpha(a), \beta(a)] - y(\xi)\}\varphi(x, a),$$

$$z(x) + \{\zeta[\alpha(a), \beta(a)] - z(\xi)\}\varphi(x, a),$$

where

$$\varphi(x, a) = \frac{x - x_2}{\xi[\alpha(a), \beta(a)] - x_2}.$$

The arcs of this family intersect the curve $\Gamma$ for $x = \xi\,[\alpha(a), \beta(a)]$ and pass through the point *2*, and the family further contains the arc $E_{12}$ for the parameter value $a = a_1$. According to Theorem 8·1, the value of the integral $I$ taken along a curve of the family is a function of the parameter $a$, whose differential at the value $a_1$ defining $E_{12}$ in the family is

$$dI = -f\,dx - (dy - y'dx)\,f_{y'} - (dz - z'dx)\,f_{z'}\,|^1,$$

where the differentials $dx$, $dy$, $dz$ belong to $\Gamma$ and the element $(x, y, z, y', z')$ in $f$ and in its derivatives belongs to $E_{12}$. If $I(E_{12})$ is to be a minimum, this differential must vanish; and since $\Gamma$ is an arbitrary curve on $S$ through the point *1*, the following theorem is established:

THEOREM 57·1. THE TRANSVERSALITY CONDITION. *An admissible arc* $E_{12}$ *is said to satisfy the transversality condition at its intersection point* 1 *with a surface* S *if the equation*

$$(f - y'f_{y'} - z'f_{z'})\,dx + f_{y'}dy + f_{z'}dz = 0$$

*is satisfied by every direction* dx:dy:dz *tangent to* S *at the point* 1, *the arguments* x, y, z, y', z' *in* f *and its derivatives being those of the arc* $E_{12}$ *at* 1. *Under these circumstances the surface* S *is said to cut the arc* $E_{12}$ *transversally at the point* 1, *according to the definition of Section 28. Every minimizing arc for the problem of this section must satisfy the transversality condition.*

The necessary condition analogous to that of Jacobi, which is now to be deduced, applies only in case the minimizing arc $E_{12}$ is a non-singular extremal arc cut transversally by the surface $S$ at the point *1* and not tangent to $S$ at the point *1*. Besides these properties, we shall also assume that the surface $S$ is non-singular at the point *1*. Then there is a two-parameter family of extremals

$$y(x, \alpha, \beta), \quad z(x, \alpha, \beta) \tag{57·2}$$

containing $E_{12}$ for parameter values $(\alpha_1, \beta_1)$ and having the following properties. The members of the family are cut by $S$ transversally at $x = \xi(\alpha, \beta)$. The functions (57·2) and their first and second derivatives with respect to $x$ have continuous second partial derivatives for values $(x, \alpha, \beta)$ in a neighborhood of those belonging to $E_{12}$. Finally, the determinant

$$\Delta(x, \alpha, \beta) = y_\alpha z_\beta - y_\beta z_\alpha$$

is not identically zero along $E_{12}$. The existence of this family is a consequence of the arguments already applied to equations (20·7) for the particular case when the function $W$ in those equations is identically zero. The determinant $\Delta$ of the family is different from zero at the point *1* on $E_{12}$, since the identities

$$\eta(\alpha, \beta) = y(\xi, \alpha, \beta), \qquad \zeta(\alpha, \beta) = z(\xi, \alpha, \beta)$$

shows that at $x = \xi(\alpha, \beta)$

$$y_\alpha = \eta_\alpha - y'\xi_\alpha, \qquad z_\alpha = \zeta_\alpha - z'\xi_\alpha,$$

$$y_\beta = \eta_\beta - y'\xi_\beta, \qquad z_\beta = \zeta_\beta - z'\xi_\beta.$$

As in the argument following equations (20·7), the determinant of these quantities is different from zero at the point *1* when $S$ has an ordinary point and $E_{12}$ is not tangent to $S$ at *1*, as has been presupposed.

Definition of Focal Points. Let $E_{12}$ be an extremal arc cut transversally by a non-singular surface $S$ at the point *1* and not tangent to $S$ at *1*. If $\Delta(x, \alpha, \beta)$ is the determinant of the two-parameter family of extremals (57·2) cut transversally by the surface $S$ and containing $E_{12}$ for the parameter values $\alpha_1, \beta_1$, then the points determined on $E_{12}$ by the zeros of $\Delta(x, \alpha_1, \beta_1)$ are called the *focal points* of $S$ on $E_{12}$. As we have seen in Section 13, they will, in general, be points of contact of $E_{12}$ with the enveloping surface of the family (57·2).

It is not difficult to see that the focal points of the surface $S$, so defined, are independent of the parametric representation chosen for $S$. For, if in the functions (57·1) defining $S$ the parameters $\alpha, \beta$ are replaced by functions $\alpha(\gamma, \delta)$, $\beta(\gamma, \delta)$ of two new parameters, the family (57·2) with the original parameters $\alpha, \beta$ will go into a second family with similar properties. The determinants $\Delta(x, \alpha, \beta)$ and $\Delta(x, \gamma, \delta)$ of the two families will differ only by a non-vanishing factor independent of $x$.

The argument used in the proof of Theorem 13·2 shows that, except in special circumstances, there will be associated with a focal point on $E_{12}$ a one-parameter family of extremals belonging to the family (57·2), containing $E_{12}$, and having an envelope which touches $E_{12}$ at the focal point. The envelope theorem, Theorem 10·2, then holds for this family; and the method used in Section 10 for the proof of Jacobi's condition justifies the following theorem:

Theorem 57·2. The Focal-Point Condition. *A non-singular extremal arc* $E_{12}$ *cut transversally by a non-singular surface* S *at the point* 1, *and not tangent to* S *at* 1, *is said to satisfy the focal-point condition if there is no focal point of* S *on* $E_{12}$ *between* 1 *and* 2. *Every non-singular minimizing arc for the problem of this section must be an extremal and satisfy the focal-point condition.*

The proof of this theorem indicated above has the same limitations as the corresponding geometric proof of the Jacobi condition in the fixed end-point case. However, as in the case of fixed end-points, the theorem can be proved with greater generality by the use of the second variation. This will be done for a more general problem in Section 60 below.

The sufficiency theorems for the problem of this section are readily deducible from the reasoning in Sections 16 and 19 of Chapter II. The Roman numeral I will be here used to designate the necessary condition of Section 6 plus the transversality condition of Theorem 57·1. This grouping is justified by the fact that the two analogous conditions for the more general problem of Bolza, which will be discussed in Part II of this book, are provable together, and together constitute the famous multiplier rule for that problem. The notations $II_N$ and III′ will denote, as in Section 16, the strengthened conditions of Weierstrass and Legendre; and the symbol IV′ will be used to denote the focal-point condition strengthened so as to exclude the point *2* on $E_{12}$ from being a focal point of $S$. Sufficient conditions for a minimum are then as follows:

THEOREM 57·3. *Let* $E_{12}$ *be an admissible arc without corners cut at a single point* 1 *by a surface* S *which is non-singular and not tangent to the arc* $E_{12}$ *at* 1. *If* $E_{12}$ *satisfies the conditions I, III′, IV′ defined above in this section, there is a neighborhood* $R_1$ *of the values* (x, y, z, y′, z′) *belonging to* $E_{12}$ *such that the inequality* $I(C_{32}) > I(E_{12})$ *holds for every admissible arc* $C_{32}$ *in* $R_1$ *joining* S *with* 2 *and not identical with* $E_{12}$. *If* $E_{12}$ *is non-singular and satisfies the conditions I,* $II_N$*, IV′, then there is a neighborhood* F *of the values* (x, y, z) *on* $E_{12}$ *such that the inequality holds for every admissible arc* $C_{32}$ *in* F *joining* S *with* 2 *and not identical with* $E_{12}$.

To prove these results, one should first notice that the conditions I, III′ imply, as in the fixed end-point case, that $E_{12}$ is a non-singular extremal arc and hence belongs to a two-parameter family (57·2) of extremals cut transversally by the surface $S$. The determinant $\Delta(x, \alpha_1, \beta_1)$ of this family is different from zero, not only at the point *1* but at every point of $E_{12}$, since the surface $S$ has no focal point on $E_{12}$ according to the condition IV′. For a sufficiently small value $\epsilon$ the extremal arcs defined in the family by values $x$, $\alpha$, $\beta$ satisfying the conditions

$$x_1-\epsilon < x < x_2+\epsilon\,, \qquad |\alpha-\alpha_1| < \epsilon\,, \qquad |\beta-\beta_1| < \epsilon$$

will simply cover an open region $F$ of $xyz$-space. No two of them can, in fact, intersect when $\epsilon$ is small, as one sees by an argument similar to that of Section 15. Furthermore, the usual implicit function theorems applied to the equations

$$y = y(x,\ \alpha,\ \beta)\,, \qquad z = z(x,\ \alpha,\ \beta)$$

show that every point $(x, y, z)$ which is covered by the extremals, has a neighborhood which is also covered, so that $F$ is an open region. For sufficiently small values $\epsilon$ no one of the extremals will intersect the surface $S$ more than once, since $E_{12}$ itself has this property by hypothesis. According to Theorem 20·1, the region $F$ is a field with the slope functions of the family, since the extremals of the family are cut transversally by the surface $S$. The value of the Hilbert integral $I^*$ with the slope functions $p(x, y, z)$, $q(x, y, z)$ of the field is zero along every arc $L$ in $F$ on the transversal surface $S$.

The integral formula

$$(57\cdot 3) \quad I(C_{32}) - I(E_{12}) = \int_{C_{32}} E(x, y, z, p, q, y', z')\,dx ,$$

analogous to the formula (19·1), holds for every admissible arc $C_{32}$ in $F$ joining the surface $S$ with the point *2*. For, if $L_{13}$ be an arc on $S$ in $F$ joining the points *1* and *3*, then it follows, from the properties of the invariant integral $I^*$ of the field, that

$$\begin{aligned} I(C_{32}) - I(E_{12}) &= I(C_{32}) - I^*(E_{12}) \\ &= I(C_{32}) - I^*(L_{13}+C_{32}) \\ &= I(C_{32}) - I^*(C_{32}) , \end{aligned}$$

since $I^*(L_{13}) = 0$. When the integrals for $I(C_{32})$ and $I^*(C_{32})$ are substituted in the second member of the last equation, the formula (57·3) is obtained. The remainder of the sufficiency proof is a repetition of the reasoning used in the proofs of Theorems 16·1 and 16·2.

**58. Problems in three-space with one end-point variable on a curve.** The problem of minimizing an integral $I$ in the class of admissible arcs joining a fixed curve $L$ to a fixed point *2* in *xyz*-space has been studied by Bliss and Mason[1] for the parametric case. The theory of the problem is complicated, relative to that of the last section, by the fact that the two-parameter family of extremals cut transversally by the fixed curve $L$ does not simply cover a neighborhood of $L$, namely, the points on the curve $L$ itself. In the following paragraphs a method suggested by Hestenes, and quite different from that of Bliss and Mason, has been adopted for the non-parametric case. It makes use of the results in the last section for the problem with one end-point variable on a surface.

For the development of the theory of the problem here to be discussed, it can first be shown, by methods used in preceding pages, that for a minimizing arc $E_{12}$ the conditions I, II, III described in the earlier paragraphs of this chapter must be satisfied. The transversality requirement in condition I follows from Theorem 57·1 if in the proof and statement of this theorem we replace the surface $S$ by the curve $L$. The curve $L$ is supposed to be defined by functions

$$\xi(a) , \quad \eta(a) , \quad \zeta(a) \qquad\qquad (a' \leqq a \leqq a'') ,$$

which have continuous third derivatives and which are such that $L$ does not intersect itself and has on it no singular point.

In order to formulate a condition IV for this problem with first end-point variable, we assume that the arc $E_{12}$ whose minimizing properties are to be stud-

[1] "The Properties of Curves in Space Which Minimize a Definite Integral," *Transactions of the American Mathematical Society*, IX (1908), 440–66; "Fields of Extremals in Space," *ibid.*, XI (1910), 325–40.

ied is a non-singular extremal arc cut transversally by $L$ so that at the intersection point $1$ of $E_{12}$ and $L$ the condition

$$(f - y'f_{y'} - z'f_{z'})\,\xi_a + f_{y'}\eta_a + f_{z'}\zeta_a = 0 \tag{58·1}$$

is satisfied. Furthermore, we assume that the function $f$ is different from zero at the element $(x, y, z, y', z')$ belonging to the point $1$ on $E_{12}$. This condition implies that the curve $L$ is not tangent to $E_{12}$ at the point $1$, since equation (58·1) and the identity of the lines through $1$ having the directions $1:y':z'$ and $\xi_a:\eta_a:\zeta_a$ would imply that $f = 0$ at 1. Let us consider, then, a two-parameter family of extremals

$$y(x, a, \beta), \qquad z(x, a, \beta) \tag{58·2}$$

containing the arc $E_{12}$ for values $x, a, \beta$ satisfying conditions of the form $x_1 \leqq x \leqq x_2$, $a = a_0$, $\beta = \beta_0$, and such that each extremal of the family is cut transversally by the curve $L$ at the point defined on the extremal by the value $x = \xi(a)$. If the determinant $\Delta(x, a, \beta) = y_a z_\beta - y_\beta z_a$ of the family is not identically zero along $E_{12}$, a point defined on $E_{12}$ by a zero of $\Delta(x, a_0, \beta_0)$ distinct from $x_1$ is called a *focal point of the curve* L *on* $E_{12}$. The focal-point condition of Theorem 57·2 is then easily seen to be applicable to the present problem if in its proof and statement the surface $S$ is replaced by the curve $L$.

In order to prove the existence of a family of extremals (58·2) cut transversally by the arc $L$ and having the properties described above, consider a direction $l:m:n$ transversal to $E_{12}$ at the point $1$ and not in the plane determined by the tangents to $L$ and $E_{12}$ at that point. The equations

$$\begin{aligned} -H\xi_a + u\eta_a + v\zeta_a &= 0\,, \\ -Hl + um + vn &= \beta - \beta_0\,, \end{aligned} \tag{58·3}$$

in which $\beta_0$ is a quite arbitrarily selected constant and the arguments of the Hamiltonian function $H$ are $(x, y, z, u, v) = [\xi(a), \eta(a), \zeta(a), u, v]$, are similar to equations (20·7) with the variables $x, y, z, y', z'$ replaced by the canonical variables $x, y, z, u, v$. They have the special solution $(a, \beta, u, v) = (a_0, \beta_0, u_1, v_1)$, where $u_1$ and $v_1$ are the values of $f_{y'}$ and $f_{z'}$ at the point $1$ on $E_{12}$. At this solution the functional determinant of the first members of equations (58·3) with respect to $u, v$ is

$$\begin{vmatrix} \eta_a - y'\xi_a & \zeta_a - z'\xi_a \\ m - y'l & n - z'l \end{vmatrix} = \begin{vmatrix} 1 & \xi_a & l \\ y' & \eta_a & m \\ z' & \zeta_a & n \end{vmatrix}, \tag{58·4}$$

since on the extremal arc $E_{12}$ we have $y' = H_u$, $z' = H_v$. The last determinant is different from zero at the point $1$ because at that point the three ratios $(1:y':z')$, $(\xi_a:\eta_a:\zeta_a)$, $(l:m:n)$ determine lines which are not coplanar, according to the hypothesis made above. Consequently, the equations (58·3) have solutions $u(a, \beta)$, $v(a, \beta)$ with continuous second derivatives near the values $(a_0, \beta_0)$ and such that $u(\alpha_0, \beta_0) = u_1$, $v(\alpha_0, \beta_0) = v_1$. The family of extremals obtained by substituting the initial values $\xi(\alpha)$, $\eta(\alpha)$, $\zeta(\alpha)$, $u(\alpha, \beta)$, $v(\alpha, \beta)$ in equations (27·4) is a two-parameter family (58·2) cut transversally by the arc $L$ at the value $x = \xi(\alpha)$.

If the Legendre condition III holds at the initial point *1* of the non-singular extremal arc $E_{12}$, then the family (58·2) has a determinant $\Delta(x, \alpha_0, \beta_0)$ which vanishes at $x_1$ but is different from zero near $x_1$, so that there is no focal point of the curve $L$ determined by this family on $E_{12}$ near the point *1*. To prove this we note first that the equations

$$(58\cdot5) \quad \eta(\alpha) = y[\xi(\alpha), \alpha, \beta], \qquad \zeta(\alpha) = z[\xi(\alpha), \alpha, \beta]$$

hold along the curve $L$. By differentiation with respect to $\alpha$ and $\beta$ these equations evidently imply that at the point *1*

$$y_\alpha = \eta_\alpha - y'\xi_\alpha = c_1, \quad y_\beta = 0,$$

$$z_\alpha = \zeta_\alpha - z'\xi_\alpha = c_2, \quad z_\beta = 0,$$

where $c_1$ and $c_2$ are merely notations for what precedes them. By an application of Taylor's formula to the column $y_\beta$, $z_\beta$ of the determinant $\Delta(x, \alpha_0, \beta_0)$ it follows that this determinant is the product of $(x - x_1)$ by a factor which reduces at $x = x_1$ to

$$(58\cdot6) \qquad \begin{vmatrix} y_\alpha & y'_\beta \\ z_\alpha & z'_\beta \end{vmatrix} = \begin{vmatrix} c_1 & y'_\beta \\ c_2 & z'_\beta \end{vmatrix}.$$

Differentiation with respect to $\beta$ of equations (58·3) with their solutions $u(\alpha, \beta)$, $v(\alpha, \beta)$ substituted gives the equations

$$c_1 u_\beta + c_2 v_\beta = 0, \qquad (m - H_u l)\, u_\beta + (n - H_v l)\, v_\beta = 1,$$

which show that the derivatives $u_\beta$, $v_\beta$ are not both zero and that the determinant (58·6) is $u_\beta y'_\beta + v_\beta z'_\beta$ except for a non-vanishing factor. But

$$u(\alpha, \beta) = f_{y'}\{\xi(\alpha), \eta(\alpha), \zeta(\alpha), y'[\xi(\alpha), \alpha, \beta], z'[\xi(\alpha), \alpha, \beta]\}$$

with a similar expression for $v$, so that

$$(58\cdot7) \qquad \begin{aligned} u_\beta &= f_{y'y'}y'_\beta + f_{y'z'}z'_\beta, \qquad v_\beta = f_{z'y'}y'_\beta + f_{z'z'}z'_\beta, \\ u_\beta y'_\beta + v_\beta z'_\beta &= f_{y'y'}y'^2_\beta + 2f_{y'z'}y'_\beta z'_\beta + f_{z'z'}z'^2_\beta. \end{aligned}$$

Since $u_\beta$, $v_\beta$ are not both zero, it follows that this last expression is different from zero because of the non-singularity of $E_{12}$ and the condition III, which is supposed to hold at *1*. Evidently $\Delta(x, \alpha_0, \beta_0)$ is zero at $x = x_1$ but different from zero elsewhere near that value.

It should perhaps be noted that the assumption of the validity of the condition III at the point *1* on the arc $E_{12}$ is more than is necessary to insure that the determinant $\Delta(x, \alpha_0, \beta_0)$ does not vanish near $x = x_1$. It would suffice merely to assume that the particular expression (58·7) is different from zero at the point *1*.

The following theorem is analogous to Theorem 57·3:

THEOREM 58·1. *Let* $E_{12}$ *be an admissible arc without corners in* xyz-*space, cut at a single point* 1 *by a non-singular curve* L *and such that the integrand function* f *is different from zero at the point* 1 *on* $E_{12}$. *Then for the problem of minimizing the integral* I *in the class of admissible arcs joining the curve* L *to the point* 2 *the conditions I, III′, IV′ of the preceding paragraphs are sufficient for* $I(E_{12})$ *to be a weak relative minimum, and the conditions I,* $II_N$, *IV′ with the non-singularity of* $E_{12}$ *are sufficient for* $I(E_{12})$ *to be a strong relative minimum.*

The proof of this theorem is an immediate consequence of Theorem 57·3 and the following lemma:

LEMMA 58·1. *If a non-singular extremal arc* $E_{12}$ *is cut transversally at the point* 1 *by a curve* L, *has* $f \neq 0$ *at the point* 1, *and contains no focal point of* L, *then through the curve* L *there is a non-singular surface* S *transversal and not tangent to* $E_{12}$ *at the point* 1, *and such that on* $E_{12}$ *there is no focal point of* S.

It is easy to see from the results of Section 57 that when this lemma has been proved the minimizing property of the arc $E_{12}$ will be established. From Theorem 57·3 it follows, in fact, that $E_{12}$ will be a minimizing arc in the class of admissible arcs joining the surface $S$ to the point *2*, and hence also in the class of such arcs joining the curve $L$ to *2*.

To prove the lemma we may consider the functions $A(\alpha, \beta)$, $B(\alpha, \beta)$, $C(\alpha, \beta)$ defined by the equations

$$A = l - \frac{\beta - \beta_0}{f}, \qquad B = m - H_u\frac{\beta - \beta_0}{f}, \qquad C = n - H_v\frac{\beta - \beta_0}{f},$$

in which $l, m, n$ are the values appearing in equations (58·3) and the arguments of $H_u, H_v, f$ are those associated with the solutions $u(\alpha, \beta)$, $v(\alpha, \beta)$ of those equations. The surface defined by the functions

$$\xi_0(\alpha, \beta, \epsilon) = \xi(\alpha) + \epsilon \int_{\beta_0}^{\beta} A(\alpha, \beta)\, d\beta$$

$$\eta_0(\alpha, \beta, \epsilon) = \eta(\alpha) + \epsilon \int_{\beta_0}^{\beta} B(\alpha, \beta)\, d\beta\,, \tag{58·8}$$

$$\zeta_0(\alpha, \beta, \epsilon) = \zeta(\alpha) + \epsilon \int_{\beta_0}^{\beta} C(\alpha, \beta)\, d\beta$$

has continuous derivatives of at least the second order in $\alpha, \beta, \epsilon$, contains the curve $L$ for $\beta = \beta_0$, and is non-singular along that curve, provided that $\epsilon \neq 0$, as one may readily verify. The equations

$$\begin{aligned} -H\xi_{0\alpha} + u\eta_{0\alpha} + v\zeta_{0\alpha} &= 0\,, \\ -HA + uB + vC &= 0 \end{aligned} \tag{58·9}$$

with the arguments $(x, y, z, u, v) = (\xi_0, \eta_0, \zeta_0, u, v)$ are equivalent to equations (58·3) when $\epsilon = 0$ and therefore have the initial solutions $(\alpha, \beta, \epsilon, u, v) = [\alpha, \beta,$

$0, u(\alpha, \beta), v(\alpha, \beta)]$ on which the functional determinant of their first members with respect to $u, v$ is (58·4) and different from zero near the values $(\alpha_0, \beta_0)$. Hence these equations (58·9) have solutions $u(\alpha, \beta, \epsilon)$, $v(\alpha, \beta, \epsilon)$, with continuous derivatives of the second order and reducing to the solutions $u(\alpha, \beta)$, $v(\alpha, \beta)$ of (58·3) for $\epsilon = 0$. When substituted with $\xi_0, \eta_0, \zeta_0$ from (58·8) as initial values in the functions (27·4), these solutions define a three-parameter family of extremals

$$Y(x, \alpha, \beta, \epsilon) \qquad Z(x, \alpha, \beta, \epsilon) . \tag{58·10}$$

When $\epsilon \neq 0$ this family is cut transversally at $x = \xi_0(\alpha, \beta, \epsilon)$ by the surface (58·8), on account of equations (58·9), in which

$$\xi_{0\beta} = \epsilon A , \qquad \eta_{0\beta} = \epsilon B , \qquad \zeta_{0\beta} = \epsilon C ;$$

and when $\epsilon = 0$ it contains the family (58·2) cut transversally at $x = \xi(\alpha)$ by the curve $L$. As a result of these properties

$$\begin{aligned} Y(\xi_0, \alpha, \beta, \epsilon) &= \eta_0(\alpha, \beta, \epsilon) , \qquad & Z(\xi_0, \alpha, \beta, \epsilon) &= \zeta_0(\alpha, \beta, \epsilon) , \\ Y(x, \alpha, \beta, 0) &= y(x, \alpha, \beta) , \qquad & Z(x, \alpha, \beta, 0) &= z(x, \alpha, \beta) . \end{aligned} \tag{58·11}$$

The determinant $\Delta(x, \alpha, \beta, \epsilon) = Y_\alpha Z_\beta - Y_\beta Z_\alpha$ for the family (58·10) has now the expansion

$$\Delta(x, \alpha_0, \beta_0, \epsilon) = \Delta(x, \alpha_0, \beta_0, 0) + \epsilon \Delta_\epsilon(x, \alpha_0, \beta_0, \theta\epsilon) \qquad (0 < \theta < 1) , \tag{58·12}$$

in which the first term is the corresponding determinant for the family (58·2) and consequently different from zero on the interval $x_1 < x \leqq x_2$ because of condition IV′. Furthermore, by differentiating the first two equations (58·11) and using equations (58·8) the value of $\Delta_\epsilon(x_1, \alpha_0, \beta_0, 0)$ can be shown to be the determinant (58·4), which is different from zero. Consequently, there will be positive constants $h, k$ such that $\Delta_\epsilon(x, \alpha_0, \beta_0, \theta\epsilon)$ will be different from zero for $x_1 \leqq x < x_1 + h$, $0 < |\epsilon| < k$. Hence for an $\epsilon$ satisfying $0 < |\epsilon| < k$ and giving $\epsilon\Delta_\epsilon$ the same sign as $\Delta(x, \alpha_0, \beta_0, 0)$ on the interval $x_1 < x < x_1 + h$, the expression (58·12) will be different from zero on $x_1 \leqq x < x_1 + h$; and it will also be different from zero on the whole interval $x_1 \leqq x \leqq x_2$ if $\epsilon$ is still further restricted so that on the interval $x_1 + h \leqq x \leqq x_2$ the second term in (58·12) has absolute value less than that of the first term. This establishes Lemma 58·1 and therefore also Theorem 58·1.

The method used by Mason and Bliss for the discussion of the problem of the calculus of variations with first end-point variable on a curve $L$ depends upon an analysis of the properties of the field covered by the two-parameter family of extremals cut transversally by the curve $L$, a field which is not simply covered along the curve $L$ itself. In the method of the present section the critical step is the construction of the surface $S$ through the curve $L$, transversal to the extremal $E_{12}$ and having no focal point on $E_{12}$, as described in Lemma 58·1. In the following sections a more general theory of problems with variable end-points is given, depending upon a theorem due to Hahn. This theory is also applicable to the more special problems of the preceding section and the present one.

**59. A more general problem with variable end-points.** The problem to be considered in this and immediately succeeding sections is that of finding a minimizing arc $E_{12}$ for a generalization of the integral $I$ of equation (35·1) in the class of admissible arcs $y_i(x)$ ($x_1 \leqq x \leqq x_2$; $i = 1, \ldots, n$) whose end-values $x_1, y(x_1), x_2, y(x_2)$ lie on an $r$-dimensional subspace $S$ of the $2(n+1)$-dimensional space of points $(x_1, y_{i1}, x_2, y_{i2})$. Such a subspace $S$ may be defined by functions of the form

$$(59\cdot 1) \qquad x_s(t_1, \ldots, t_r), \qquad y_{is}(t_1, \ldots, t_r) \qquad (s = 1, 2;\ r \leqq 2n+2)$$

for which the parameters $t = (t_1, \ldots, t_r)$ range over a bounded closed set $T$ of points $t$. The functions (59·1) are supposed to have continuous third derivatives on the set $T$, and the space $S$ is supposed to be non-singular and not to intersect itself.

Besides the generalization to $(n + 1)$-space and the generalization of the manifold on which the end-points $x_1, y(x_1)$ and $x_2, y(x_2)$ lie we may also modify our problem further by adding to the integral $I$ a function of the coordinates of the end-points, so that the functional to be minimized has the form

$$J = g[x_1, y(x_1), x_2, y(x_2)] + \int_{x_1}^{x_2} f(x, y, y')\,dx .$$

This is the form in which the most general problem without side conditions so far studied was formulated by Bolza.[2] Since on the end-space (59·1) the function $g$ depends upon $t$, we may write $J$ in the form

$$(59\cdot 2) \qquad J = g(t) + \int_{x_1}^{x_2} f(x, y, y')\,dx .$$

The problem is then to find, in a class of admissible arcs $y_i(x)$ ($x_1 \leqq x \leqq x_2$; $i = 1, \ldots, n$) satisfying the end-conditions

$$(59\cdot 3) \quad x_s = x_s(t), \qquad y_i(x_s) = y_{is}(t) \qquad (s = 1, 2;\ i = 1, \ldots, n)$$

for a value $t$ in $T$, one which minimizes the sum $J$ in (59·2). The form (59·2) for $J$ was introduced by M. Morse[3] and is in some respects more convenient than that of Bolza, since the accessory minimum problem associated with it appears at once in the same form, as will be emphasized again in a later section.

Since, by hypothesis, the end-space $S$ does not intersect itself, an admissible

[2] "Über den anormalen Fall beim Lagrangeschen und Mayerschen Problem mit gemischten Bedingungen und variablen Endpunkten," *Mathematische Annalen*, LXXIV (1913), 430–46.

[3] "Sufficient Conditions in the Problem of Lagrange with Variable End Points," *American Journal of Mathematics*, LIII (1931), 517–46.

arc $C$ with ends on $S$ determines uniquely the value $t$ belonging to its ends. The value $J(C)$ of the sum (59·2) is therefore uniquely determined by $C$, and $J(C)$ is the function which is to be minimized. As before, we consider a particular admissible arc $E_{12}$ with ends on $S$ whose minimizing properties are to be studied, and for convenience we let $t_h = 0$ $(h = 1, \ldots, r)$ be the parameter values of the point on $S$ belonging to $E_{12}$. The assumption of the non-singularity of the space $S$ is equivalent to saying that the matrix of derivatives of the functions (59·1) with respect to the variables $t_h$ is of rank $r$ everywhere in $T$. The function $g$ is supposed to have continuous second derivatives in $T$.

Since every admissible arc joining the ends of $E_{12}$ has its end-values on the space $S$, it is clear that if $E_{12}$ is a minimizing arc it must satisfy all the necessary conditions for the problem with fixed end-points, described in Chapter IV. More specifically, it must satisfy the condition I of Section 35 as well as the conditions II and III of Weierstrass and Legendre. Moreover, if the arc $E_{12}$ is a non-singular minimizing arc without corners, it is an extremal, and there can be no point *3* conjugate to *1* on $E_{12}$ between *1* and *2*.

If the arc $E_{12}$ is a non-singular extremal, it can be imbedded in a $2n$-parameter family of extremals $y(x, a, b)$ of the form (36·1) with properties analogous to those described in Theorem 7·1. It is evident that if $E_{12}$ is a minimizing arc the value $J(t, a, b)$ of the sum $J$ taken from $x_1(t)$ to $x_2(t)$ along an extremal $y(x, a, b)$ must have a minimum at the values $(t, a, b) = (0, a_0, b_0)$ belonging to $E_{12}$ in the class of sets $(t, a, b)$ satisfying the equations

$$y_i[x_s(t), a, b] = y_{is}(t) \qquad (s = 1, 2;\ i = 1, \ldots, n). \tag{59·4}$$

The problem of determining the minima of the so-called "extremal integral" $J(t, a, b)$ is a problem in the theory of functions of a finite number of variables.

If the ends of the non-singular extremal arc $E_{12}$ are not conjugate, the functional determinant of equations (59·4) with respect to the variables $a_i, b_i$ at the initial solution $(0, a_0, b_0)$ is the determinant $D(x_2, x_1, a_0, b_0)$ of equation (36·7) and different from zero. Equations (59·4) therefore have solutions $a_i(t)$, $b_i(t)$ which have continuous partial derivatives of the second order near $t = 0$ and which further take the initial values $a_i(0) = a_{i0}$, $b_i(0) = b_{i0}$. The functions

$$Y_i(x, t) = y_i[x, a(t), b(t)] \qquad [x_1(t) \leqq x \leqq x_2(t)] \tag{59·5}$$

now define an $r$-parameter family of extremals containing the arc $E_{12}$ for $t = 0$ and having their end-points on the end-space $S$, as indicated by equations (59·4). From what has been said above, it is clear that the function

$$J(t) = J[t, a(t), b(t)] \tag{59·6}$$

must have a minimum $J(0)$ if $E_{12}$ is a minimizing arc.

**60. A sufficiency theorem for the more general problem with variable end-points.** The purpose of this section is to establish a sufficiency theorem for the problem with variable end-points described in Section 59. The proof of the theorem depends upon an important auxiliary theorem due to H. Hahn.[4] We consider an extremal arc $E_0$ in $(x, y)$-space which is imbedded in an $r$-parameter family of extremals (59·5). The theorem to be proved is to be applied to the particular family of the last section; but it is also applicable to other families of extremals, depending upon arbitrary numbers of parameters and having similar continuity properties. The theorem to be proved is as follows:

THEOREM 60·1. THE THEOREM OF HAHN. *Let* $E_0$ *be a non-singular extremal arc imbedded for parameter values* $t_h = 0$ $(h = 1, \ldots, r)$ *in an* r*-parameter family* (59·5) *of extremal arcs of the kind described in the last section, having on it no point conjugate to its initial point, and satisfying the strengthened condition* $II_N$ *of Weierstrass. Then there exist a constant* $\epsilon > 0$ *and a neighborhood* F *of* $E_0$ *in* (x, y)*-space such that for every extremal arc* E *of the family* (59·5) *whose parameters* t *satisfy the conditions* $|t_h| < \epsilon$ *the inequality* $I(C) > I(E)$ *is satisfied for every admissible arc* C *in* F *joining the ends of* E *but not identical with* E.

*If* $E_0$ *satisfies the condition III instead of* $II_N$, *then there exist a constant* $\epsilon > 0$ *and a neighborhood* $R_1$ *of the elements* $(x, y, y')$ *on* $E_0$ *such that the last sentence above is true with* F *replaced by* $R_1$ *and* (x, y)*-space replaced by* (x, y, y')*-space.*

In the proof of this theorem we use the canonical variables $x$, $y_i$, $z_i = f_{y'_i}$. From the imbedding theorem as proved in Section 38, we know that the nonsingular extremal arc $E_0$ is a member of a $2n$-parameter family of extremals

$$(60\cdot2) \qquad y_i(x, a, b), \qquad z_i(x, a, b)$$

in which the constants $a_i$, $b_i$ are the initial values of the variables $y_i$, $z_i$ at a value $x_0$ on the $x$-interval belonging to $E_0$. We know, also, from the results of Sections 23 and 39 that, since $E_0$ has on it no point conjugate to its initial point, there exists a conjugate system of solutions $\eta_{ik}(x)$, $\zeta_{ik}(x)$ of the accessory canonical equations along $E_0$ with $|\eta_{ik}(x)| \neq 0$ on the interval $x_1 \leqq x \leqq x_2$ belonging to $E_0$. The functions (60·2) with

$$(60\cdot3) \quad a_i = Y_i(x_0, t) + \eta_{ik}(x_0)\,\alpha_k \qquad b_i = Z_i(x_0, t) + \zeta_{ik}(x_0)\,\alpha_k$$

then define an $(r + n)$-parameter family of extremals

$$(60\cdot4) \qquad y_i = y_i(x, t, \alpha), \qquad z_i = z_i(x, t, \alpha)$$

which contains the family (59·5) for $\alpha = 0$. The family (60·4) contains the arc $E_0$ for values $(x, t, \alpha)$ satisfying the conditions $x_1 \leqq x \leqq x_2$, $t_h = 0$, $\alpha_k = 0$. The derivatives $y_{i\alpha_k}$, $z_{i\alpha_k}$ are equal to $\eta_{ik}$, $\zeta_{ik}$ at $x = x_0$, and along $E_0$ satisfy the canonical accessory equations (39·12). Hence these equalities hold along $E_0$ for all values of $x$, and we have $|y_{i\alpha_k}| = |\eta_{ik}| \neq 0$ along $E_0$. It is evident, then, from the usual implicit function theorems, that the first $n$ equations (60·4) have solutions $\alpha_k(x, y, t)$ with continuous derivatives of the second order for values $(x, y, t)$

[4] "Über Variationsprobleme mit variablen Endpunkten," *Monatshefte für Mathematik und Physik*, XXII (1911), 127–36.

with $(x, y)$ in a neighborhood $F$ of the arc $E_0$ in $xy$-space and with $|t_h| \leqq \epsilon$ when $F$ and $\epsilon$ are sufficiently small. The functions

$$p_i(x, y, t) = y_i'[x, t, a(x, y, t)] \tag{60·5}$$

are the slope functions of the family.

For every fixed set of values $t$ with $|t_h| \leqq \epsilon$ the slope functions (60·5) form a field in the region $F$, according to the results in Section 37. This is a consequence of the fact that on the hyperplane $x = x_0$ the integrand $f_{y_i'}dy_i$ of the Hilbert integral $I^*$ is the sum $b_i da_i$, which from (60·3) and the relations

$$\zeta_{ik}\eta_{il} - \eta_{ik}\zeta_{il} = 0$$

expressing the conjugacy of the accessory extremals $\eta_{ik}$, $\zeta_{ik}$ has the value

$$\begin{aligned} b_i da_i &= [Z_i(x_0, t) + \zeta_{ik}(x_0) a_k]\, \eta_{il}(x_0)\, da_l \\ &= d\,[Z_i(x_0, t)\, \eta_{il}(x_0)\, a_l + \tfrac{1}{2}\zeta_{ik}(x_0)\, \eta_{il}(x_0)\, a_k a_l]\,. \end{aligned}$$

The Hilbert integral is thus independent of the path on the hyperplane $x = x_0$ and therefore has the same property in the whole region $F$.

As has been seen in Lemma 16·1, the condition $\text{II}_N$ satisfied by the non-singular arc $E_0$ implies the condition $\text{II}_N'$ which says that the inequality

$$E[x, y, p(x, y, t), y'] > 0 \tag{60·6}$$

holds for all sets $(x, y, p, y')$ with $(x, y, p)$ in $N$ and $(x, y, y')$ admissible and different from $(x, y, p)$. If the region $F$ and the constant $\epsilon$ of the preceding paragraphs are suitably restricted, then the inequality (60·6) will hold for all sets $(t, x, y, y')$ with $(x, y)$ in $F$, $|t_h| < \epsilon$, and $(x, y, y') \neq (x, y, p)$ and admissible. The conclusion of the first paragraph of the theorem now follows by an easy application of the fundamental sufficiency theorem, Theorem 19·2.

If the arc $E_0$ satisfies the condition III, it will also satisfy III$'$, since it is non-singular. With the help of Corollary 9·1 extended to $(n + 1)$-dimensional space it can now be seen that there will be a neighborhood $R_1$ of the sets $(x, y, y')$ on $E_0$ and a constant $\epsilon > 0$ such that the inequality (60·6) holds whenever $(x, y, y') \neq (x, y, p)$ is in $R_1$ and $|t_h| < \epsilon$. Then for each fixed $t$ satisfying the last inequality the region $F$ with the slope functions $p(x, y, t)$ will be a field to which the fundamental sufficiency theorem is applicable if we define admissible sets $(x, y, y')$ to be those interior to $R_1$. Thus the statement in the last paragraph of the theorem is proved.

By means of the theorem of Hahn we may establish the following sufficiency theorem for both weak and strong relative minima for the problem with variable end-points described in Section 59.

THEOREM 60·2. *Let* $E_0$ *be an admissible arc without corners, with end-points on the end-space* S *and having on it no other point of* S.

*If* $E_0$ *satisfies the sufficient conditions for a strong relative minimum for the problem with fixed end-points, it is a member for* $t = 0$ *of an* r*-parameter family*

*(59·5) of extremal arcs whose end-points are on the end-space* S. *If, further, the values* J(t) *in (59·6) of* $J = g + I$ *on these extremal arcs have a relative minimum at* $t = 0$ *then* $J(E_0)$ *is a strong relative minimum in the sense that there is a neighborhood* F *of* $E_0$ *in* xy*-space such that the inequality* $J(C) \geqq J(E_0)$ *is valid for every admissible arc* C *in* F *with end-points on the space* S. *If the minimum of* J(t) *at* $t = 0$ *is proper, the same is true of the minimum* $J(E_0)$.

*If* $E_0$ *satisfies the sufficient conditions for a weak relative minimum for the problem with fixed end-points, then the statements in the preceding paragraph are still valid if we replace the word "strong" by the word "weak," and the neighborhood* F *by a neighborhood* $R_1$ *of the values* (x, y, y′) *on* $E_0$.

To prove the theorem we first note that, when $E_0$ satisfies the sufficient conditions for a relative minimum for the fixed end-point problem, the arguments of the last section show that it is a member of a family (59·5) of extremal arcs as stated in the theorem, and it also satisfies the hypothesis of the theorem of Hahn.

We may next show that for every positive constant $\epsilon$ there is a neighborhood $F$ of $E_0$ such that for every admissible arc $C$ in $F$ with ends on the space $S$ the parameter values $t_h$ defining the ends of $C$ on $S$ are in the $\epsilon$-neighborhood of the values $t_h = 0$. Suppose that this were not true. Then there would exist a constant $\epsilon > 0$ such that every neighborhood $(E_0)_{1/m}$ would contain an admissible arc $C_m$ with end-points on the end-space $S$ for parameter values $(t)_m$ not in the open neighborhood $|t_h| < \epsilon$. The values $(t)_m$ would have an accumulation point not in the neighborhood $|t_h| < \epsilon$; and the corresponding point of $S$ would necessarily lie on $E_0$, since the neighborhoods $(E_0)_{1/m}$ condense on $E_0$. But this is contrary to the hypothesis that $E_0$ has no points in common with $S$ except its end-points which correspond to the values $t_h = 0$.

To complete the proof of the first part of the theorem let us consider a constant $\epsilon > 0$ and a neighborhood $F$ which have the properties described in the theorem of Hahn. It is evident that if the Hahn theorem holds for a particular $\epsilon$ and $F$ it will also hold for every smaller pair. We may therefore choose $\epsilon$ so that the extremal integral $J(t)$ has $J(0)$ as its minimum in the neighborhood $|t_h| < \epsilon$ and we may choose $F$ so small that, relative to $\epsilon$, it has the property described in the last paragraph. Then for every admissible arc $C$ in $F$, with ends on the end-space $S$ at the point with the parameter values $t_h$, we have

$$\begin{aligned} J(C) - J(E_0) &= [J(C) - J(t)] + [J(t) - J(0)] \\ &= [I(C) - I(t)] + [J(t) - J(0)]. \end{aligned}$$

On account of the theorem of Hahn the first difference on the right is positive unless the arc $C$ coincides with the extremal arc $E_t$ of the family (59·5), whose ends coincide with those of $C$. The second difference is non-negative, since $J(0)$ is a minimum; and if $J(0)$ is a proper minimum it is positive unless $E_t$ coincides with $E_0$. Thus the first part of the theorem is proved. The proof of the second part is similar.

**61. The transversality condition.** The purpose of this and succeeding sections is the deduction of conditions which are necessary for a minimum for the general problem with variable end-points of Section 59, and which, when suitably strengthened, are sufficient for a minimum. These conditions are analogous to those of preceding sections in this and earlier chapters. The sufficiency proofs are intimately dependent upon the sufficiency theorem of Section 60.

The first of the necessary conditions remaining to be deduced is the following one:

THEOREM 61·1. THE TRANSVERSALITY CONDITION. *An admissible arc* $E_{12}$ *is said to satisfy the transversality condition for the problem with variable end-points described in Section 59 if the equation*

$$(61\cdot 1) \qquad [(f - y_i' f_{y_i'})\, dx + f_{y_i'} dy_i]_1^2 + dg = 0$$

*is satisfied identically in the variables* $dt_h (h = 1, \ldots, r)$ *when the differentials* $dx_s$, $dy_{is}$ $(s = 1, 2)$ *are expressed in terms of the* $dt_h$ *by means of the end-conditions (59·3). This is equivalent to saying that the equation (61·1) is satisfied by every direction* $dx_s$, $dy_{is}$ *tangent to the end-space* S *at the intersection* $(x_1, y_{i1}, x_2, y_{i2})_0$ *of* S *and* $E_{12}$. *If this condition is satisfied, we say that the space* S *cuts* $E_{12}$ *transversally. It is understood that the arguments of* f *and its derivatives in equation (61·1) are the end-elements of* $E_{12}$. *Every minimizing arc for the problem of Section 59 must satisfy this transversality condition.*

The proof is similar to the ones made for simpler cases in Sections 57 and 58. Let $dx_s$, $dy_{is}$ $(s = 1, 2)$ be an arbitrary direction tangent to the space (59·1) at the point $P$ determined by the end-values of $E_{12}$ in the $(2n + 2)$-dimensional space $S$ of points $(x_s, y_{is})$. Consider a curve $\Gamma$ defined on the space $S$ by functions $t_h(a)$ having continuous first derivatives near the value $a = 0$, passing through $P$ for $a = 0$, and having the direction $dx_s$, $dy_{is}$ at $P$. When the functions $t_h(a)$ are substituted in the functions (59·1), two end-curves $C$ and $D$ are determined in $xy$-space, defined by two sets of functions $x_s(a)$, $y_{is}(a)$ $(s = 1, 2)$. Consider, now, the family of admissible arcs

$$y_i(x, a) \qquad [x_1(a) \leqq x \leqq x_2(a)]$$

for which

$$y_i(x, a) = y_i(x) + \{y_{i1}(a) - y_i[x_1(a)]\} \frac{x_2(a) - x}{x_2(a) - x_1(a)}$$
$$+ \{y_{i2}(a) - y_i[x_2(a)]\} \frac{x - x_1(a)}{x_2(a) - x_1(a)}.$$

The family contains for $a = 0$ the arc $E_{12}$ whose defining functions are $y_i(x)$, and for arbitrary values $a$ the end-points of its arcs are all on $S$. According to Theorem 8·1, the sum $J = g + I$ evaluated on this family of arcs is a function of $a$, whose first differential is the first member of the equation (61·1). Hence if $J(E_{12})$ is to be a minimum, this differential must be zero on $E_{12}$, as was to be proved.

**62. The second variation and a fourth necessary condition.** For the purpose of deducing further necessary conditions for the general problem with variable end-points it is desirable to compute the value of the so-called "second variation" of the sum $J = g + I$ along an arc $E_{12}$ whose minimizing properties are to be investigated. It is assumed that $E_{12}$ is an extremal cut transversally by the end-space $S$. We may consider now what would happen if we had a one-parameter family of admissible arcs defined by functions

$$y_i(x, a) \qquad [x_1(a) \leqq x \leqq x_2(a)] \tag{62·1}$$

containing the extremal arc $E_{12}$ for the value $a = 0$, and satisfying the end-conditions (59·3). The analytic expression of these properties is that there would be a set of functions $t_h(a)$ with $t_h(0) = 0$ such that if we define the functions $x_s(a)$ by the first of the equations

$$x_s(a) = x_s[t(a)], \qquad y_i[x_s(a), a] = y_{is}[t(a)], \tag{62·2}$$

the remaining ones will also be satisfied. The functions $y_i(x, a)$, $y_{ix}(x, a)$, $t_h(a)$ will be supposed to have continuity and differentiability properties sufficient to carry through the following computations. The existence of such a family will be established in the proof of Theorem 62·1.

After differentiating the identities (62·2) with respect to $a$ and setting $a = 0$, one sees that

$$\eta_i(x_s) = C_{ish}\tau_h \qquad (s = 1, 2;\ i = 1, \ldots, n), \tag{62·3}$$

provided that $\eta_i(x)$, $\tau_h$, and $C_{ish}$ are defined, in accordance with the notations of M. Morse, by the equations

$$\eta_i(x) = y_{ia}(x, 0) \qquad \tau_h = t'_h(0),$$

$$C_{ish} = y_{ish}(0) - y'_i(x_s)\, x_{sh}(0) \qquad (h = 1, \ldots, r).$$

In these equations the subscript $h$ on $x_s$ and $y_{is}$ indicates partial derivatives with respect to $t_h$, the functions $y_i(x)$ are the ones which define the arc $E_{12}$, and the repeated index $s$, by exception, does not indicate a sum. The set $\eta_i(x)$, $\tau_h$ will be designated as *the variations of the family* (62·1) along the arc $E_{12}$. The differentials associated with this family satisfy the relations

$$
\begin{aligned}
&\delta y_i = y_{ia}(x, a)\, da, \qquad \delta^2 y_i = y_{iaa}(x, a)\, da^2 \\
&dy_i = y'_i dx + \delta y_i, \\
&d^2 y_i = y'_i d^2 x + y''_i dx^2 + 2\,\delta y'_i dx + \delta^2 y_i,
\end{aligned}
\tag{62·4}
$$

where the symbol $\delta$ indicates a differential taken with respect to the parameter $a$ alone, and the symbol $d$ a differential with respect to $a$ occurring explicitly and also in $x$.

Along the arcs of the family (62·1) the values of the sum $J$ define a function $J(a)$ whose first differential clearly has the form

$$dJ = J'(a)\,da = f\,dx\,\Big|_1^2 + \int_{x_1}^{x_2} [f_{y_i}\delta y_i + f_{y'_i}\delta y'_i]\,dx + dg\,.$$

Along the extremal arc $E_{12}$ where $a = 0$ an integration by parts shows that $J'(0)$ is zero, since this extremal satisfies the transversality condition (61·1).

The second differential $d^2J = J''(0)da^2$ is expressible in the form

$$d^2J = [\,f d^2x + f' dx^2 + 2 f_{y_i}\delta y_i dx + 2 f_{y'_i}\delta y'_i dx\,]_1^2 + d^2 g$$
$$+ \int_{x_1}^{x_2} [\,f_{y_i}\delta^2 v_i + f_{y'_i}\delta^2 y'_i + 2\omega(x,\ \delta y,\ \delta y')\,]\,dx$$

where $2\omega$ is the quadratic form (36·4). The notation $f'$ is used to represent the derivative of $f$ with respect to the $x$ occurring in all of its arguments $x$, $y_i(x, a)$, $y'_i(x, a)$. If the usual integration by parts is applied to the first two terms under the integral sign in the expression for $d^2J$ and if the $\delta$-differentials are eliminated by means of the relations (62·4) with $a = 0$, it turns out that

$$d^2J = [\,f d^2x + (d^2y_i - y'_i d^2x)\, f_{y'_i}]_1^2 + d^2 g$$
$$+ [\,(f_x - y'_i f_{y_i})\, dx^2 + 2 f_{y_i} dy_i dx\,]_1^2 + \int_{x_1}^{x_2} 2\omega dx\,.$$

If the identities (62·2) are differentiated with respect to the parameter $a$, one sees that at $a = 0$

$$dx_s = x_{sh} dt_h \qquad d^2x_s = x_{shl} dt_h dt_l + x_{sh} d^2 t_h\,,$$
$$dy_i = y_{ish} dt_h\,, \qquad d^2y_i = y_{ishl} dt_h dt_l + y_{ish} d^2 t_h\,.$$

It is to be understood that the subscripts $h$, $l$ on the function $g$, as well as on $x_s$, $y_{is}$, will indicate partial derivatives with respect to $t_h$ and $t_l$. With the help of the transversality condition (61·1) and the relation

$$d^2 g = g_h d^2 t_h + g_{hl} dt_h dt$$

it is seen that the terms in $d^2t_h$ disappear from $d^2J$ and that $J''(0)$ is equal to the expression

$$J_2(\eta,\ \tau) = b_{hl}\tau_h\tau_l + \int_{x_1}^{x_2} 2\omega(x,\ \eta,\ \eta')\,dx\,, \tag{62·5}$$

where $b_{hl} = b_{lh}$ is defined by the equation

$$\begin{aligned} b_{hl} = g_{hl} &+ [\,(f - y'_i f_{y'_i})\, x_{hl} + f_{y'_i} y_{ihl}]_1^2 \\ &+ [\,(f_x - y'_i f_{y_i})\, x_h x_l + f_{y_i}(y_{ih} x_l + y_{il} x_h)\,]_1^2. \end{aligned} \tag{62·6}$$

The expression $J_2(\eta, \tau)$ is called the *second variation of the sum* J *along the extremal arc* E$_{12}$.

A *set of admissible variations* $\eta_i(x)$, $\tau_h$ $(x_1 \leqq x \leqq x_2)$ is one for which the parameters $\tau_h$ are constants and the functions $\eta_i(x)$ define a continuous arc in $x\eta$-space consisting of a finite number of sub-arcs having continuously turning tangents. For such sets of variations we can now prove the following necessary condition:

THEOREM 62·1. *An extremal arc* $E_{12}$ *cut transversally by the end-space* S *is said to satisfy the condition IV if the second variation* $J_2(\eta, \tau)$ *along* $E_{12}$ *is non-negative for every set of admissible variations* $\eta_i(x)$, $\tau_h$ *satisfying the end-conditions (62·3). Every minimizing extremal arc* $E_{12}$ *is necessarily cut transversally by the end-space* S *and satisfies the condition IV.*

To prove this, consider a set of variations identical on the interval $x_1x_2$ with the variations $\eta_i(x)$, $\tau_h$ of the theorem but with functions $\eta_i(x)$ defined and having continuous derivatives $\eta_i'(x)$ in neighborhoods of $x_1$ and $x_2$ on an extension of the interval $x_1x_2$ beyond these values. It will be proved, in accordance with a suggestion of Hestenes, that these extended variations belong to a family (62·1) with continuity and differentiability properties sufficient to carry through the operations involved in the computation of the second variation. The function $J(a)$ belonging to the family will then have first and second derivatives at $a = 0$, and if $E_{12}$ is a minimizing arc it will also be true that $J'(0) = 0$ and $J_2(\eta, \tau) = J''(0) \geqq 0$. The theorem will therefore be proved.

Let $\eta_{i\nu}(x)$ $(\nu = 1, \ldots, 2n)$ be a set of functions having continuous second derivatives on an interval including the interval $x_1x_2$ in its interior, and such that the determinant

$$(62\cdot7) \qquad \begin{vmatrix} \eta_{i\nu}(x_1) \\ \eta_{i\nu}(x_2) \end{vmatrix}$$

is different from zero. Then the $2n$ equations

$$(62\cdot8) \qquad y_{is}(t) = y_i[x_s(t)] + a\eta_i[x_s(t)] + B_\nu \eta_{i\nu}[x_s(t)]$$
$$(i = 1, \ldots, n;\ s = 1, 2;\ \nu = 1, \ldots, 2n)$$

with $t_h = a\tau_h$, are linear in the parameters $B_\nu$ and have unique solutions $B_\nu(a)$; and $B_\nu(0) = 0$ since the end-points of $E_{12}$ lie on the end-space $S$ for $(t) = (0)$. These solutions $B_\nu(a)$ have continuous first derivatives near $a = 0$, as can be seen by differentiating equations (62·8). Furthermore, $B_\nu'(0) = 0$, since from (62·8) differentiated and (62·3)

$$0 = -C_{ish}\tau_h + \eta_i(x_s) + \eta_{i\nu}(x_s)B_\nu'(0) = \eta_{i\nu}(x_s)B_\nu'(0)\,.$$

At $a = 0$ the second derivatives $B_\nu''(0)$ also exist, as one can prove by a second differentiation of equations (62·8) at $a = 0$. It will be seen that, because $\eta_i'$ occurs only with a factor $a$, this differentiation can be performed at $a = 0$ even though the functions $\eta_i[x_s(t)]$ have only first derivatives.

The family

$$(62\cdot9) \qquad y_i(x, a) = y_i(x) + a\eta_i(x) + B_\nu(a)\,\eta_{i\nu}(x)$$
$$[x_1(a) \leqq x \leqq x_2(a)]$$

with

$$t_h(a) = a\tau_h\,, \qquad x_s(a) = x_s[t(a)]$$

satisfies the end-conditions (62·2) on account of equations (62·8), contains the arc $E_{12}$ for $a = 0$, and has the set $\eta_i(x)$, $\tau_h$ as its variations along $E_{12}$. It has, furthermore, the first differentials $\delta y_i(x, a)$ occurring in the equations (62·4), and also the second differentials $\delta^2 y_i(x, 0)$. Hence the first differential $dJ = J'(a)da$ is well defined, and the second differential $d^2J = J''(0)da^2$ will also exist, provided that the function

$$f\{x_s(a),\ y[x_s(a),\ a],\ y'[x_s(a),\ a]\}$$

occurring in the expression for $dJ$ has a derivative at $a = 0$. But this function can be easily seen to have a derivative, since its first two arguments clearly have derivatives near $a = 0$ and since it follows from equations (62·9), with the help of the values $B_\nu(0) = B'_\nu(0) = 0$, that at $a = 0$

$$\frac{d}{da}\, y'_i[x_s(a),\ a] = y''_i(x_s)\, x_{sh}(0)\, \tau_h + \eta'_i(x_s)\ .$$

The last equation (62·4) is also satisfied at $a = 0$ by the differentials of the family (62·9), as can be proved without difficulty.

**63. Further sufficiency theorems.** The purpose of this section is the formulation of necessary conditions and of sufficient conditions for a minimum analogous to those of Sections 17 and 35 for problems with fixed end-points. In order to state such theorems we may designate by the Roman numeral I the corresponding condition of Section 35 plus the transversality condition of Section 61. These conditions are grouped together because they turn out to be naturally associated in the multiplier rule, which will be proved in a later chapter for the more general problem of Bolza. For the fixed end-point problem, which is a special case of the general problem with variable end-points, the transversality condition imposes no restriction on the minimizing arc, as one may readily verify. The conditions II, III, and their associated conditions are the same as for problems with fixed end-points. The second variation is said to be *non-negative* if it satisfies the condition of Theorem 62·1, which we shall designate as IV. The second variation $J_2(\eta, \tau)$ is said to be *positive definite* if it is non-negative and vanishes only when the variations $\eta_i(x)$, $\tau_h$ are identically zero. The condition IV′ is that $J_2(\eta, \tau)$ be positive definite.

THEOREM 63·1. *For an admissible arc* $E_{12}$ *without corners, with end-points on the end-space* S *and having no other pair of distinct or coincident points forming a point on* S, *the table of necessary conditions and of sufficient conditions for a minimum in Section 17 is applicable to the problem with variable end-points of Section 59.*

The statements of the table concerning necessary conditions have been proved in the preceding sections.

The condition IV′ of this section for the arc $E_{12}$ of the theorem implies that there is no point conjugate to *1* between the end-points *1* and *2* or at *2* on the arc $E_{12}$. This is a consequence of the fact that if there were such a conjugate point the second variation $J_2(\eta, \tau)$ along $E_{12}$ would vanish for a set of admissible variations $(\eta_i, \tau_h) = (\eta_i, 0)$ with functions $\eta_i(x)$ vanishing at $x_1$ and $x_2$ but not identically zero, as one sees by an argument similar to that immediately following equations (11·2).

In order to prove the effectiveness for the problem with variable end-points of the sufficient conditions in the last column of the table of Section 17, we may first note, as a result of the comment in the last paragraph, that these conditions imply in each case the analogous conditions for the problem with fixed end-points. From the sufficiency theorem already proved, Theorem 60·2, it follows, then, that the extremal integral $J(t)$ of that theorem exists. With the help of arguments quite like those of Section 62 it may be seen that at $(t) = (0)$

$$dJ = dg + [f dx]_1^2 + \int_{x_1}^{x_2} [f_{y_i}\delta y_i + f_{y'_i}\delta y'_i]\, dx$$

$$d^2J = J_2(\delta y,\ dt)\,,$$

where

$$\delta y_i = y_{it_h} dt_h \qquad \delta^2 y_i = y_{it_h t_l} dt_h dt_l\,.$$

With the help of the usual integration by parts it follows that $dJ = 0$ as a result of the transversality condition. The condition IV′ of this section implies, further, that the quadratic form $d^2J$ in the variables $dt_h$ is positive definite, so that $J(0)$ is a minimum for the function $J(t)$. The conclusion of Theorem 63·1 is now an immediate consequence of Theorem 60·2.

**64. Another form of the fourth condition.** In order to state the condition which is to be discussed in this section, it is desirable to formulate for the problem with variable end-points an accessory minimum problem analogous to those of Sections 11 and 36 for problems with fixed end-points. In Section 62 it has been shown that the second variation $J_2(\eta, \tau)$ along a minimizing extremal arc must be non-negative. This suggests the accessory problem of minimizing

$$J_2(\eta,\ \tau) = b_{hl}\tau_h\tau_l + \int_{x_1}^{x_2} 2\omega(x,\ \eta,\ \eta')\, dx \tag{64·1}$$

in the class of sets of admissible variations $\eta_i(x)$, $\tau_h$ satisfying the accessory end-conditions

$$\eta_i(x_s) = C_{ish}\tau_h, \qquad x_s = \text{const.} \qquad (s = 1,\ 2)\,, \tag{64·2}$$

a problem in $x\eta$-space of the same form as the original problem of Section 60 in $xy$-space.

The accessory equations are, as before, the differential equations (36·5) of the extremals of the accessory problem. If $2n$ linearly independent solutions

$\eta_{i\nu}(x)$ ($\nu = 1, \ldots, 2n$) of these equations are known, the general solution has the form

$$(64\cdot3) \qquad \eta_i(x) = c_\nu \eta_{i\nu}(x) .$$

The accessory transversality conditions are the conditions

$$(64\cdot4) \qquad [C_{ish}\omega_{\eta'_i}(x_s)]_1^2 + b_{hl}\tau_l = 0 .$$

They are the interpretation for the accessory problem of the transversality condition (61·1) for the original problem.

In the discussion of the necessary condition which is to be formulated in this section it will be understood that the extremal arc $E_{12}$ along which the second variation is taken is non-singular and cut transversally by the end-space $S$. Let $x_3$ be an arbitrarily selected value between $x_1$ and $x_2$; and let $\eta_{i\mu}(x, x_3)$ ($\mu = 1, \ldots, m$) be a maximal set of linearly independent broken accessory extremals which have no corner, or possibly one corner at $x_3$, and which, furthermore, satisfy the accessory end-conditions (64·2) with corresponding sets of constants $\tau_{h\mu}(\mu = 1, \ldots, m)$. We know that there is such a maximal set since the requirement that two families of the form (64·3) adjoin continuously at the value $x_3$ and satisfy the end-conditions (64·2) imposes only linear homogeneous conditions on their two sets of constants $c_\nu$ and their common set of constants $\tau_h$. For the linear family of variations

$$(64\cdot5) \qquad \eta_i(x) = a_\mu \eta_{i\mu}(x) , \qquad \tau_h = a_\mu \tau_{h\mu}$$

the second variation belonging to the arc $E_{12}$ is a homogeneous quadratic form

$$(64\cdot6) \qquad Q(x_3, a) = J_2(a_\mu \eta_\mu, a_\mu \tau_\mu)$$

in the coefficients $a_\mu$.

It is evident that when the arc $E_{12}$ is a minimizing arc the quadratic form (64·6) is necessarily non-negative. This form vanishes when the constants $a_\mu$ define an unbroken accessory extremal (64·5) satisfying the transversality conditions (64·4). For in that case the formula

$$2\omega = \eta_i \omega_{\eta_i} + \eta'_i \omega_{\eta'_i}$$

and an integration by parts, together with equations (64·2) and (64·4), show that

$$(64\cdot7) \qquad J_2(\eta, \tau) = b_{hl}\tau_h\tau_l + [C_{ish}\tau_h\omega_{\eta'_i}(x_s)]_1^2 = 0 .$$

Furthermore, $Q(x_3, a)$ vanishes only for such values $a_\mu$, since a set of admissible variations $\eta_i(x)$, $\tau_h$ which gives $J_2$ the value zero is necessarily a minimizing set for the accessory problem. Since $E_{12}$ is non-singular, the arc $\eta_i(x)$ belonging to such a set $a_\mu$ can have no corners and must be an accessory extremal and, further, must satisfy the accessory transversality condition.

The accessory end-conditions (64·2) are said to be *conjugate end-conditions* if there exists a set of admissible variations $\eta_i(x)$, $\tau_h$, not identically zero, which satisfy them and also the accessory transversality conditions and for which, further, the arc $\eta_i(x)$ is an accessory extremal.

THEOREM 64·1. *Let* $E_{12}$ *be a non-singular extremal arc cut transversally by the end-space* S *and satisfying the condition III of Legendre.*

*Necessary and sufficient conditions for the second variation* $J_2(\eta, \tau)$ *along* $E_{12}$ *to be non-negative are then that it have this property on all accessory extremal arcs with at most one corner satisfying the accessory end-conditions (64·2) and, further, that it vanish only on unbroken extremal arcs satisfying both the accessory end-conditions (64·2) and transversality conditions (64·4). Analytically, this is equivalent to requiring that for every value* $x_3$ *between* $x_1$ *and* $x_2$ *the quadratic form* $Q(x_3, a)$ *in (64·6) be non-negative and vanish only when the constants* $a_\mu$ *define an unbroken extremal (64·5) satisfying the accessory end and transversality conditions.*

*Necessary and sufficient conditions for* $J_2(\eta, \tau)$ *to be positive definite are the same as the above, with the additional restriction that the end-conditions be non-conjugate. This means that the positive definiteness of* $J_2(\eta, \tau)$ *is equivalent to the positive definiteness of* $Q(x_3, a)$ *for every* $x_3$ *between* $x_1$ *and* $x_2$.

The necessity of the conditions in the theorem is a consequence of arguments which have already been made.

To prove the sufficiency we note, first, that if there were a point conjugate to *1* between *1* and *2* on $E_{12}$ the second variation would vanish for a set $[\eta_i(x), \tau_h] = [\eta_i(x), 0]$, for which $\eta_i(x)$ defines a broken extremal arc with one corner, as can be seen by an argument similar to that immediately following equations (11·2). This broken arc would satisfy the end-conditions (64·2) with $\tau_h = 0$, which contradicts the hypothesis of both parts of the theorem that $Q(x_3, a)$ vanishes only for values $a$ defining an unbroken extremal satisfying the accessory end and transversality conditions. A similar argument shows that there is no point conjugate to *2* on $E_{12}$ between *1* and *2*. Consider, then, an arbitrary set of admissible variations $\eta_i(x)$, $\tau_h$ satisfying the end-conditions (64·2). Let $x_3$ be a value between $x_1$ and $x_2$. The ends of the arc $\eta_i(x)$ on the interval $x_1x_3$ can be joined by an accessory extremal, since $x_1$ and $x_3$ are not conjugate values, and similarly for the ends of $\eta_i(x)$ on $x_3x_2$. Each of these extremal arcs gives to the integral in (64·1) a value not greater than that given by the corresponding arc of $\eta_i(x)$, as one may infer from the analogue for $(n + 1)$-dimensional space of Theorem 23·3. Consequently, the broken extremal arc which they form, taken with the constants $\tau_h$, gives to $J_2$ a value not greater than that given by $\eta_i(x)$, $\tau_h$; and this value is non-negative on account of the hypothesis that $Q(x_3, a)$ is non-negative. It is actually positive if the arc defined by $\eta_i(x)$ does not coincide with the broken extremal or if $Q(x_3, a) > 0$. This last inequality will surely be true, when the end-conditions are not conjugate, unless the broken extremal and its values $\tau$ are identically zero. Thus the theorem is proved.

If one examines the proof of Theorem 64·1 which has just been made, it will be seen that the requirement of the theorem on the quadratic form $Q(x_3, a)$ can be weakened. This requirement is that at every value $x_3$ between $x_1$ and $x_2$ the quadratic form $Q(x_3, a)$ be non-negative and vanish only for values $a$ defining an extremal without corners satisfying the accessory end and transversality conditions. For $J_2(\eta, \tau)$ to be non-negative it is evidently necessary, and also sufficient, that these properties hold only at every value $x_3$ conjugate to $x_1$ or $x_2$ between $x_1$ and $x_2$ and that $Q$ have the property of being non-negative in any case at one point at least between $x_1$ and $x_2$.

The criterion for the non-negativeness of the second variation given in the theorem is the outgrowth of a number of preceding results. In a paper concerning the problem of Bolza a fourth condition was formulated by Bliss[5] in terms of a quadratic form similar to $Q(x_3, a)$ but involving only unbroken accessory extremals satisfying the end-conditions. For the problem of Bolza with so-called "separated end-conditions" Hestenes[6] used, similarly, a family of accessory extremals each with at most one corner and satisfying both end and transversality conditions. A condition similar to this for a problem in the plane with end-points variable on two curves was previously given by Bliss.[7] The modification of these criteria described in the theorem, involving accessory extremals each with at most one corner and satisfying only the end-conditions, is due to Goldstine. This modification is more effective than the method of Bliss, for which the spread between necessary conditions and sufficient conditions for the second variation to be non-negative is greater than desirable in some not too exceptional cases. It has the advantage over the criterion of Hestenes that it is applicable even if the end-conditions are not separated.

**65. Focal points for problems with one end-point variable.** The problem to be treated in this section is that of finding in the class of admissible arcs joining a fixed end-space $S$ to a fixed point *2* one which minimizes the sum $J$ in (59·2). The end-space $S$ on which the first end-point only is variable is defined by functions

$$x_1(t_1, \ldots, t_r), \qquad y_{i1}(t_1, \ldots, t_r). \tag{65·1}$$

The purpose of this section is to formulate for this problem a condition, in terms of so-called "focal points," equivalent to the condition IV of Section 62. As in the three-dimensional cases, discussed in Sections 57 and 58, focal points play the same role, for the problem just proposed above, that conjugate points do for problems with fixed end-points.

It will be understood in this section that $E_{12}$ is a non-singular extremal arc joining the end-space $S$ to the fixed point *2*, cut transversally by this end-space $S$

[5] "The Problem of Bolza in the Calculus of Variations," *Annals of Mathematics*, XXXIII (1932), 261–74.

[6] "Sufficient Conditions for the Problem of Bolza in the Calculus of Variations," *Transactions of the American Mathematical Society*, XXXVI (1934), 793–818.

[7] "A Boundary Value Problem in the Calculus of Variations," *Bulletin of the American Mathematical Society*, XXXII (1926), 317–31.

but not tangent to $S$ at its intersection point *1*. It will be understood, as in preceding sections, that the point *1* is defined on $S$ by the parameter values $t_h = 0$.

The computations of Section 62 tell us that along $E_{12}$ the second variation has the value (62·5) and that all the terms in the brackets of formula (62·6) vanish at the fixed end-point *2*. It is evident that at the point *1* the accessory end and transversality conditions, (64·2) and (64·4), now have the form

$$\eta_i(x_1) = C_{il}\tau_l, \quad \zeta_i(x_1) C_{ih} = b_{hl}\tau_l \qquad (h = 1, \ldots, r) \tag{65·2}$$

where

$$\zeta_i = \omega_{\eta_i'}, \qquad C_{ih} = y_{i1h}(0) - y_i'(x_1)\, x_{1h}\,.$$

Since $E_{12}$ is not tangent to the end-space $S$, the matrix $\|C_{ih}\|$ has rank $r$, as can be readily verified. At the value $x_2$ the end-conditions of the accessory minimum problem are simply $x_2 =$ constant, $\eta_i(x_2) = 0$, and there are no transversality conditions.

In terms of the second variation the analytic definition of a focal point of the end-space $S$ on the arc $E_{12}$ is given in the following statement:

Definition of a Focal Point. On a non-singular extremal arc $E_{12}$ cut transversally at its initial point by an end-space $S$ a value $x_3$ is said to define a focal point of $S$ if the accessory equations along $E_{12}$ have a solution $u_i(x)$ satisfying the accessory end and transversality conditions (65·2) at $x = x_1$ with constants $\tau_h$, and having $u_i(x_3) = 0$, but not vanishing identically on the interval $x_1x_3$.

The following theorem gives an important criterion for the determination of focal points. It is a generalization of Theorem 12·3 for the determination of conjugate points.

Theorem 65·1. *The totality of solutions of the canonical accessory equations (39·12) along* $E_{12}$ *satisfying the accessory end and transversality conditions (65·2) with constants* $\tau_h$ *is a linear family whose basis is a system* $\eta_{ik}(x)$, $\zeta_{ik}(x)$, $\tau_{hk}$ $(k = 1, \ldots, n)$ *for which the accessory extremals* $\eta_{ik}$, $\zeta_{ik}$ *form a conjugate system. The focal points of the end-space* S *on* $E_{12}$ *are determined by the zeros* $x_3 \neq x_1$ *of the determinant* $|\eta_{ik}(x)|$.

To prove the theorem we may first note that every system $\eta_{ik}(x)$, $\zeta_{ik}(x)$ $(k = 1, \ldots, n)$ of linearly independent solutions of the canonical accessary equations (39·12) satisfying the accessory end- and transversality conditions (65·2) with constants $\tau_{hk}$ is necessarily a conjugate system. This follows because the expressions $\eta_{ik}\zeta_{il} - \zeta_{ik}\eta_{il}$, shown to be constants in Section 39, vanish at $x = x_1$, as can easily be seen with the help of the conditions (65·2) with $\eta_{ik}$, $\zeta_{ik}$, $\tau_{lk}$ in place of $\eta_i$, $\zeta_i$, $\tau_l$. To show that there exists such a conjugate system we observe that the $(n + r)$ equations (65·2) have a maximal set of $n$ linearly independent solutions $\eta_{ik}(x_1)$, $\zeta_{ik}(x_1)$, $\tau_{hk}$ $(k = 1, \ldots, n)$, since the matrix $\|C_{ih}\|$ has, by hypothesis, rank $r$. It is also easy to see that for these solutions the matrix $\|\eta_{ik}(x_1), \zeta_{ik}(x_1)\|$ has rank $n$, since the equations (65·2) have no non-vanishing solution $\eta_i(x_1)$, $\zeta_i(x_1)$, $\tau_h$ with values $\eta_i(x_1)$, $\zeta_i(x_1)$ all zero. Well-known existence theorems now tell us that the canonical accessory equations have $n$ independent solutions $\eta_{ik}(x)$, $\zeta_{ik}(x)$ $(k = 1, \ldots, n)$ with the initial values $\eta_{ik}(x_1)$, $\zeta_{ik}(x_1)$.

Consider now an accessory extremal $\eta_i(x)$, $\zeta_i(x)$ satisfying the conditions (65·2) with constants $\tau_h$. From what has been said above, it is evident that the initial values $\eta_i(x_1)$, $\zeta_i(x_1)$, $\tau_h$ are linearly expressible in terms of the corresponding initial values at $x = x_1$ of the conjugate system described in the last paragraph. It follows at once that for all values of $x$ we have relations of the form

$$(65\cdot 3) \qquad \eta_i = \eta_{ik} a_k , \qquad \zeta_i = \zeta_{ik} a_k , \qquad \tau_h = \tau_{hk} a_k ,$$

in which the coefficients $a_k$ are constants. In particular, if $\eta_i(x)$ characterizes a focal point *3* of $S$ on $E_{12}$, then it is evident from the equations (65·3) that the determinant $|\eta_{ik}(x)|$ vanishes at $x = x_3$, since $\eta_i(x_3) = 0$. Conversely, if this determinant vanishes at a value $x_3 \neq x_1$ then the constants $a_k (k = 1, \ldots, n)$ may be chosen so that the corresponding set $\eta_i(x)$, $\zeta_i(x)$, $\tau_h$ in (65·3), which satisfies the condition (65·2), has $\eta_i(x_3) = 0$. The functions $\eta_i(x)$ are not identically zero on the interval $x_1x_3$ since otherwise the functions $\zeta_i = \omega_{\eta_i'}$ linearly expressible in terms of the $\eta_i$ and $\eta_i'$ would also vanish identically, and the system $\eta_{ik}$, $\zeta_{ik}$ $(k = 1, \ldots, n)$ could not be linearly independent. Thus, every zero $x_3 \neq x_1$ of the determinant $|\eta_{ik}(x)|$ determines a focal point, and the theorem is proved.

For the proof of the next theorem below it is convenient to note that the conjugate system $\eta_{ik}(x)$, $\zeta_{ik}(x)$, $\tau_{hk}$ $(k = 1, \ldots, n)$ of Theorem 65·1 may be so chosen that

$$\begin{aligned} &\eta_{il}(x_1) = C_{il} , \qquad &&\zeta_{il}(x_1) C_{ih} = b_{hl} \qquad &&\tau_{hl} = \delta_{hl} \\ (65\cdot 4) \qquad &\eta_{i\rho}(x_1) = 0 , &&\zeta_{i\rho}(x_1) C_{ih} = 0 , &&\tau_{h\rho} = 0 \\ & && (h, l = 1, \ldots, r ; \ \rho = r+1, \ldots, n) , \end{aligned}$$

as one may verify by an examination of equations (65·2).

We are now in a position to state and prove the following theorem, which is the purpose of this section:

THEOREM 65·2. *Let* $E_{12}$ *be a non-singular extremal arc cut transversally by the end-space* S *at the point* 1 *and satisfying the condition III of Legendre. Then the second variation (62·5) along* $E_{12}$ *is non-negative if and only if the arc* $E_{12}$ *contains no focal point of the end-space* S *between the points* 1 *and* 2. *It is, furthermore, positive definite if and only if* $E_{12}$ *contains no focal point of* S *between* 1 *and* 2 *or at* 2.

To prove the necessity of the conditions in the theorem, we may first note that a focal point *6* of the end-space $S$ on $E_{12}$ between *1* and *2* has associated with it, as in Section 11, a broken accessory extremal $\eta_i(x)$, $\zeta_i(x)$, $\tau_h$ having a corner at $x_6$ and no other corner. By an argument like that in Sections 11 and 64 it follows, then, that

$$J_2(\eta, \tau) = b_{hl}\tau_h\tau_l - \zeta_i(x_1) C_{il}\tau_l = 0 ,$$

since the extremal satisfies the conditions (65·2). This result implies immediately that, if the second variation is non-negative, there can be no focal point *6* between *1* and *2* and, further, from Theorem 64·1, that if the second variation is positive definite the end-conditions cannot be conjugate. The end-conditions are evidently non-conjugate if and only if the point *2* is not a focal point of the end-space $S$ on $E_{12}$. This completes the proof of the necessity of the conditions in the theorem.

The sufficiency part of the theorem is the statement that, if there is no focal point of the end-space $S$ on $E_{12}$ between *1* and *2* or at *2*, then the second variation is positive definite, and if there is no focal point between *1* and *2*, the second variation is at least non-negative. To prove the first of these statements let $\eta_i(x)$, $\tau_h$ be an admissible set of variations not identically zero and satisfying the end-conditions

$$(65\cdot5) \qquad \eta_i(x_1) = C_{ih}\tau_h \,, \qquad \eta_i(x_2) = 0 \,.$$

We wish to show that for such a set the second variation is positive, and to do so we make use of the field in $x\eta$-space which is covered by the $n$-parameter family of accessory extremals in Theorem 65·1. If the functions $\eta_{ik}(x)$ are those belonging to this family, determined as in the paragraph preceding Theorem 65·2, the equations

$$(65\cdot6) \qquad \eta_i(x) = a_h\eta_{ih}(x) + a_\rho\eta_{i\rho}(x)$$
$$(h = 1, \ldots, r;\ \rho = r+1, \ldots, n)$$

will determine uniquely the coefficients $a_k$ as functions $a_k(x)$ on the interval $x_1 < x \leqq x_2$, since there is no focal point of $S$ on this interval. We shall presently see that these functions have definite limits $a_h(x_1)$, $a_\rho(x_1)$ as $x$ approaches $x_1$ and that $a_h(x_1) = \tau_h$. Furthermore, it is evident that $a_h(x_2) = a_\rho(x_2) = 0$, since $|\eta_{ik}(x_2)| \neq 0$.

The determinant $|\eta_{ih}(x_1),\ \eta'_{i\rho}(x_1)|$ is different from zero. Otherwise there would be a set of constants $C_h$, $C_\rho$, not all zero, satisfying the linear equations

$$C_h\eta_{jh}(x_1) + C_\rho\eta'_{j\rho}(x_1) = 0 \,.$$

Multiplication by $f_{y'_iy'_j}C_l\,\eta_{il}(x_1)$ and summation with respect to $i$ and $j$ would give

$$C_l\eta_{il}(x_1)\, f_{y'_iy'_j}C_h\eta_{jh}(x_1) + C_l\eta_{il}(x_1)\,C_\rho\zeta_{i\rho}(x_1) = 0 \,.$$

The last term would be zero, since $\eta_{i\rho}(x_1) = 0$ and the solutions $\eta_{il}$, $\zeta_{il}$ and $\eta_{i\rho}$, $\zeta_{i\rho}$ are conjugate; and the vanishing of the first term would imply $C_l\,\eta_{il}(x_1) = C_lC_{il} = 0$ on account of the non-singularity of $E_{12}$ and the condition III. But this would further imply $C_l = 0$, since the matrix $\|C_{il}\|$ is of rank $r$. The accessory extremal $C_\rho\,\eta_{i\rho}(x)$ would thus vanish with its derivatives at $x_1$ and be identically zero, which is impossible, since the solutions $\eta_{i\rho}$, $\zeta_{i\rho}$ are linearly independent.

If the equations (65·6) are written in the form

$$(65\cdot 7)\quad \eta_i(x) = a_h \eta_{ih}(x) + (x - x_1)\, a_\rho \int_0^1 \eta'_{i\rho}[x_1 + \theta(x - x_1)]\, d\theta\ ,$$

it is evident from the result of the last paragraph that the functions $a_h(x)$, $(x - x_1)a_\rho(x)$ approach definite limits as $x$ approaches $x_1$. The numerator determinant of the quotient representing $(x - x_1)a_\rho(x)$ will retain its value if the column $\eta_i(x)$ in it is replaced by the column $\eta_i(x) - \tau_h \eta_{ih}(x)$, all of whose elements vanish at $x = x_1$ on account of equations (65·2) and the initial values (65·4). Hence the functions $a_\rho(x)$ also have unique limits at $x = x_1$. From equations (65·6) or (65·7) at $x = x_1$, with (65·2) and (65·4), it follows that $a_h(x_1) = \tau_h$.

To prove that the value $J_2(\eta, \tau)$ of the second variation is positive for the set $\eta_i(x)$, $\tau_h$, we may define $u_i$ and $v_i$ for arbitrary values $x$, $x_3$ on the interval $x_1x_2$ by the equations

$$(65\cdot 8)\quad u_i(x, x_3) = a_k(x_3)\, \eta_{ik}(x)\ , \qquad v_i(x, x_3) = a_k(x_3)\, \zeta_{ik}(x)$$

and consider the function

$$\Phi(x_3) = b_{hl} a_h a_l + \int_{x_1}^{x_3} 2\omega(x, u, u')\, dx + \int_{x_3}^{x_2} 2\omega(x, \eta, \eta')\, dx\ ,$$

in which the argument of $a_h(x)$ is understood to be $x = x_3$. Since $a_h(x_1) = \tau_h$ and $a_i(x_2) = 0$, this function has the values

$$(65\cdot 9)\qquad \Phi(x_1) = J_2(\eta, \tau)\ , \qquad \Phi(x_2) = 0\ .$$

Furthermore, with the help of the usual integration by parts and the equations

$$u_i(x_3, x_3) = \eta_i(x_3)\ , \qquad u'_i(x_3, x_3) + u_{ix_3}(x_3, x_3) = \eta'_i(x_3)\ ,$$

the derivative of $\Phi$ at a point $x_3 \neq x_1$ is seen to be

$$\Phi'(x_3) = 2 b_{hl} a_h a'_l - [2u_{ix_3} v_i]^1 - [2E_\omega(x, \eta, \pi, \eta')]^3\ ,$$

where $E_\omega$ is the Weierstrassian $E$-function for the function $\omega$ and the $\pi_i(x, \eta)$ are the slope functions of the family (65·6). But from equations (65·8) and (65·4) it follows that

$$[u_{ix_3} v_i]^1 = a'_h(x_3)\, C_{ih} v_i(x_1, x_3) = a'_h(x_3)\, b_{hl} a_l(x_3)\ ,$$

so that the first two terms in $\Phi'(x_3)$ cancel; and after evaluation of the $E$-function we find

$$\Phi'(x_3) = -[f_{y'_i y'_k}(\eta'_i - \pi_i)(\eta'_k - \pi_k)]^3\ .$$

On account of the condition III and the non-singularity of the extremal arc $E_{12}$ this derivative is negative, and the values (65·9) show that $J_2(\eta, \tau)$ is positive unless the equations $\eta'_i = \pi_i(x, \eta)$ are everywhere satisfied. But these equations are not satisfied, since their only solution through the point $(x, \eta) = (x_2, 0)$ is the set $\eta_i(x) \equiv 0$. Thus, using again the fact that the matrix $\|C_{ih}\|$ is of rank $r$, we see that $J_2(\eta, \tau)$ is positive for every set $\eta_i(x)$, $\tau_h$ satisfying the end-conditions (65·5) and not identically zero.

If there is no focal point of $S$ between *1* and *2* on the arc $E_{12}$, then the second variation $J_2(\eta, \tau)$ is at least non-negative. The proof can be made by an argument quite similar to that used in proving Corollary 23·1.

Theorem 65·2, which has thus been proved, shows that for problems with one end-point variable on a space $S$ the conditions IV and IV′, stated in terms of the second variation and used in Theorems 62·1 and 63·1, are equivalent to the non-existence on the intervals $x_1 < x < x_2$ and $x_1 < x \leqq x_2$, respectively, of values defining focal points of $S$. For the problem with one end-point variable these conditions are also equivalent, therefore, to those formulated in Theorem 64·1 in terms of the quadratic form $Q(x_3, a)$.

**66. Dependence of the focal point of a curve on curvature.**[8] In this section we shall restrict the problem of the preceding section by supposing that the end-space $S$ transversal to the non-singular extremal arc $E_{12}$ at the point *1* is a curve $L$. Without loss of generality we may assume that the single parameter $t$ in the functions (65·1) defining $L$, and in the function $g(t)$ of the sum (59·2), is the Euclidean length of arc on $L$ measured from the point *1*. It will be supposed that $E_{12}$ satisfies the Legendre condition III and has on it no point conjugate to *1* between *1* and *2*, and that $f \neq 0$ at its initial point *1*. The numbers

$$A = [f - y'_k f_{y'_k}]^1 \qquad B_i = [f_{y'_i}]^1$$

are then not all zero and define a direction in $xy$-space through the point *1* such that every other direction through the point *1* orthogonal to this one is transversal to the extremal arc $E_{12}$ at *1*.

We shall be concerned with the totality of curves $L$ tangent at the point *1* to a fixed straight line through *1* transversal to the arc $E_{12}$. It will be shown that the focal point of $L$ on $E_{12}$ is completely determined by the projection $\sigma$ on the direction $A$, $B_i$ of the first curvature $1/\rho$ of $L$ at the point *1*. When $\sigma$ varies monotonically, the focal point moves monotonically on the arc $E_{12}$.

The direction cosines of the fixed line through *1* transversal to $E_{12}$ will be denoted by $\alpha$, $\beta_i$. Since the single parameter $t$ now appearing in (65·1) is the length of arc measured from the point *1* along $L$, we have $\alpha = x_{1t}(0)$, $\beta_i = y_{i1t}(0)$. If the angle at the point *1* between the principal normal of the curve $L$ and the vector $A$, $B_i$ is designated by $\theta$, then the *projected curvature* $\sigma$ *of* $L$ at the point *1* is defined to be the value

$$(66{\cdot}1) \qquad \sigma = \frac{1}{\rho}\cos\theta = \frac{A x_{1tt} + B_i y_{i1tt}}{(A^2 + B_i B_i)^{1/2}},$$

[8] See Householder, "The Dependence of a Focal Point upon Curvature in the Calculus of Variation" (diss., University of Chicago), in *Contributions 1933–1937*, p. 485, where other references to G. A. Bliss and M. B. White are given.

where the first curvature $1/\rho$ of $L$ is, by definition,

$$\frac{1}{\rho} = (x_{1tt}^2 + y_{i1tt}y_{i1tt})^{1/2}.$$

For the problem with initial end-point variable on a curve the second variation from formula (62·5) has the value

$$(66 \cdot 2) \qquad J_2(\eta, \tau, \sigma) = b\tau^2 + \int_{\tau_1}^{x_2} 2\omega(x, \eta, \eta')\, dx ,$$

in which $b$ is defined, from (62·6), by the formulas

$$(66 \cdot 3) \qquad \begin{aligned} b &= g_{tt} - [A x_{1tt} + B_i y_{i1tt}]^1 - D = g_{tt} - \sigma(A^2 + B_i B_i)^{1/2} - D , \\ D &= [(f_x - y_k' f_{y_k}) a^2 + 2 f_{y_i} a \beta_i]^1 . \end{aligned}$$

Furthermore, the accessory end and transversality conditions (65·2) now have the form

$$(66 \cdot 4) \qquad \eta_i(x_1) = C_i \tau , \qquad \zeta_i(x_1) C_i = b\tau ,$$

where the constants

$$(66 \cdot 5) \qquad C_i = \beta_i - y_i'(x_1)\, a$$

are not all zero, since the curve $L$ cannot be tangent to $E_{12}$ when $f$ is different from zero at the point *1*, as was seen in Section 58. It is evident that the second variation $J_2$ is completely determined by the projected curvature $\sigma$ and the variations $\eta_i(x)$, $\tau$ when $E_{12}$ and the direction cosines $a$, $\beta_1$ of the curve $L$ at *1* are fixed.

In order to study the dependence of the focal point of $L$ on the parameter $\sigma$, we consider the family of accessory extremals $\eta_i(x, x_3)$, $\zeta_i(x, x_3)$ determined by the conditions

$$(66 \cdot 6) \qquad \eta_i(x_1, x_3) = C_i , \qquad \eta_i(x_3, x_3) = 0 ,$$

where $x_3$ is an arbitrary value on the interval $x_1 < x < x_2$. For each such value $x_3$ the corresponding extremal of the family is uniquely determined, since there is no value conjugate to $x_1$ on the interval $x_1 < x < x_2$. The value of the second variation $J_2(\eta, \tau, \sigma)$ on the set $\eta_i(x, x_3)$, $\tau = 1$ and on the interval $x_1 x_3$ is then a function of the form

$$(66 \cdot 7) \qquad \begin{aligned} a(x_3, \sigma) &= b + \int_{x_1}^{x_3} 2\omega(x, \eta, \eta')\, dx \\ &= b - C_i \zeta_i(x_1, x_3) , \end{aligned}$$

the last equality being justified by the formula $2\omega = \eta_i \omega_{\eta_i} + \eta_i' \omega_{\eta_i'}$, the usual integration by parts, and the initial values (66·6).

THEOREM 66·1. *Consider an extremal arc* $E_{12}$ *with the properties described above, and the totality of curves* L *transversal to* $E_{12}$ *at the point* 1 *in a fixed direction* $\alpha, \beta_i$. *The linear equation in* $\sigma$

$$q(x_3, \sigma) = 0 \tag{66·8}$$

*is necessary and sufficient for a value* $x_3$ *on the interval* $x_1 < x_3 < x_2$ *to define the first focal point on* $E_{12}$ *of all the curves* L *whose projected curvatures are* $\sigma$. *If* $x_2$ *is not conjugate to* $x_1$ *then the solution* $\sigma(x_3)$ *of the equation (66·8) decreases monotonically from* $+\infty$ *to its finite value* $\sigma(x_2)$ *as* $x_3$ *increases from* $x_1$ *to* $x_2$.

To prove the necessity of the condition (66·8) as stated in the theorem, let $x_3$ define the first focal point of a curve $L$ with projected curvature $\sigma$. There will then be a set $\eta_i(x)$, $\tau$ satisfying the end and transversality conditions (66·4) and the conditions $\eta_i(x_3) = 0$, with $\eta_i(x)$ belonging to an accessory extremal $\eta_i(x)$, $\zeta_i(x)$. The constant $\tau$ cannot be zero, since there is no value conjugate to $x_1$ on the interval $x_1 < x < x_2$; and we may therefore suppose, without loss of generality, that $\tau = 1$. The accessory extremal $\eta_i(x)$, $\zeta_i(x)$ is then identical with the $\eta_i(x, x_3)$, $\zeta_i(x, x_3)$ of equations (66·6), and the equation (66·8) is a consequence of (66·4) and (66·7).

Conversely, if the equation (66·8) is satisfied, the accessory extremal $\eta_i(x, x_3)$, $\zeta_i(x, x_3)$ satisfies the transversality conditions (66·4) with $\tau = 1$ because of equation (66·7); and hence $x_3$ defines a focal point of the curve $L$ with projected curvature $\sigma$. This focal point is the first one after $x_1$ since the solution $\sigma(x_3)$ of equation (66·8) is finite and varies monotonically with $x_3$, as we shall see in the next paragraph.

The partial derivatives of the function $q(x_3, \sigma)$ have the values

$$q_{x_3} = -[f_{y_i'y_k'}\eta_i'\eta_k']^3, \qquad q_\sigma = -(A^2 + B_iB_i)^{1/2}, \tag{66·9}$$

in which the functions $\eta_i$ are those in equations (66·6). The first of these is found by differentiating the first equation (66·7) with respect to $x_3$, applying the usual integration by parts, and using the fact that the derivatives $\eta_{ix_3}$ vanish at $x_1$ and have the values $-\eta_i'$ at $x_3$, as one sees by differentiating equations (66·6) with respect to $x_3$. The value so determined is

$$q_{x_3} = [2\omega - 2\eta_i'\omega_{\eta_i'}]^3;$$

and this is readily identifiable with the first expression (66·9), since the functions $\eta_i$ vanish at $x_3$. Because of the condition III and the non-singularity of $E_{12}$, both of the derivatives (66·9) are negative; and the equation

$$q_{x_3} + q_\sigma \sigma'(x_3) = 0$$

shows that $\sigma'(x_3)$ is everywhere negative, so that $\sigma(x_3)$ monotonically decreases.

To prove that the limit of $\sigma(x_3)$ as $x_3$ approaches $x_1$ is $+\infty$, we may first select an arbitrary set of admissible variations $\eta_i(x)$, $\tau$ with $\tau \neq 0$ and satisfying the end-conditions

$$\eta_i(x_1) = c_i\tau, \qquad \eta_i(x_2) = 0.$$

For every sufficiently large positive value $\Sigma$ the second variation $J_2(\eta, \tau, \Sigma)$ is then negative, since the coefficient of $\sigma$ in (66·3) is negative. Hence from Theorem 65·2 it follows that a curve $L$ with projected curvature $\Sigma$ necessarily has a focal point $x_3$ on the interval $x_1 < x < x_2$, and from the first part of Theorem 66·1 it follows that $\sigma(x_3) = \Sigma$. This means that $\sigma(x_3)$ takes on arbitrarily large positive values, and that it must approach $+\infty$ as $x_3$ approaches $x_1$.

In order to discuss the behavior of the function $\sigma(x_3)$ as $x_3$ approaches $x_2$, when $x_2$ is conjugate to $x_1$, we shall need to distinguish between two cases. A transversal direction $\alpha$, $\beta_i$ at the point *1* will be said to be *exceptional* if for every accessory extremal $\eta_i(x)$, $\zeta_i(x)$ with $\eta_i(x_1) = \eta_i(x_2) = 0$ the transversality condition $\zeta_i(x_1)C_i = 0$ is satisfied. We then have the following theorem:

THEOREM 66·2. *If* $x_2$ *is conjugate to* $x_1$ *and if the direction* $\alpha$, $\beta_i$ *transversal to the extremal* $E_{12}$ *at the point* 1 *is not exceptional, then the solution* $\sigma(x_3)$ *of equation (66·8) decreases monotonically from* $+\infty$ *to* $-\infty$ *as* $x_3$ *increases from* $x_1$ *to* $x_2$.

To prove this let $\eta_i$, $\zeta_i$ be an accessory extremal with elements $\eta_i$ vanishing at $x_1$ and $x_2$ but not satisfying the condition $\zeta_i(x_1)C_i = 0$. The set $\eta_i(x)$, $\tau = 0$ then makes $J_2(\eta, \tau, \sigma)$ vanish whatever the value of $\sigma$. But this set does not minimize the second variation in the class of sets $\eta_i$, $\tau$ satisfying the conditions

$$\eta_i(x_1) = C_i\tau , \qquad \eta_i(x_2) = 0$$

since it does not satisfy the accessory transversality condition $\zeta_i(x_1)C_i = 0$. Hence, from Theorem 65·2 it follows that for every curve $L$ through the direction $\alpha$, $\beta_i$ at the point *1* there must be a focal value $x_3$ on the interval $x_1 < x < x_2$. Since this is true whatever the projected curvature $\sigma$ of $L$ may be, it follows that $\sigma(x_3)$ must take on all real values for values $x_3$ on the interval $x_1 < x < x_2$, and the conclusion of the theorem can be justified with the help of Theorem 66·1.

THEOREM 66·3. *If* $x_2$ *is conjugate to* $x_1$ *and the direction* $\alpha$, $\beta_i$ *is exceptional, then the solution* $\sigma(x_3)$ *of equation (66·8) decreases from* $+\infty$ *to a finite value* $\sigma_0$ *as* $x_3$ *increases from* $x_1$ *to* $x_2$. *The value* $\sigma_0$ *is a projected curvature for which* $x_2$ *is a focal value of* L *on* $E_{12}$ *as well as a value conjugate to* $x_1$.

To prove this let $\eta_{ik}(x)$, $\zeta_{ik}(x)$ be the conjugate system of accessory extremals whose elements $\eta_{ik}$ all vanish at $x_2$. If there are $n - r$ linearly independent accessory extremals with elements $\eta_i$ vanishing at both $x_1$ and $x_2$, the matrix $\|\eta_{ik}(x_1)\|$ is of rank $r$ and can be so chosen that it has zeros in its last $n - r$ columns. On account of the conjugacy of the system it follows that

$$\eta_{i\mu}(x_1)\,\zeta_{i\nu}(x_1) = 0 \qquad (\mu = 1, \ldots, r;\ \nu = r+1, \ldots, n);$$

and, since $\alpha$, $\beta_i$ is exceptional,

$$C_i\zeta_{i\nu}(x_1) = 0 \qquad (\nu = r+1, \ldots, n).$$

Hence the matrix $\|\eta_{i\mu}(x_1), C_i\|$ is of rank $r$. It is easy to see, therefore, that there is a set of constants $a_\mu$, $\tau$ and a projected curvature $\sigma_0$ such that the accessory extremal $u_i = a_\mu \eta_{i\mu}$, $v_i = a_\mu \zeta_{i\mu}$ satisfies the conditions

$$u_i(x_1) = C_i \tau \,, \qquad v_i(x_1) C_i = b_0 \tau \,, \qquad \eta_i(x_2) = 0 \,,$$

in which $b_0$ is the expression (66·3) with $\sigma_0$ in place of $\sigma$. The constant $\tau$ does not vanish and can be chosen equal to unity. With the help of the well-known formula

$$2\omega = \eta_i \omega_{\eta_i} + \eta'_i \omega_{\eta'_i}$$

and the usual integration by parts it follows that

$$J_2(u,\ 1,\ \sigma_0) = b_0 - C_i v_i(x_1) = 0 \,.$$

Since there is no value conjugate to $x_1$ between $x_1$ and $x_2$, an extension to higher space of Corollary 23·1 implies that $J_2(u, 1, \sigma_0)$ is a minimum of the values $J_2(\eta, 1, \sigma_0)$ in the class of admissible sets $\eta_i(x)$ satisfying the conditions

(66·10) $$\eta_i(x_1) = C_i \,, \qquad \eta_i(x_2) = 0 \,.$$

Hence, in particular for the broken extremal $\eta_i$ on the interval $x_1x_2$, a part of which is $\eta_i(x, x_3)$, we have

$$q(x_3,\ \sigma_0) = J_2(\eta,\ 1,\ \sigma_0) \geqq J_2(u,\ 1,\ \sigma_0) = 0 \,.$$

The value $\sigma(x_3)$ which makes $q(x_3, \sigma)$ vanish must therefore be greater than or equal to $\sigma_0$, since the coefficient of $\sigma$ in $q(x_3, \sigma)$ is positive; and it follows that $\sigma(x_3)$ approaches a limiting value $\sigma'_0 \geqq \sigma_0$ as $x_3$ approaches $x_2$.

To prove that $\sigma'_0 = \sigma_0$ we may use the facts that for the interval $x_1x_3$ and the extremal $\eta_i(x, x_3)$ the value $J_2[\eta, 1, \sigma(x_3)]$ is zero and that, according to the extension of Corollary 23·1 cited above, this value is a minimum for the class of admissible sets $\eta_i(x)$ on the interval $x_1x_3$ satisfying the conditions

$$\eta_i(x_1) = C_i \,, \qquad \eta_i(x_2) = 0 \,.$$

As a consequence of this fact, it can be seen that on the class of admissible variations $\eta_i$ satisfying on $x_1x_2$ the end-conditions (66·10) the function $J_2(\eta, 1, \sigma'_0)$ has a minimum less than or equal to zero. Furthermore, by a continuity argument similar to that used in proving Corollary 23·1 it follows that the minimum of $J_2(\eta, 1, \sigma'_0)$ cannot be less than zero. Hence $J_2(\eta, 1, \sigma'_0)$ has minimum zero, as was seen in the last paragraph to be the case for $J_2(\eta, 1, \sigma_0)$. This is possible only if $\sigma'_0 = \sigma_0$.

THEOREM 66·4. *If two directions are exceptional, so is every linear combination of them. The number of linearly independent exceptional directions is* r, *when* n − r *is the number of linearly independent accessory extremals* $\eta_i(x)$, $\zeta_i(x)$ *with elements* $\eta_i$ *vanishing at* $x_1$ *and* $x_2$.

To prove this we use now $\alpha$, $\beta_i$ as direction ratios instead of direction cosines. The first statement of the theorem is an immediate consequence of the definitions of an exceptional direction and of the constant $C_i$ in (66·5). In terms of the notations used above, necessary and sufficient conditions for a direction $\alpha$, $\beta_i$ to be transversal and exceptional are the $n - r + 1$ equations

$$A\alpha + B_i\beta_i = 0 ,$$

$$\zeta_{i\nu}(x_1) C_i = -y_i'(x_1)\zeta_{i\nu}(x_1)\alpha + \zeta_{i\nu}(x_1)\beta_i = 0$$

$$(\nu = r+1, \ldots, n) .$$

These equations are independent, since otherwise there would be constants $k$, $k_\nu$, not all zero, such that

$$kA - k_\nu y_i'(x_1)\zeta_{i\nu}(x_1) = 0 ,$$

$$kB_i + k_\nu\zeta_{i\nu}(x_1) = 0 .$$

If the last equation is multiplied by $y_i'(x_1)$, summed for $i$, and added to the first, it is found that $k = 0$, since the function $f$ is, by hypothesis, different from zero at the point *1* on $E_{12}$. The last equation would then be impossible, since the accessory extremals $\eta_{i\nu}$, $\zeta_{i\nu}$ are linearly independent. Hence the number of linearly independent sets $\alpha$, $\beta_i$ defining exceptional directions is $r$.

**67. Problems with variable end-points in the plane.** The problem in the $xy$-plane analogous to those of Sections 57 and 58 is that of finding in the class of admissible arcs

$$y(x) \qquad (x_1 \leqq x \leqq x_2) \tag{67·1}$$

joining a fixed curve $L$ to a fixed point *2* one which minimizes the integral

$$I = \int_{x_1}^{x_2} f(x, y, y')\,dx . \tag{67·2}$$

The curve $L$ is supposed to be non-singular and defined by functions

$$\xi(a), \quad \eta(a) \qquad (a' \leqq a \leqq a'') .$$

For this problem an admissible arc $E_{12}$ joining $L$ to *2* is said to satisfy the condition I if it satisfies the equation

$$f_{y'} = \int_{x_1}^{x} f_y\,dx + c \tag{67·3}$$

and if at the intersection point *1* of $E_{12}$ and $L$ the differentials $dx$, $dy$ of $L$ and the element $(x, y, y')$ of $E$ satisfy the transversality condition

$$(f - y'f_{y'})\,dx + f_{y'}dy = 0 .$$

The conditions II and III are those stated in Section 35.

To obtain an analogue of Jacobi's condition for the problem, we suppose that $E_{12}$ is a non-singular extremal arc cut transversally by the curve $L$ at the point *1* and not tangent to $L$ at *1*. By the method described for the problem of Section 57 it is known then that a one-parameter family of extremals $y(x, a)$ exists containing $E_{12}$ for values $(x, a)$ satisfying conditions of the form $x_1 \leqq x \leqq x_2$, $a = a_1$ and such that each extremal of the family is cut transversally by the curve $L$ at the value $x = \xi(a)$. A *focal point of the curve* $L$ on $E$ is then a point *3* defined by a zero $x_3$ of the function $y_a(x, a_1)$, that is, a contact point of $E$ with an envelope of the extremal family. The arc $E_{12}$ is said to satisfy the condition IV if there is no focal point of $L$ on $E_{12}$ between its end-points *1* and *2*.

With these definitions of the conditions I–IV the theorems implied in the table of Section 17 concerning necessary conditions and sufficient conditions for a minimum are again valid, provided that $E$ is an admissible arc without corners intersecting the curve $L$ in a single point *1* but not tangent to $L$ at *1*. The proofs may be made by methods quite similar to those of Section 57, or the problem may be regarded as a special case of the more general ones discussed in Sections 59–66.

A second problem with variable end-points in the plane is that of finding in the class of admissible arcs (67·1) joining two fixed curves $L$ and $M$ one which minimizes the integral (67·2). The curves $L$ and $M$ are supposed to be non-singular and defined by functions

$$\xi_1(a), \quad \eta_1(a) \qquad (a' \leqq a \leqq a''),$$
$$\xi_2(\beta), \quad \eta_2(\beta) \qquad (\beta' \leqq \beta \leqq \beta''),$$

respectively. This problem is also a special case of those considered in Sections 59–66, but there is an interesting interpretation of its condition IV which has been justified by Bliss.[9]

An admissible arc $E_{12}$ joining the curves $L$ and $M$ is said to satisfy the condition I for the problem just formulated if it satisfies the equation (67·3) and if, furthermore, it is cut transversally by $L$ and $M$ at its intersection points *1* and *2* with them. The conditions II and III are again those of Section 35. The second variation (62·5) along a non-singular extremal arc $E_{12}$ cut transversally by the curves $L$ and $M$ has the form

$$J_2(\eta, \tau) = b_1\tau_1^2 + b_2\tau_2^2 + \int_{x_1}^{x_2} 2\omega(x, \eta, \eta')\,dx,$$

in which $2\omega$ is the quadratic form (36·4); and from (62·6)

$$b_1 = -\left[(f - y'f_{y'})\,\xi_{aa} + f_{y'}\eta_{aa} + (f_x - y'f_y)\,\xi_a^2 + 2f_y\xi_a\eta_a\right]^1,$$

$$b_2 = \quad \left[(f - y'f_{y'})\,\xi_{\beta\beta} + f_{y'}\eta_{\beta\beta} + (f_x - y'f_y)\,\xi_\beta^2 + 2f_y\xi_\beta\eta_\beta\right]^2.$$

The condition IV of Theorem 62·1 requires this second variation to be non-negative in the class of admissible sets $\eta(x)$, $\tau_1$, $\tau_2$ satisfying the end-conditions (62·3), which now have the form

$$(67\cdot4) \qquad \eta(x_1) = C_1\tau_1, \qquad \eta(x_2) = C_2\tau_2,$$

with

$$C_1 = \eta_{1a} - y'(x_1)\,\xi_{1a}, \qquad C_2 = \eta_{2\beta} - y'(x_2)\,\xi_{2\beta}.$$

[9] "Jacobi's Criterion When Both End Points Are Variable," *Mathematische Annalen*, LVIII (1904), 70–80, and "A Boundary Value Problem in the Calculus of Variations," *Bulletin of the American Mathematical Society*, XXXII (1926), 317–31.

We shall assume henceforth that the extremal arc $E_{12}$ under consideration is not tangent to either of the curves $L$ and $M$, so that the constants $C_1$ and $C_2$ are both different from zero. We may further assume, without loss of generality, that these constants are both positive, since $C_1$, for example, can be made positive by replacing $a$ by $-a$ if necessary.

The focal points of the curve $L$ on the extremal arc $E_{12}$ are defined by the zeros of a solution $u(x)$ of the accessory equation determined by the initial conditions

$$(67\cdot 5) \qquad u(x_1) = C_1 , \qquad [\omega_{\eta'}(x, u, u')]^1 C_1 = b_1 ,$$

as one sees from equations (65·2) and the subsequent definition of a focal point in Section 65. Similarly, the focal points of the curve $M$ are defined by the zeros of an accessory extremal $v(x)$ satisfying

$$(67\cdot 6) \qquad v(x_2) = C_2 , \qquad [\omega_{\eta'}(x, v, v')]^2 C_2 = -b_2 ,$$

the negative sign in the last equation being due to the fact that the curve $M$ is transversal to $E_{12}$ at the second end-point *2* instead of *1*. From Theorem 65·2, or by a direct proof like the one given for that theorem, it follows that when $E_{12}$ satisfies the condition IV it can have on it between *1* and *2* no focal point of either of the curves $L$ and $M$. The functions $u(x)$ and $v(x)$ are, therefore, both positive on the interval $x_1 < x < x_2$. The sets $\eta(x)$, $\tau_1$, $\tau_2$ determined by the conditions

$$(67\cdot 7) \qquad \begin{aligned} \eta(x) &= u(x)\tau_1 \quad \text{on} \quad x_1 \leqq x \leqq x_3 \\ &= v(x)\tau_2 \quad \text{on} \quad x_3 \leqq x \leqq x_2 \\ u(x_3)\tau_1 &= v(x_3)\tau_2 \end{aligned}$$

satisfy the accessory end and transversality conditions

$$\eta(x_1) = C_1\tau_1 , \qquad \eta(x_2) = C_2\tau_2 ,$$

$$\omega_{\eta'}(x_1) C_1 = b_1\tau_1 , \qquad \omega_{\eta'}(x_2) C_2 = -b_2\tau_2 ,$$

as may be seen with the help of equations (67·5) and (67·6). Using the usual integration by parts and simple manipulations, we find for such a set $\eta(x)$, $\tau_1$, $\tau_2$ the value

$$(67\cdot 8) \qquad J_2(\eta, \tau) = \tau_1\tau_2[(vu' - uv') f_{y'y'}]^3 .$$

The third equation (67·7) shows that $\tau_1$ and $\tau_2$ have the same sign, so that the condition IV requires the bracket to be non-negative. The bracket has the same value at all points $x_3$ on the interval $x_1x_2$, since, if we define $J(\eta)$ by the equation

$$J(\eta) = \frac{d}{dx}\omega_{\eta'} - \omega_\eta$$

if follows that

$$\frac{d}{dx}[(uv' - vu') f_{y'y'}] = uJ(v) - vJ(u) = 0 .$$

We can now prove the following theorem:

THEOREM 67·1. *For a non-singular extremal arc* $E_{12}$ *in the* xy*-plane, cut transversally at* 1 *and* 2 *by the curves* L *and* M, *the condition* IV, *the non-negativeness of the second variation, is equivalent to requiring that* L *and* M *have no focal points on the arc* $E_{12}$ *and that for the accessory extremals* u(x), v(x) *whose zeros define these focal points the expression* $vu' - uv'$ *is zero or has the same sign as the product* uv *at each value* $x_3$ *between* $x_1$ *and* $x_2$. *The condition* IV' *is equivalent to the same requirements with the additional one that* $vu' - uv' \neq 0$.

In the preceding paragraphs and here we are assuming $C_1$ and $C_2$ both positive and $u$ and $v$ therefore positive at $x_1$ and $x_2$, respectively. The statements of the theorem for the other cases follow readily from this one.

If the condition IV is satisfied, the curve $L$ cannot have a focal point at *2*. Otherwise we should have $u(x_2) = 0$, $u'(x_2) < 0$, $v(x_2) = C_2 > 0$; and the expression (67·8) for the second variation would be negative. A similar argument shows that the curve $M$ cannot have a focal point at *1*. The other consequences of the condition IV stated in the theorem have been justified above.

It will next be proved that the requirements stated in the theorem imply the non-negativeness of the second variation and, consequently, the condition IV. This can be proved in a number of ways, but most simply, perhaps, by the use of a formula analogous to the formula (39·5). Let $\eta(x)$, $\tau_1$, $\tau_2$ be an arbitrary set of admissible variations satisfying the end-conditions (67·4). We wish to calculate the value $J_2(\eta, \tau)$ in the third equation preceding (67·4). Two values, $w_1$ and $w_2$, may first be determined by the equations

$$w_1 u\,(x_3) = \eta\,(x_3) = w_2\, v\,(x_3)$$

where $u$ and $v$ are the accessory extremals defined above and $x_3$ is an arbitrarily selected value between $x_1$ and $x_2$. In Figure 67·1, $C_{12}$ represents the curve in the $x\eta$-plane defined by $\eta(x)$, and $E_{43}$ and $E_{35}$ are the particular extremals $w_1 u$ and

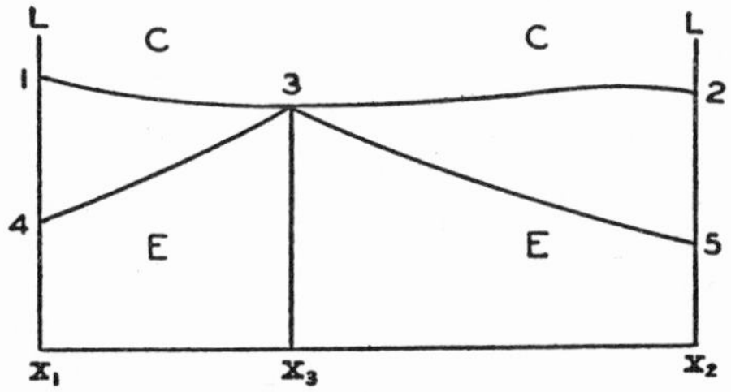


FIG. 67·1

$w_2 v$, respectively. If $I_2$ represents the integral in $J_2(\eta, \tau)$, then with the help of the properties of the invariant integral $I_2{}^*$ in the field of accessory extremals $au$ it follows that

$$I_2(C_{13}) = [I_2(C_{13}) - I_2^*(C_{13})] + I_2^*(L_{14}) + I_2(E_{43})\,.$$

When the integrals on the right are evaluated with the help of equations (67·5), it turns out that

$$I_2(C_{13}) = \int_{x_1}^{x_3} (\eta' - \pi)^2 f_{y'y'}\,dx - b_1\tau_1^2 + w_1w_2[v\omega_{\eta'}(x, u, u')]^3 .$$

If this value and a similar one for $I_2(C_{32})$ are substituted in $J_2(\eta, \tau)$, it follows that

$$(67\cdot 9) \quad J_2(\eta, \tau) = \int_{x_1}^{x_2} (\eta' - \pi)^2 f_{y'y'}\,dx + w_1w_2[(vu' - uv') f_{y'y'}]^3 ,$$

in which the slope functions of the two fields involved are $\pi = \eta u'/u$ and $\pi = \eta v'/v$ on the intervals $x_1x_3$ and $x_3x_2$, respectively. The remaining conclusions of the theorem follow readily from (67·10).

If there is an extension of the extremal arc $E_{12}$ on which the curves $L$ and $M$ have focal points *1′* and *2′*, the results of the last theorem can be given a still different interpretation. The symbols *1′* and *2′* will always be used to designate the first focal points of $L$ and $M$ on the right or on the left.

THEOREM 67·2. *If there is an extension of the extremal arc* $E_{12}$ *on which the curves* L *and* M *have focal points* 1′ *and* 2′, *then the condition IV is equivalent to requiring that the arc* $E_{12}$ *contain neither of these focal points and that the arc* 11′ *of* E *contain neither or both of the points* 2 *and* 2′. *The condition IV′ is equivalent to the same requirements, with the addition that* 1′ *and* 2′ *are distinct.*

The case when *1′* is the first focal point at the right of *1* will be discussed in this paragraph. At the point *1′* we then have $u = 0$, $u' < 0$. The relation $vu' - uv' \geqq 0$ of Theorem 67·1 implies that $v \leqq 0$. The focal point *2′* of $M$ is consequently either coincident with *1′* when $v = 0$ or between *1* and *1′* when $v < 0$. With the help of these remarks the conclusions of the theorem follow readily from those of Theorem 67·1. The argument depends upon the well-known facts that a solution $u(x) \not\equiv 0$ of a linear differential equation of the second order never vanishes with its derivative and that two such solutions have zeros which separate each other.

A similar proof can be made in the case when *1′* is the first focal point of $L$ at the left of *1*.

For an admissible arc $E_{12}$ without corners and having only its end-points *1* and *2* in common with the curves $L$ and $M$ the theorems concerning necessary conditions and sufficient conditions for a minimum are those indicated in the table of Section 17 with the interpretations given in this section for the conditions I–IV. The proofs of the necessary conditions have been indicated in the preceding paragraphs, and the theorems concerning sufficient conditions are consequences of the theorems of Section 63. Independent proofs applicable to the problem of this section have been given by Bliss in the references cited above.

# PART II

# THE PROBLEM OF BOLZA

# CHAPTER VII

## THE MULTIPLIER RULE

**68. Introduction.** The problems of Lagrange, Mayer, and Bolza with variable end-points are the most general problems of the calculus of variations involving only simple integrals for which a theory having some degree of completeness can now be formulated. The most economical theory of the three problems can be attained by studying, first of all, the problem of Bolza, since this type includes the other two by means of simple specializations and since in each of the three cases the so-called "accessory minimum problem" of the second variation, which plays an important auxiliary role in the theory, appears as a problem of Bolza and requires no new theory for its analysis.

Theoretically, the three problems are equivalent. It has been known for some time[1] that the problem of Bolza can be transformed into a problem of Mayer. It is also true that there is a very simple transformation, apparently not hitherto noted, which takes the problems of Mayer and Bolza into problems of Lagrange. In Section 69, below, these relationships between the various problems are discussed in more detail.

The multiplier rule for the problems mentioned in the preceding paragraphs and the necessary conditions for a minimum usually designated as those of Weierstrass and Clebsch have been deduced by several writers.[2] A necessary condition analogous to those of Jacobi for simpler problems is suggested in early papers by Mayer [1, 3]; and a corresponding condition, stated in terms of the smallest characteristic number of a boundary-value problem associated with the second variation, was deduced by Cope [16]. The first published discussion of sufficient conditions is that of Morse [23] for the problem of Bolza. Shortly after the appearance of Morse's paper Bliss [25] published a quite different theory of sufficient conditions, which he had long known and which was suggested by the papers of Mayer (to which reference is made above) and which involves an important theorem due to Hahn [7]. Still later, a third discussion of sufficient conditions for the problem of Bolza was made by Hu [31]. On account of rather strong assumptions concerning the so-called "normality of the minimizing arc," the methods of these writers cannot be applied to the problem of Mayer with variable end-points without serious modifications. The method of Bliss has, however, been extended by Bliss and Hestenes [30, 34] to include this case.

[1] See Bliss [11], p. 314. The bracketed numbers here and in later references, as well as in the text, indicate items in the Bibliography of the Problem of Bolza, which appears on pp. 274–83, below.

[2] See, e.g., Bolza [8]; Bliss [11, 17]; Morse and Myers [24]; Bliss and Schoenberg [26]; McShane [64].

That the normality assumptions used by Morse and also by Bliss and Hestenes are stronger than necessary is shown in a number of recent papers. Graves [29] modified the proof of the necessary condition of Weierstrass in ingenious fashion so that it is effective under much weaker normality assumptions; and McShane [64] has recently shown that this condition, like the multiplier rule, can be established without normality assumptions of any kind. Hestenes [38] generalized for the problem of Bolza a necessary condition for a minimum which had earlier been applied by Bliss [15] to a relatively very special problem in the plane. He further made a sufficiency proof for the problem which is remarkable in that it applies not only to normal extremal arcs which are not necessarily normal on every subinterval but also to some abnormal cases. The results of Graves and Hestenes bring to a satisfactory close the important chapter of the theory of the problem of Bolza which applies to minimizing arcs that are normal but have not necessarily the property of normality on every subinterval which was previously undesirably presupposed. The conclusions of the theory, established by the methods now possible in view of their researches, are applicable without modification to the problems of Mayer and Lagrange with variable endpoints as specializations of the problem of Bolza. Such applications were not possible for the earlier theories, as has been indicated above explicitly by Bliss [56].

The attention of students of the calculus of variations has been attracted to the so-called "abnormal" problems by two papers by Carathéodory [27, 36] in which he studies the theory of the second variation in such cases and makes a classification of abnormal problems. It seems unlikely to the present writer that a comprehensive theory without any normality assumption whatever can be developed in the near future, in view of the enormous variety of singular possibilities which present themselves. These singularities are analogous to those possible for implicit functions but are even more numerous and complicated. The results of Hestenes [38] did, however, extend our knowledge to special abnormal cases, and in the domain of sufficiency proofs they were the first such extensions. At the September, 1934, meeting of the American Mathematical Society, Reid [44] announced an interesting auxiliary theorem which seems to make it possible to extend the method of Bliss for the problem of Bolza to the more general cases studied by Hestenes. Reid's theorem has also been proved independently by Morse [41] and Hestenes [46]. In papers by Hestenes [38, p. 794; 50, p. 141] and Morse [41, p. 147] the statement is made that the hypotheses of the sufficiency theorems there proved contain no assumptions with regard to normality. This seems to me only superficially true, since the theorems in question are reducible in simple fashion to ones for normal problems, as has been shown by Bliss [56, p. 370]. Quite recently McShane [64, 69, 71, 76, 74] and Myers [77] have published interesting results concerning abnormal cases.

The purpose of the following pages is the presentation of the theory of the problem of Bolza in the relatively complete form which has been made possible by the researches briefly described in the preceding paragraphs. The problem is formulated approximately as stated by Bolza himself, and the emphasis is on the normal problems, which seem to be by far the most important ones. The more important results so far deduced for abnormal problems can be established by making the proofs for suitably phrased normal problems, as indicated in Section 92, below.

**69. The equivalence of various problems.** The problem of Bolza [8] as formulated by Bliss [25] is that of finding, in a class of arcs

(69·1) $$y_i(x) \qquad (i=1, \ldots, n;\; x_1 \leqq x \leqq x_2)$$

satisfying differential equations and end-conditions of the form

(69·2) $$\phi_\beta(x, y, y') = 0 \qquad (\beta = 1, \ldots, m<n),$$

(69·3) $$\psi_\mu[x_1, y(x_1), x_2, y(x_2)] = 0 \qquad (\mu = 1, \ldots, p \leqq 2n+2)$$

one which minimizes a sum of the form

(69·4) $$J = g[x_1, y(x_1), x_2, y(x_2)] + \int_{x_1}^{x_2} f(x, y, y')\,dx .$$

In these expressions, and often in the following pages, the symbols $y$ and $y'$ stand for the sets $(y_1, \ldots, y_n)$ and $(y_1', \ldots, y_n')$; and similar notations will be used for other sets when convenient. In an analogous statement of the problem of Bolza by Morse[3] the conditions (69·3) are replaced by parametric equations of the form

(69·5) $$x_s = x_s(t), \qquad y_i(x_s) = y_{is}(t) \qquad (i = 1, \ldots, n;\; s = 1, 2),$$

where $t$ is a set of parameters $(t_1, \ldots, t_r)$, and the function to be minimized is taken in the form

(69·6) $$J = g(t) + \int_{x_1}^{x_2} f(x, y, y')\,dx .$$

The problem of Mayer with variable end-points as formulated by Bliss [11] is the problem of Bolza first described above with its integrand function $f$ identically zero, and the problem of Lagrange with variable end-points is similarly the case when $g$ is absent from $J$ in (69·4). In Morse's form it would be the case when $g$ is absent from $J$ in (69·6).

It is easy to see, with the help of very simple considerations, that the problem of Bolza is transformable into a problem of either Mayer or Lagrange with variable end-points. It is, in the first place, equivalent, as one readily verifies, to the problem of Mayer having a class of arcs

$$y_i(x), \qquad y_{n+1}(x) \qquad (i = 1, \ldots, n;\; x_1 \leqq x \leqq x_2)$$

[3] [22], pp. 518–19; Morse and Myers [24], pp. 235–36.

subjected to conditions of the form

$$\phi_\beta = 0 , \qquad y'_{n+1} - f(x, y, y') = 0 ,$$
$$\psi_\mu = 0 , \qquad y_{n+1}(x_1) = 0$$

and having the function $J = g + y_{n+1}(x_2)$ to be minimized. It is, furthermore, equivalent to a problem of Lagrange with a class of arcs

$$y_i(x) , \qquad y_{n+1}(x) \qquad (i = 1, \ldots, n; \; x_1 \leqq x \leqq x_2)$$

satisfying conditions of the form

$$\phi_\beta = 0 , \qquad y'_{n+1} = 0 ,$$
$$\psi_\mu = 0 , \qquad y_{n+1}(x_1) - \frac{g}{x_2 - x_1} = 0$$

and with an integral to be minimized of the form

$$I = \int_{x_1}^{x_2} (f + y_{n+1}) \, dx .$$

This last transformation is the one mentioned above in the second paragraph of the introduction (Sec. 68). Since the problem of Bolza contains the problems of Lagrange and Mayer as specializations, it is evident from the two transformations of this paragraph that the three problems possess the same degree of generality.

One can also verify, without difficulty, the equivalence of the problem of Bolza having non-parametric end-conditions and sum $J$ of the forms (69·3) and (69·4) with the one having parametric end-conditions and sum (69·5) and (69·6). For, in the first place, $r = 2n + 2 - p$ new functions $\psi_{p+h}[x_1, y(x_1), x_2, y(x_2)]$ $(h = 1, \ldots, r)$ can be chosen in such a way that the $2n + 2$ equations

$$\psi_\mu [x_1, y(x_1), x_2, y(x_2)] = 0 ,$$
$$\psi_{p+h} [x_1, y(x_1), x_2, y(x_2)] = t_h$$

are solvable for the $2n + 2$ end-values $x_1$, $y(x_1)$, $x_2$, $y(x_2)$. Then the equations (69·3) are expressible in the form (69·5), and the function $g$ in (69·4) becomes a function $g(t)$. The choice of the functions $\psi_{p+h}$ is possible since in the development of the theory it is always presupposed that the matrix of derivatives of the functions $\psi_\mu$ with respect to their arguments $x_1$, $y(x_1)$, $x_2$, $y(x_2)$ has rank $p$. On the other hand, a parametric problem is expressible as a non-parametric one, since the non-parametric problem with a class of arcs

$$y_i(x) , \qquad t_h(x) \qquad (i = 1, \ldots, n; \; h = 1, \ldots, r; \; x_1 \leqq x \leqq x_2)$$

satisfying the conditions

$$(69\cdot7) \qquad \begin{array}{ll} \phi_\beta = 0 & t'_h = 0 , \\ x_s - x_s[t(x_1)] = 0 & y_i(x_s) - y_{is}[t(x_1)] = 0 \end{array}$$

and with the function

$$J = g[t(x_1)] + \int_{x_1}^{x_2} f(x, y, y')\, dx$$

to be minimized, is equivalent to the original problem with parametric conditions in the forms[4] (69·5) and (69·6).

The problem of Bolza associated with the expressions (69·1) to (69·4) is said to have *separated end-conditions* if the conditions (69·3) fall into two groups of the form

$$\psi_\rho[x_1, y(x_1)] = 0, \qquad \psi_\sigma[x_2, y(x_2)] = 0 \qquad (\rho = 1, \ldots, r; \ \sigma = r+1, \ldots p) \tag{69·8}$$

and if, furthermore, the function $g$ in (69·4) is a difference

$$g = g_1[x_1, y(x_1)] - g_2[x_2, y(x_2)].$$

Otherwise the problem is said to have *mixed end-conditions.* The problem of finding, in a class of arcs

$$y_i(x), \quad y_{n+a}(x) \qquad (i = 1, \ldots, n; \ a = 1, \ldots, n+2; \ x_1 \leqq x \leqq x_2) \tag{69·9}$$

satisfying the different equations and end-conditions

$$\begin{aligned} &\phi_\beta(x, y, y') = 0, \qquad y'_{n+a} = 0, \\ &\psi_\mu[y_{2n+1}(x_1), y_i(x_1), y_{2n+2}(x_1), y_{n+i}(x_1)] = 0, \\ &y_{2n+1}(x_1) - x_1 = 0, \\ &y_{n+i}(x_2) - y_i(x_2) = 0, \qquad y_{2n+2}(x_2) - x_2 = 0, \end{aligned} \tag{69·10}$$

one which minimizes the functional

$$J = g[y_{2n+1}(x_1), y_i(x_1), y_{2n+2}(x_1), y_{n+i}(x_1)] + \int_{x_1}^{x_2} f(x, y, y')\, dx$$

is a problem with separated end-conditions equivalent to the original one.

Similarly, the problem of Bolza in the form (69·2, 5, 6) is said to have *separated parametric end-conditions* if equations (69·5) have the form

$$\begin{aligned} x_1 &= x_1(t_1, \ldots, t_\rho), \qquad y_i(x_1) = y_{i1}(t_1, \ldots, t_\rho), \\ x_2 &= x_2(t_{\rho+1}, \ldots, t_r), \qquad y_i(x_2) = y_{i2}(t_{\rho+1}, \ldots, t_r) \end{aligned}$$

and if the function $g(t)$ has the form

$$g = g_1(t_1, \ldots, t_\rho) - g_2(t_{\rho+1}, \ldots, t_r).$$

Otherwise the end-conditions are said to be *mixed parametric end-conditions.* The problem with a class of arcs

$$y_i(x), \quad y_{n+h}(x) \qquad (i = 1, \ldots, n\cdot \ h = 1, \ldots, r; \ x_1 \leqq x \leqq x_2) \tag{69·11}$$

[4] See Bliss and Schoenberg [26].

satisfying differential equations and end-conditions

$$\phi_\beta = 0\,, \qquad y'_{n+h} = 0$$

$$(69\cdot 12) \qquad \begin{aligned} x_1 &= x_1(t_1, \ldots, t_r)\,, & y_i(x_1) &= y_{i1}(t_1, \ldots, t_r)\,, \\ & & y_{n+h}(x_1) &= t_h\,, \\ x_2 &= x_2(t_{r+1}, \ldots, t_{2r}\,, & y_i(x_2) &= y_{i2}(t_{r+1}, \ldots, t_{2r})\,, \\ & & y_{n+h}(x_2) &= t_{r+h}\,, \end{aligned}$$

and with the function $J$ in (69·6) to be minimized, has separated end-conditions and is equivalent to the original one [Hestenes, 38, p. 815].

When $x_1$ and $x_2$ are allowed to vary, the end-points of an arc (69·1) describe a two-dimensional subspace of the $(2n + 2)$-dimensional space of points $(x_1, y_{i1}, x_2, y_{i2})$. An arc (69·1) satisfying the end-conditions of the problem of Bolza is said to satisfy the *non-tangency condition* if the two-dimensional locus of its end-points has no tangent in common with the space of $(2n + 2)$-dimensional points defined by the end-conditions of the problem. The tangents to the two-dimensional space have the direction ratios

$$a_1 : a_1 y'_i(x_1) : a_2 : a_2 y'_i(x_2)\,,$$

in which $a_1$ and $a_2$ are arbitrary constants not both zero. Such a direction is tangent to the space defined by the equations (69·3) if and only if for every $\mu = 1, \ldots, p$ the condition

$$a_1[\psi_{\mu,1} + \psi_{\mu,i1}\, y'_i(x_1)] + a_2[\psi_{\mu,2} + \psi_{\mu,i2}\, y'_i(x_2)] = 0$$

is satisfied, in which

$$\psi_{\mu,1} = \frac{\partial \psi_\mu}{\partial x_1}\,, \qquad \psi_{\mu,i1} = \frac{\partial \psi_\mu}{\partial y_i(x_1)}$$

and $\psi_{\mu,2}$ and $\psi_{\mu,i2}$ have similar interpretations. Hence it is evident that a necessary and sufficient condition for an arc to satisfy the non-tangency condition is that the matrix

$$\| \psi_{\mu,1} + \psi_{\mu,i1}\, y'_i(x_1)\,, \qquad \psi_{\mu,2} + \psi_{\mu,i2}\, y'_i(x_2) \|$$

has rank two. A curve (69·9) satisfying the differential equations in (69·10) has always this property relative to the end-conditions in (69·10), as one readily verifies.

If the end-conditions are given in the parametric form (69·5), let us use the notations

$$x_{sh} = \frac{\partial x_s}{\partial t_h}\,, \qquad y_{ish} = \frac{\partial y_{is}}{\partial t_h}\,, \qquad y'_{is} = y'_i(x_s)\,,$$

$$(69\cdot 13) \qquad c_{ish}(t) = y_{ish} - y'_{is} x_{sh}\,,$$

$$(i = 1, \ldots, n;\; h = 1, \ldots, r;\; s = 1, 2)\,.$$

Then the criterion for non-tangency is that the equations

$$x_{sh}\tau_h = a_s , \qquad y_{ish}\tau_h = a_s y'_{is}$$

have only the solutions $(\tau_h, a_s) = (0, 0)$. This is equivalent to saying that the matrix

$$(69\cdot 14) \qquad \left\| \begin{matrix} x_{1h} & 1 & 0 \\ y_{i1h} & y'_{i1} & 0 \\ x_{2h} & 0 & 1 \\ y_{i2h} & 0 & y'_{i2} \end{matrix} \right\|$$

has maximum rank or that the slightly transformed matrix

$$\left\| \begin{matrix} c_{i1h} \\ c_{i2h} \end{matrix} \right\|$$

has the same property. An arc (69·11) satisfying the differential equations in (69·12) has always this property relative to the end-conditions in (69·12); and, furthermore, these end-conditions are *non-singular* at the ends of the arc in the sense that the matrix of the first $r$ columns of (69·14) has rank $r$.

The upshot of the remarks which have been made in the preceding paragraphs of this section is that the problems of Mayer and Lagrange with variable end-points and the problem of Bolza with either non-parametric or parametric end-conditions are all of equal generality and equivalent by relatively simple transformations. Furthermore, there is no loss of generality if it is assumed that the end-conditions are separated or non-singular or that the arcs satisfying the differential equations $\phi_\beta = 0$ of the problem all satisfy the non-tangency condition also. In the next section a more explicit description is given of the form in which the problem of Bolza will be studied in this book.

**70. Analytic formulation of the problem of Bolza.** In order to secure a firm analytic foundation for the theories of the following pages, let $R_1$ be an open region of $(2n + 1)$-dimensional points $(x, y, y')$ in which the functions $\phi_\beta$ and $f$ have continuous partial derivatives of at least the third order. In order that the equations $\phi_\beta = 0$ may be independent differential equations, it is assumed that the matrix $\|\phi_{\beta y'_i}\|$ is everywhere of rank $m$ in $R_1$, the subscripts $y'_i$ here, as elsewhere, indicating partial derivatives. Similarly, $R_2$ is supposed to be an open set of $(2n + 2)$-dimensional points $(x_1, y_{i1}, x_2, y_{i2})$ in which the functions $\psi_\mu$ and $g$ have continuous partial derivatives of at least the third order and in which the matrix

$$(70\cdot 1) \qquad \| \psi_{\mu,1} \quad \psi_{\mu,i1} \quad \psi_{\mu,2} \quad \psi_{\mu,i2} \|$$

has rank $p$. In these statements the symbol $y_{i1}$, for example, stands for $y_i(x_1)$ and

$$\psi_{\mu,1} = \frac{\partial \psi_\mu}{\partial x_1}, \qquad \psi_{\mu,i1} = \frac{\partial \psi_\mu}{\partial y_{i1}},$$

with similar notations for other derivatives. A set $(x, y, y')$ or $(x_1, y_{i1}, x_2, y_{i2})$ is said to be *admissible* if it is in $R_1$ or $R_2$, respectively.

The arcs of the type (69·1) to be considered are supposed to be continuous and to consist of a finite number of sub-arcs on each of which the functions $y_i(x)$ have continuous derivatives. Such an arc is said to lie in $R_1$ if its elements $(x, y, y')$ are admissible, and it is said to be an *admissible arc* if its elements $(x, y, y')$ and $[x_1, y(x_1), x_2, y(x_2)]$ are all admissible. On every such arc the functions $\phi_\beta$, $\psi_\mu$, $f$, $g$ and the function $J$ have well-defined values. One should notice that this definition of an admissible arc is not that previously adopted by Bliss [17, p. 677] or that of Morse [23, p. 518]. The definition given here is designed merely to make sure that on each admissible arc $C$ of the type (69·1) the sum $J$ in (69·4) has a unique value $J(C)$. With the definition of admissibility formulated in this way it is believed that the statements of the various theorems are more self-contained.

The problem of Bolza is now that of finding, in the class of admissible arcs (69·1) satisfying the differential equations $\phi_\beta = 0$ in (69·2) and the end-conditions $\psi_\mu = 0$ in (69·3), one which minimizes the function $J$ in (69·4). If we designate by $\mathfrak{M}$ the class of admissible arcs satisfying $\phi_\beta = 0$ and $\psi_\mu = 0$, then the problem is that of finding in $\mathfrak{M}$ an arc $C$ on which $J(C)$ is a minimum.

For the problem of Bolza in the form (69·5–6) one may presuppose an open set $T$ of points $t = (t_1, \ldots, t_r)$ in which the functions $x_s(t)$, $y_{is}(t)$, $g(t)$ in the end-conditions (69·5) and the expression (69·6) for $J$ have continuous partial derivatives of at least the third order. An admissible set

$$(70\cdot2)\qquad y_i(x), \qquad t_h \qquad (i = 1, \ldots, n;\ h = 1, \ldots, r;\ x_1 \leqq x \leqq x_2)$$

is one for which the arc $y_i(x)$ is an arc in $R_1$ and the set $t$ is in $T$. The problem is then that of finding in the class of admissible sets (70·2) satisfying the differential equations (69·2) and the end-conditions (69·5) one which minimizes the sum $J$ in (69·6).

**71. Variations and the equations of variation.** In the following pages families of arcs with special continuity properties are frequently considered. In order to describe, once for all, the properties of these families, one may begin by defining an *elementary family*

$$(71\cdot1)\qquad y_i(x\quad b) \qquad (x' \leqq x \leqq x'';\ |b| \leqq \epsilon)$$

as one for which the derivatives $y_i'(x, b)$ exist and, with the functions $y_i(x, b)$, have continuous derivatives of at least the first order with respect to $b$ in a neighborhood of the region of points $(x, b)$ indicated in the parenthesis on the right. Two such families are said to be *adjacent* if they are defined on adjoining intervals $x' \leqq x \leqq x''$ and $x'' \leqq x \leqq x'''$ and if, furthermore, their defining functions form continuous functions $y_i(x, b)$ on the region $x' \leqq x \leqq x'''$, $|b| \leqq \epsilon$. The families of the somewhat more general form

$$(71\cdot2)\qquad y_i(x,\ b) \qquad [x_1(b) \leqq x \leqq x_2(b);\ |b| < \epsilon]$$

to be considered are supposed to have functions $x_1(b)$, $x_2(b)$ with continuous derivatives of at least the first order with respect to $b$ in the region $|b| < \epsilon$, and each such family is supposed to be a part of a sequence of adjacent elementary families defined on adjoining intervals $x'x''$, $x''x'''$, . . . , $x^{(k-1)}x^{(k)}$ such that

$$x' < x_1(b) < x'', \qquad x^{(k-1)} < x_2(b) < x^{(k)} .$$

A family (71·2) with these properties, all of whose arcs are admissible, is called an *admissible family.*

The differentials of the family (71·2) will be represented by the notations

$$\begin{aligned} dx_1 &= x_{1b}\, db , \qquad dx_2 = x_{2b}\, db \\ dy_i &= y_i' dx + \delta y_i , \\ d^2 y_i &= y_i' d^2 x + y_i'' dx^2 + 2\,\delta y_i' dx + \delta^2 y_i , \end{aligned} \tag{71·3}$$

where the symbol $\delta$ indicates differentials taken with respect to the parameter $b$ alone. Every admissible family has the differentials in the first two rows of (71·3), but not necessarily the differential $\delta^2 y_i$, since in the definition of such a family no assumption is made concerning the derivatives $y_i''$. But we shall see later, in Corollary 77·2, that admissible families with these differentials can be constructed when the arc $E$ contained in the family (71·2) for $b = 0$ has continuous second derivatives.

The *set of variations of the family along* $E$ is the set $\xi_1$, $\xi_2$, $\eta_i(x)$ defined by the equations

$$\begin{aligned} dx_1 &= x_{1b}(0)\, db = \xi_1\, db , \qquad dx_2 = x_{2b}(0)\, db = \xi_2\, db , \\ \delta y_i &= y_{ib}(x, 0)\, db = \eta_i(x)\, db. \end{aligned} \tag{71·4}$$

The symbols $\xi_1$, $\xi_2$ represent constants; and as a result of the continuity properties of the family (71·2), it is easily seen that the functions $\eta_i(x)$ have the continuity properties of admissible arcs $y_i(x)$ on the interval $x_1(0) \leqq x \leqq x_2(0)$ belonging to $E$. Every set $\xi_1$, $\xi_2$, $\eta_i(x)$ with these properties is called a set of *admissible variations along* $E$.

If the arcs of an admissible family all satisfy the equations

$$\phi_\beta [x, y(x, b), y'(x, b)] = 0$$

then the variations $\eta_i(x)$ along the arc $E$ contained in the family for $b = b_0$, satisfy the equations

$$\Phi_\beta (x, \eta, \eta') = \phi_{\beta y_i}\eta_i + \phi_{\beta y_i'}\eta_i' = 0 , \tag{71·5}$$

in which the arguments of the derivatives of $\phi_\beta$ are the functions $y_i(x, b_0)$ belonging to $E$. The equations (71·5) are called the *equations of variation along* $E$. Their coefficients are completely determined, irrespective of any family, when the arc $E$ is given. The repeated subscripts in these equations indicate that sums for $i = 1, \ldots, n$ are to be taken, as customary in tensor analysis. This convention is used freely in the following pages.

If the end-values of the arcs of an admissible family satisfy the equations

$$\Psi_\mu\{x_1(b),\ y[x_1(b),\ b],\ x_2(b),\ y[x_2(b),\ b]\} = 0\,,$$

then by differentiation with respect to $b$ it is seen that the variations of the family along $E$ satisfy the equations

$$(71\cdot 6) \qquad \Psi_\mu[\xi_1,\ \eta(x_1),\ \xi_2,\ \eta(x_2)] = 0\,,$$

where

$$(71\cdot 7)\ \Psi_\mu = (\psi_{\mu,1} + y'_{i1}\psi_{\mu,i1})\xi_1 + \psi_{\mu,i1}\eta_i(x_1) + (\psi_{\mu,2} + y'_{i2}\psi_{\mu,i2})\xi_2 + \psi_{\mu,i2}\eta_i(x_2)$$

and the arguments of the derivatives of $\psi_\mu$ are the end-values of $E$. The equations (71·7) are called the *equations of variation on* E *of the end-conditions.*

It should be noted that the definitions in the preceding paragraphs can be extended at once to families (71·2) for which the symbol $b$ stands for a set of parameters $(b_1, \ldots, b_s)$. The family (71·2) will then have a set of variations $\xi_{1\sigma}$, $\xi_{2\sigma}$, $\eta_{i\sigma}(x)$ for each parameter $b_\sigma$ $(\sigma = 1, \ldots, s)$. The modifications necessary in the differentials (71·3) and (71·4) can be readily inferred.

**72. A fundamental imbedding lemma.** If an admissible arc $E$ satisfying the equations $\phi_\beta = 0$, $\psi_\mu = 0$ is given, one cannot conclude without proof that there are other arcs with the same properties. If there are no others, the problem of Bolza, described in Section 69 and formulated more precisely analytically in Section 70 above, is, of course, trivial. The lemma of this section establishes the fact that under the hypotheses made on the functions $\phi_\beta$ every arc $E$ in $R_1$ satisfying the equations $\phi_\beta = 0$ is imbedded in families of arcs of the same sort. In a later section it will be shown that every admissible arc $E$, satisfying the equations of both the sets $\phi_\beta = 0$ and $\psi_\mu = 0$, is imbedded in families of admissible arcs satisfying these equations, provided that $E$ has a certain property called "normality." The following lemma plays an important role in this latter proof, as well as in other parts of the theory.

LEMMA 72·1. *If an admissible arc* E *satisfies the equations* $\phi_\beta = 0$, *and if* $\xi_1$, $\xi_2$, $\eta_i(x)$ *is a set of admissible variations satisfying the equations of variation* $\Phi_\beta = 0$ *on* E, *then there is an admissible one-parameter family (71·2) of arcs containing* E *for the parameter value* $b = 0$, *satisfying the equations* $\phi_\beta = 0$, *and having the set* $\xi_1$, $\xi_2$, $\eta_i(x)$ *as the variations of the family along* E.

In order to prove this it is desirable first to extend the system of equations $\phi_\beta = 0$ to a system of the form

$$(72\cdot 1) \qquad \phi_\beta = 0\,, \qquad \phi_m = z_\gamma \qquad (\beta = 1, \ldots, m;\ \gamma = m+1, \ldots, n)\,,$$

in which the functions $\phi_\gamma(x, y, y')$ have continuous partial derivatives of at least the third order in a neighborhood of the values $(x, y, y')$ belonging to $E$ and are such that the functional determinant of the functions $\phi_\beta$, $\phi_\gamma$ with respect to the variables $y'$ is different from zero along $E$. The functions $\phi_\gamma$ can, in fact, be chosen linear in the variables $y'$ with coefficients functions of $x$, as has been shown by Bliss [11, pp. 307, 312]. When the functions $y_i(x)$ defining $E$ are substituted, the equations (72·1) determine a set of functions $z_\gamma(x)$ belonging to $E$ which are continuous except possibly at the corners of $E$. Equations (72·1) have a set of equations of variation

$$(72\cdot 2)\qquad \Phi_\beta = 0\,, \qquad \Phi_\gamma = \zeta_\gamma \qquad (\beta = 1, \ldots, m;\ \gamma = m+1, \ldots, n)$$

which determine functions $\zeta_\gamma(x)$ corresponding to the arc $E$ and the functions $\eta_i(x)$ of the lemma. The functions $\zeta_\gamma(x)$ are continuous except possibly at values $x$ defining corners of $E$ or at discontinuities of the derivatives of the functions $\eta_i(x)$.

According to well-known implicit function theorems, the equations (72·1) have solutions

$$y_i' = \chi_i(x, y, z)\,,$$

for which the functions $\chi_i$ have continuous partial derivatives of at least the third order in a neighborhood of the values $x, y, z$ belonging to $E$, since the functions $\phi_\beta$, $\phi_\gamma$ have such derivatives. Let $x'$ be the first value following $x_1$ and defining a corner of $E$ or a discontinuity of the functions $\eta_i'(x)$, or let $x' = x_2$ if there are no such values and let $E_1$ be the sub-arc of $E$ corresponding to the interval $x_1x'$. The functions $z_\gamma(x)$, $\zeta_\gamma(x)$ as defined on the interval $x_1x'$ can be extended arbitrarily so that they are continuous on a slightly larger interval. The second members of the equations

$$(72\cdot 3)\qquad y_i' = \chi_i[x, y, z(x) + b\zeta(x)]$$

are then continuous in $x, y, b$ and have continuous third partial derivatives with respect to the variables $y_i$, $b$ in a neighborhood of the values $(x, y, b = 0)$ belonging to $E_1$. According to known existence theorems for differential equations,[5] equations (72·3) have, therefore, solutions

$$(72\cdot 4)\qquad y_i = Y_i(x, x_0, y_0, b)$$

with initial point $(x_0, y_0) = (x_0, y_{10}, \ldots, y_{n0})$ for which the functions $Y_i$, $Y_i'$ are continuous and have continuous partial derivatives of at least the third order with respect to the variables $y_{i0}$, $b$ in a neighborhood of the sets $(x, x_0, y_0, b)$ belonging to $E$. The functions

$$(72\cdot 5)\qquad y_i = Y_i[x, x_1, y(x_1) + b\eta(x_1), b] = y_i(x, b)$$

then define an elementary family satisfying the equations $\phi_\beta = 0$ on an interval including $x_1x'$.

[5] For these existence theorems see Appen., pp. 269–83, where further references are given.

The functions $y_i(x, b)$ defined in equations (72·5) have at $x_1$ the initial values

$$y_i(x_1, b) = Y_i[x_1, x_1, y(x_1) + b\eta(x_1), b] = y_i(x_1) + b\eta_i(x_1),$$

and hence their variations $y_{ib}(x, 0)$ along $E_1$ have at $x = x_1$ the initial values $\eta_i(x_1)$. Furthermore, the functions (72·5) satisfy equations (72·3) and therefore also the equations

$$\phi_\beta = 0, \qquad \phi_\gamma = z_\gamma(x) + b\zeta_\gamma(x).$$

Consequently, the derivatives $y_{ib}(x, 0)$ satisfy the equations (72·2) along $E_1$ and must be identical with the variations $\eta_i(x)$, since these functions are the only solutions of the equations (72·2) with the initial values $\eta_i(x_1)$.

Thus an elementary family of the form (71·1) has been determined, defined on an interval including $x_1x'$, satisfying the equations $\phi_\beta = 0$, and having as its variations $y_{ib}(x, 0)$ along $E_1$ the functions $\eta_i(x)$ of the lemma. Let $x''$ be the next value following $x'$ and defining a corner of $E$ or a discontinuity of the functions $\eta_i'(x)$. It can similarly be proved that the functions

$$y_i = Y_i[x, x', y(x', b), b],$$

found from (72·4) by substituting the initial values $x_0 = x'$, $y_{i0} = y_i(x', b)$, define a new elementary family on an interval including $x'x''$, adjacent to the elementary family previously determined on $x_1x'$, satisfying the equations $\phi_\beta = 0$, and having the variations $\eta_i(x)$ along $E$. A continuation of this process provides an admissible one-parameter family (71·2) of arcs in $R_1$ with the properties of the lemma. The functions $x_1(b)$ and $x_2(b)$ may be defined by the equations

$$x_1(b) = x_1 + b\xi_1, \qquad x_2(b) = x_2 + b\xi_2$$

where $x_1$ and $x_2$ are the end-values of $E$.

COROLLARY 72·1. *If an admissible arc* E *satisfies the equations* $\phi_\beta = 0$ *and if* $\xi_{1\sigma}, \xi_{2\sigma}, \eta_{i\sigma}(x)$ $(\sigma = 1, \ldots, s)$ *are* s *sets of admissible variations satisfying the equations of variation* $\Phi_\beta = 0$ *along* E, *then there is an admissible* s-*parameter family* (71·2) *of arcs containing* E *for the parameter values* $b_\sigma = 0$ $(\sigma = 1, \ldots, s)$, *satisfying the equations* $\phi_\beta = 0$, *and having for each* $\sigma = 1, \ldots, s$ *the set* $\xi_{1\sigma}, \xi_{2\sigma}, \eta_{i\sigma}(x)$ *as the variations of the family along* E *with respect to the parameter* $b_\sigma$.

The proof of this corollary can be made by steps which are so closely analogous to those of the proof of the lemma that they do not need to be repeated here.

The admissible families (71·2) constructed for Lemma 72·1 and Corollary 72·1 have more continuity properties than are required by the definition of an admissible family in Section 71. In the definition there given an admissible family is assumed to be one consisting of elementary families whose functions $y_i(x, b)$, $y_i'(x, b)$ have continuous first partial derivatives with respect to $b$ at $b = 0$. The second members of equations (72·4) are continuous in $x$, $x_0$, $y_0$, $b$ and have continuous partial derivatives of the third order in the variables $y_0$, $b$.

It follows readily, then, that the functions $y_i(x, b)$, $y_i'(x, b)$ of the elementary families constructed for Lemma 72·1 and its corollary will have partial derivatives of the third order with respect to the variables $b$ continuous in a neighborhood of the values $x$, $b$ defining the sub-arc of $E$ contained in the family. With the help of a well-known theorem about interchange of order in partial derivatives[6] one can show that the order of the differentiations in one of these derivatives can be arbitrarily changed without changing the value of the derivative. These remarks will be useful in later paragraphs, especially in Section 77.

**73. The first variation of *J*.** When the functions defining an admissible one-parameter family (71·2) of arcs are substituted in the expression (69·4) for $J$, a function $J(b)$ is determined whose first differential is readily calculated, with the help of the notations (71·3), to be

$$(73\cdot 1)\qquad dJ = f\,dx\,\Big|_1^2 + dg + \int_{x_1}^{x_2} (f_{y_i}\delta y_i + f_{y_i'}\delta y_i')\,dx\,.$$

On the arc $E$ corresponding in the family to the parameter value $b = 0$ this takes the form $dJ = J_1(\xi, \eta)db$, where

$$(73\cdot 2)\quad J_1(\xi, \eta) = f\xi\,\Big|_1^2 + G[\xi_1, \eta(x_1)\quad \xi_2, \eta(x_2)] + \int_{x_1}^{x_2} (f_{y_i}\eta_i + f_{y_i'}\eta_i')\,dx$$

In this expression $\xi_1$, $\xi_2$, $\eta_i(x)$ are the variations of the family along $E$, and $G$ is the linear expression

$$(73\cdot 3)\quad G = (g_1 + y_{i1}'g_{i1})\,\xi_1 + g_{i1}\eta_i(x_1) + (g_2 + y_{i2}g_{i2})\,\xi_2 + g_{i2}\eta_i(x_2)$$

analogous to the function $\Psi_\mu$ defined for $\psi_\mu$ in (71·7). The function $J_1(\xi, \eta)$ is called the *first variation of* J *on the arc E*. Its value is completely defined when the functions $y_i(x)$ $(x_1 \leqq x \leqq x_2)$ defining $E$ and the admissible variations $\xi_1$, $\xi_2$, $\eta_i(x)$ are given.

The notation $F$ will be used for the function

$$(73\cdot 4)\qquad F(x, y, y', l) = l_0 f + l_i\phi_i\,,$$

in which the functions $\phi_i$ are the set $\phi_\beta$, $\phi_\gamma$ of equations (72·1), $l_0$ is a constant, and the multipliers $l_i$ are functions of $x$ to be determined. If the variations $\eta_i(x)$ satisfy the equations $\Phi_\beta = 0$, and therefore also the equations (72·2) with suitably determined functions $\zeta_\gamma(x)$, the value of $l_0J_1(\xi, \eta)$ will not be altered when the sum $l_\beta\Phi_\beta + l_\gamma(\Phi_\gamma - \zeta_\gamma)$ is added to its integrand function. From (73·2) it is found then that

$$l_0 J_1(\xi, \eta) = l_0 f\xi\,\Big|_1^2 + l_0 G + \int_{x_1}^{x_2} (F_{y_i}\eta_i + F_{y_i'}\eta_i' - l_\gamma\zeta_\gamma)\,dx\,.$$

It will be shown in the next paragraph that when constants $l_0$, $c_i$ $(i = 1, \ldots, n)$ are arbitrarily selected a set of multipliers $l_i(x)$, continuous on the interval $x_1x_2$

[6] See, e.g., Pierpont, *The Theory of Functions of Real Variables*, I (1905), 267, sec. 421.

except possibly at values $x$ defining corners of $E$, is uniquely determined by the equations

$$F_{y'_i} = \int_{x_1}^{x} F_{y_i}\, dx + c_i\,. \tag{73·5}$$

By the usual integration by parts of the calculus of variations it follows then that

$$l_0 J_1(\xi, \eta) = [l_0 f \xi + F_{y'_i}\eta_i]_1^2 + l_0 G - \int_{x_1}^{x_2} l_\gamma \zeta_\gamma\, dx\,. \tag{73·6}$$

This is a reduced form for the first variation (73·2), valid for all admissible variations $\xi_1$, $\xi_2$, $\eta_i(x)$ satisfying the equations $\Phi_\beta = 0$, and useful in proving the multiplier rule of the next section.

In order to prove that the equations (73·5) have solutions as described in the last paragraph, the new variables

$$v_i = F_{y'_i} = l_0 f_{y'_i} + l_k \phi_{ky'_i} \tag{73·7}$$

may be introduced. It can be easily seen then that solution of equations (73·5) is equivalent to the determination of continuous functions $v_i(x)$ satisfying equations and initial conditions of the form

$$\frac{dv_i}{dx} = A_{ik} v_k + l_0 B_i\,, \qquad v_i(x_1) = c_i \qquad (i = 1, \ldots, n)\,, \tag{73·8}$$

in which the second members of the differential equations are found by solving equations (73·7) for the $l_i$ as linear expressions in $v_i$, $l_0$ and substituting in the derivatives $F_{y_i}$. The coefficients $A_{ik}$, $B_i$ are functions of $x$ continuous on $x_1x_2$ except possibly at the values $x'$, $x''$, . . . defining corners of $E$. Equations (73·8) have unique continuous solutions on the interval $x_1x'$ with the initial values $v_i(x_1) = c_i$ and unique continuous solutions on the interval $x'x''$ with initial values at $x'$ equal to the end-values at $x'$ of the functions already determined, and so on. The result is a set of continuous functions $v_i(x)$ satisfying the conditions (73·8) and defining solutions $l_i(x)$ of equations (73·5) by means of equations (73·7). Because of the uniqueness of the solutions of equations (73·8) for prescribed initial values $v_i(x')$ at a single point $x'$ it is clear that $l_0$, $v_i(x)$ do not vanish simultaneously unless they are all identically zero, and the same is true of the multipliers $l_0$, $l_i(x)$. One can also verify readily the fact that the $l_i(x)$ have unique right and left limits at values $x'$ defining corners of $E$, since the derivatives $y'_i(x)$ for $E$ have this property.

**74. The multiplier rule.** Let us suppose now that $E$ is a minimizing arc for the problem of Bolza with defining functions

$$y_i(x) \qquad (i = 1, \ldots, n;\ x_1 \leqq x \leqq x_2)\,.$$

The so-called "multiplier rule" is a first condition which such an arc $E$ must satisfy and which can be deduced as follows:

Consider a set

$$\xi_{1\sigma}, \quad \xi_{2\sigma}, \quad \eta_{i\sigma}(x) \qquad (\sigma = 1, \ldots, p+1) \tag{74·1}$$

of $p + 1$ sets of admissible variations all of which satisfy the equations of variation $\Phi_\beta = 0$ along $E$. According to Corollary 72·1, there exists a $(p + 1)$-parameter admissible family of arcs,

$$y_i(x, b) \qquad [x_1(b) \leqq x \leqq x_2(b)], \tag{74·2}$$

containing $E$ for the parameter values $b_\sigma = 0$, satisfying the equations $\phi_\beta = 0$, and having for each $\sigma = 1, \ldots, p + 1$ the set $\xi_{1\sigma}$, $\xi_{2\sigma}$, $\eta_{i\sigma}(x)$ as its variations with respect to $b_\sigma$ along $E$. When the functions defining this family are substituted, the functions $J$, $\psi_\mu$ become functions $J(b)$, $\psi_\mu(b)$ of the parameters $b$. The equations

$$J(b) = J(0) + u, \qquad \psi_\mu(b) = 0 \tag{74·3}$$

have the solution $(b, u) = (0, 0)$ corresponding to the minimizing arc $E$. If the functional determinant of the first members of these equations with respect to the parameters $b$ is different from zero at the values $(b, u) = (0, 0)$, then existence theorems for implicit functions tell us that the equations have unique solutions $b_\sigma(u)$ continuous near $u = 0$ and having the initial values $b_\sigma(0) = 0$. But in this case $E$ cannot be a minimizing arc for the problem of Bolza, since equations (74·3) show that the arcs of the family (74·2) corresponding to parameter values $b_\sigma(u)$ with negative values of $u$ give to $J$ values $J(b)$ which are less than the value $J(0)$ belonging to $E$. It is evident, then, that for the minimizing arc $E$ the functional determinant of the first members of equations (74·3) must be zero for all choices of the sets (74·1).

From Sections 71 and 73, above, it follows that this functional determinant has the form

$$\begin{vmatrix} J_1(\xi_\sigma, \eta_\sigma) \\ \Psi_\mu(\xi_\sigma, \eta_\sigma) \end{vmatrix}, \tag{74·4}$$

in which the arguments of $\Psi_\mu$ have been abbreviated and only the second subscripts of the variations (74·1) are indicated. Let $q < p + 1$ be the maximum rank attainable for the determinant (74·4) for sets of the form (74·1), and let (74·1) be a set for which this rank is attained. Then there exist constants $l_0$, $e_\mu$, not all zero, satisfying the linear equations whose coefficients are the columns of (74·4). With these constants the equation

$$l_0 J_1(\xi, \eta) + e_\mu \Psi_\mu(\xi, \eta) = 0 \tag{74·5}$$

must be satisfied for every set of admissible variations $\xi_1$, $\xi_2$, $\eta_i(x)$ satisfying the equations of variation $\Phi_\beta = 0$ along $E$. Otherwise a set $J_1(\xi, \eta)$, $\Psi_\mu(\xi, \eta)$, not satisfying equation (74·5) and adjoined to the matrix (74·4) as a column, would give a matrix of rank $p + 1$, which by the preceding paragraph is impossible.

When the expression (73·6) for $l_0 J_1$ is substituted in equation (74·5), the resulting equation has the form

$$[l_0 f \xi + F_{y_i'} \eta_i]_1^2 + l_0 G + e_\mu \Psi_\mu - \int_{x_1}^{x_2} l_\gamma \zeta_\gamma \, dx = 0 \, .$$

The terms outside the integral sign are linear in $\xi_1$, $\xi_2$, $\eta_i(x_1)$, $\eta_i(x_2)$; and the coefficients of the terms in $\eta_i(x_1)$ can be made to vanish by properly selecting the arbitrary constants $F_{y_i'}(x_1) = c_i$, used in (73·5). The remainder of the expression must vanish for every arbitrarily selected set $\xi_1$, $\xi_2$, $\eta_i(x_2)$, $\zeta_\gamma(x)$ with $\zeta_\gamma(x)$ continuous except at a finite number of values $x$ on $x_1 x_2$, since functions $\zeta_\gamma(x)$ and initial values $\eta_i(x_2)$ determine, by means of equations (72·2), a set of admissible variations $\eta_i(x)$. By setting $\xi_1 = \xi_2 = \eta_i(x_2) = 0$ it follows from the equation above that the last $n - m$ multipliers $l_\gamma(x)$ $(\gamma = m + 1, \ldots, n)$ vanish identically, since the functions $\zeta_\gamma(x)$ can be arbitrarily selected. Similarly, by using a set for which $\xi_1 \neq 0$, $\xi_2 = \eta_i(x_2) = \zeta_\gamma(x) \equiv 0$, it follows that the coefficient of $\xi_1$ must vanish, and similarly for the other coefficients. Since $l_0 f = F$ when the arc $E$ satisfies the equations $\phi_\beta = 0$, this result is equivalent to saying that the coefficients of $\xi_1$, $\eta_i(x_1)$, $\xi_2$, $\eta_i(x_2)$ in the equation

$$(74 \cdot 6) \qquad [F \xi + F_{y_i'} \eta_i]_1^2 + l_0 G + e_\mu \Psi_\mu = 0$$

all vanish. With the help of some further simple arguments given below, this justifies the following theorem:

THEOREM 74·1. THE MULTIPLIER RULE. *An admissible arc* E, *defined on an interval* $x_1 x_2$, *is said to satisfy the multiplier rule if there exist constants* $l_0$, $e_\mu$, *not all zero, and a function*

$$(74 \cdot 7) \qquad F(x, y, y', l) = l_0 f + l_\beta(x) \phi_\beta \qquad (\beta = 1, \ldots, m)$$

*with multipliers* $l_\beta(x)$ *continuous on* $x_1 x_2$ *except possibly at values* x *defining corners of* E *where they have well-defined right and left limits, such that the equations*

$$(74 \cdot 8) \qquad F_{y_i'} = \int_{x_1}^{x} F_{y_i} dx + c_i \, , \qquad \phi_\beta = 0$$

*are satisfied along* E *and, furthermore, such that the equations*

$$(74 \cdot 9) \quad [(F - y_i' F_{y_i'}) \, dx + F_{y_i'} dy_i]_1^2 + l_0 \, dg + e_\mu d\psi_\mu \equiv 0 \qquad \psi_\mu = 0$$

*hold at the ends of* E *for every choice of the differentials* $dx_1$, $dy_{i1}$, $dx_2$, $dy_{i2}$. *For an arc* E *satisfying the multiplier rule the multipliers* $l_0$, $l_\beta(x)$ *do not vanish simultaneously at any point of the interval* $x_1 x_2$. *Every minimizing arc* E *for the problem of Bolza must satisfy the multiplier rule.*

The vanishing of the coefficients of $dx_1$, $dy_{i1}$, $dx_2$, $dy_{i2}$ in equation (74·9) is called the *transversality condition* on the arc $E$. It is equivalent to the vanishing of the coefficients of $\xi_1$, $\eta_i(x_1)$, $\xi_2$, $\eta_i(x_2)$ in equation (74·6), as can be seen by noting that the equation (74·9) is equivalent to (74·6) by means of the transformation

$$dx_1 = \xi_1\, db\,, \qquad dy_{i1} = y'_{i1} dx_1 + \eta_i(x_1)\, db\,,$$

$$dx_2 = \xi_2\, db\,, \qquad dy_{i2} = y'_{i2} dx_2 + \eta_i(x_2)\, db\,.$$

By collecting the coefficients of $dx_1$, $dy_{i1}$, $dx_2$, $dy_{i2}$ in (74·9) one sees that the transversality condition is equivalent to saying that the matrix

$$(74\cdot10) \qquad \left\| \begin{matrix} -A_1 + l_0 g_1 & -B_{i1} + l_0 g_{i1} & A_2 + l_0 g_2 & B_{i2} + l_0 g_{i2} \\ \psi_{\mu,1} & \psi_{\mu,i1} & \psi_{\mu,2} & \psi_{\mu,i2} \end{matrix} \right\|$$

has rank less than $p + 1$, where $A_1$, $B_{i1}$ and $A_2$, $B_{i2}$ are the values at $x_1$ and $x_2$ of the expressions

$$A = F - y'_i F_{y'_i}\,, \qquad B_i = F_{y'_i}\,.$$

This matrix form of the transversality condition was given by Bliss [17, p. 693] for the problem of Lagrange. The equivalence of the identity (74·6) with (74·9), and the remark just made concerning the rank of the matrix (74·10), will be useful in later sections.

The multipliers $l_0$, $l_\beta(x)$ cannot vanish at a point on $x_1x_2$, since otherwise the functions $v_i(x) = F_{y'_i}$ satisfying equations (73·5) and (73·8) would vanish simultaneously and each would be identically zero, and the same would be true of the functions $l_\beta(x)$. Equation (74·9) would then imply $e_\mu d\psi_\mu \equiv 0$; and consequently $e_\mu = 0$, since the matrix of derivatives of the functions $\psi_\mu$ is of rank $p$. This would, in turn, contradict the fact that the constants $l_0$, $e_\mu$ in (74·5) are not all zero.

It is important for the sequel to note that every set $l_0$, $l_\beta(x)$, $e_\mu$ whatsoever, having the continuity properties described in the theorem and satisfying the equations (74·8) and (74·9) along an arc $E$, must have all of its elements identically zero if $l_0$, $l_\beta(x)$ vanish simultaneously or if $l_0$, $e_\mu$ are all zero. In the former case the proof just given justifies this conclusion. In the latter case the identity (74·9) implies $F_{y'_i} = 0$ at $x_1$, with the consequent identical vanishing of $v_i = F_{y'_i}$, and equations (73·7) then show that $l_\beta(x) \equiv 0$.

The multiplier rule has the three following important corollaries analogous to those which are well known for simpler problems.

COROLLARY 74·1. THE EULER-LAGRANGE EQUATIONS. *At each point of an admissible arc* E *satisfying equations (74·8) the functions* $F_{y'_i}$ *have forward and backward derivatives, equal except at corners and such that*

$$(74\cdot11) \qquad \frac{dF_{y'_i}}{dx} = F_{y_i}\,.$$

COROLLARY 74·2. THE WEIERSTRASS-ERDMANN CORNER CONDITION. *At each corner of an admissible arc* E *satisfying equations (74·8) the functions* $F_{y'_i}$ *of Theorem 74·1 have well-defined right and left limits which are equal.*

COROLLARY 74·3. THE HILBERT DIFFERENTIABILITY CONDITION. *On each sub-arc of an admissible arc* E *satisfying the equations* $\phi_\beta = 0$ *and* (74·8) *on which the functions* $y_i(x)$ *defining* E *have continuous derivatives and the determinant*

$$(74\cdot 12)\qquad R = \begin{vmatrix} F_{y_i'y_k'} & \phi_{\gamma y_i'} \\ \phi_{\beta y_k'} & 0 \end{vmatrix} \qquad (i,\ k = 1,\ \ldots,\ n;\ \beta,\ \gamma = 1,\ \ldots,\ m)$$

*is different from zero, the functions* $y_i'(x)$, $l_\beta(x)$ *belonging to* E *have continuous derivatives of at least the first order with respect to* x.

The first two corollaries are immediate consequences of the equations (74·8). To prove the third one let $x_0$ be a value defining a point interior to a sub-arc of $E$ on which the functions $y_i(x)$ defining $E$ have continuous derivatives, and let it be such that the determinant (74·12) is different from zero at $x_0$. The equations

$$F_{y_i'}[x,\ y(x),\ u,\ \mu] = \int_{x_1}^{x} F_{y_i}[x,\ y(x),\ y'(x),\ l(x)]\,dx + c_i\,,$$

$$\phi_\beta[x,\ y(x),\ u] = 0$$

have the solutions $u_i = y_i'(x)$, $\mu_\beta = l_\beta(x)$ along the arc $E$. The functional determinant of the first members with respect to the variables $u_i$, $\mu_\beta$ is the determinant (74·12) and is, by hypothesis, different from zero at the values $(x, y, \mu) = [x_0, y'(x_0), l(x_0)]$. Hence, by well-known theorems concerning implicit functions the solutions $u_i = y_i'(x)$, $\mu_\beta = l_\beta(x)$ will have near $x_0$ continuous derivatives with respect to $x$ of as many orders as the functions in the equations have with respect to the variables $x$, $u$, $\mu$. An examination of the equations shows that this number is at least one, and Corollary 74·3 is therefore proved.

If the functions $y_i'(x)$, $l_\beta(x)$ have continuous first derivatives, the functions in the last equations have continuous partial derivatives with respect to the variables $x$, $u$, $\mu$ of at least the second order. Hence the solutions $y_i'(x)$, $l_\beta(x)$ have continuous second derivatives with respect to $x$ near $x = x_0$. A continuation of this process shows that *when the functions* f, $\phi_\beta$ *have continuous partial derivatives of order* k *with respect to the variables* x, y, y′ *the functions* $y_i'(x)$, $l_\beta(x)$ *belonging to a minimizing arc* E *must have continuous derivatives of order* k − 1 *with respect to* x *near every value* $x_0$ *defining a point on* E *at which the determinant* (74·12) *is different from zero.* This is an extension of the results stated in the corollary.

The properties described in Corollary 74·3 and in the last paragraph hold even at corners of a minimizing arc $E$ if one interprets them for one-sided derivatives only. To show this let $x_0$ be a value defining the initial element $[x_0, y(x_0), y'(x_0), l(x_0)]$ of an arc on which the functions $y_i'(x)$ belonging to $E$ are continuous, and suppose that the determinant $R$ in (74·12) is different from zero at this element. On an interval $x_0 < x < x + \epsilon$ the derivatives $y_i''(x)$, $l_\beta'(x)$ exist and are solutions of the equations

$$(74\cdot 13)\qquad \begin{aligned} F_{y_i'x} + F_{y_i'y_k}y_k' + F_{y_i'y_k'}y_k'' + l_\beta'\phi_{\beta y_i'} &= F_{y_i}\,, \\ \phi_{\beta x} + \phi_{\beta y_k}y_k' + \phi_{\beta y_k'}y_k'' &= 0\,, \end{aligned}$$

found by differentiating the equations (74·8) and $\phi_\beta = 0$. These solutions must have unique limits as $x$ approaches $x_0$ from the right, since the functions $y_i'(x)$, $l_\beta(x)$ have that property. But the well-known mean-value theorem

$$\frac{h(x) - h(x_0)}{x - x_0} = h'[x_0 + \theta(x - x_0)] \qquad (0 < \theta < 1)$$

shows that a function $h(x)$ having a derivative on an interval $x_0 < x < x_0 + \epsilon$ will have a right-hand derivative at $x_0$ if $h'(x)$ has a unique right-hand limit at $x = x_0$. Hence the functions $y_i'(x)$, $l_\beta(x)$ have right-hand derivatives at $x = x_0$. By successive differentiations of the equations (74·8) and applications of the same reasoning the existence of the forward derivatives of higher orders can successively be established.

There is an equation, indicated in the following theorem, which is sometimes useful and which should be adjoined to equations (74·8). So far as is known to the writer of these pages, it has not yet appeared in the literature. When the minimizing arc consists of a single arc on which the functions $y_i'(x)$, $l_\beta(x)$ have continuous derivatives, this equation can be deduced from equations (74·8) or from equations (74·11).

THEOREM 74·2. *For every minimizing arc* E *there exist a function* F *and constants* $c_i$, $e_\mu$, *with the properties described in Theorem 74·1, and, furthermore, a constant* c *such that the equation*

$$F - y_i'F_{y_i'} = \int_{x_1}^{x} F_x\, dx + c \tag{74·14}$$

*holds at every point of* E.

To prove this theorem the equations of the minimizing arc $E$ may be written in the parametric form

$$x = t, \qquad y_i = y_i(t) \qquad (x_1 \leqq t \leqq x_2). \tag{74·15}$$

A parametric arc of the form

$$x = X(t), \qquad y_i = Y_i(t) \qquad (t_1 \leqq t \leqq t_2), \tag{74·16}$$

with continuity properties in the space of points $(t, X, Y)$ like those described in Section 70 for admissible arcs in $(x, y)$-space, will be expressible in non-parametric form if $X_t(t)$ is different from zero on the interval $t_1t_2$. If the elements $(t, X, Y, X_t, Y_t)$ of the arc (74·16) are in a sufficiently small neighborhood of the set of similar elements of (74·15), then $X_t$ will be different from zero along (74·16), and the elements $(X, Y, Y_t/X_t)$ and $[X(t_1), Y(t_1), X(t_2), Y(t_2)]$ of (74·16) will all be admissible. The arc (74·15) must therefore minimize the sum

$$J = g[X(t_1),\ Y(t_1),\ X(t_2),\ Y(t_2)] + \int_{t_1}^{t_2} f\left[X,\ Y,\ \frac{Y_t}{X_t}\right] X_t\, dt$$

in the class of such arcs (74·16) satisfying the equations

$$\phi_\beta\left(X,\ Y,\ \frac{Y_t}{X_t}\right) X_t = 0, \qquad \psi_\mu[X(t_1),\ Y(t_1),\ X(t_2),\ Y(t_2)] = 0.$$

A simple application of Theorem 74·1 now gives equations (74·8) and (74·9) for the arc (74·15), as well as the new equation (74·14) corresponding to the variable $X$.

From equation (74·14) one can deduce two results analogous to those of Corollaries 74·1 and 74·2. At every point of a minimizing arc $E$ the expression $F - y_i' F_{y_i'}$ has forward and backward derivatives, equal except at corners of $E$, and satisfying the equation

$$\frac{d\,(F - y_i' F_{y_i'})}{dx} = F_x\,; \tag{74·17}$$

and at each corner of $E$ the function $F - y_i' F_{y_i'}$ has forward and backward limits which are equal.

If the arc $E$ consists of a single arc without corners and with continuous derivatives $y_i''$, $l_\beta'$, then equation (74·14) is a consequence of the equations $\phi_\beta = 0$ and (74·11). For in that case the derivative of the expression $F - y_i' F_{y_i'}$ may be calculated in terms of $y_i''$, $l_\beta'$ and partial derivatives of $F$, and it turns out to have the value $F_x$, as in (74·17). Since $F - y_i' F_{y_i'}$ is now continuous, the equation (74·17) implies (74·14), a conclusion which cannot be thus directly made when the arc $E$ has corners.

In concluding this section attention should perhaps be called to the fact that the transversality condition (74·9) is equivalent to saying that the equation

$$[\,(F - y_i' F_{y_i'})\,dx + F_{y_i'} dy_i\,]_1^2 + l_0\,dg = 0 \tag{74·18}$$

must hold for all sets of differentials $dx_1$, $dy_{i1}$, $dx_2$, $dy_{i2}$ satisfying the equations $d\psi_\mu = 0$. The equivalence of the two statements is deducible from simple algebraic properties of linear equations. Furthermore, the multiplier rule for the parametric problem as formulated by Morse takes the form stated in the following corollary:

COROLLARY 74·4. *For the problem with parametric end-conditions in the form*

$$x_s = x_s(t_1, \ldots, t_r), \quad y_i(x_s) = y_{is}(t_1, \ldots, t_r) \qquad (i = 1, \ldots, n;\ s = 1, 2) \tag{74·19}$$

*there must exist for every minimizing arc* E *a function* F *of the form* (74·7) *and constants* $c_i$ *such that the equations* (74·8) *hold at every point of* E *and, furthermore, such that the equation* (74·18) *is satisfied identically in* $dt_h$ (h = 1, . . . , r) *when the differentials* $dx_s$, $dy_{is}$ *from equations* (74·19) *are substituted.*

This is an easy consequence of the application of the multiplier rule in Theorem 74·1 to the transformed problem described at the end of Section 69, above.

**75. The extremals.** As has been shown in the preceding section, a minimizing arc for the problem of Bolza not only satisfies the equations $\phi_\beta = 0$ but also must have a set of multipliers $l_0$, $l_\beta(x)$ with which it satisfies equations (74·11). The solutions of these equations have, therefore, a special significance for the problem. For this reason an *extremal* is defined as an admissible arc $y_i(x)$ without corners, together with a set of multipliers

$$(75\cdot 1) \qquad y_i(x), \; l_0 = 1, \; l_\beta(x) \qquad (i = 1, \ldots, n;\; \beta = 1, \ldots, m;\; x_1 \leqq x \leqq x_2),$$

for which the functions $y_i'(x)$, $l_\beta(x)$ have continuous derivatives on the interval $x_1x_2$ and satisfy the equations $\phi_\beta = 0$ and (74·11). For such a set of functions (75·1) these equations can be written in the form

$$(75\cdot 2) \qquad F_{y_i'x} + F_{y_i'y_k}y_k' + F_{y_i'y_k'}y_k'' + F_{y_i'l_\gamma}l_\gamma' = F_{y_i}, \qquad \phi_\beta = 0.$$

They are called the *differential equations of the extremals.* An extremal is said to be *non-singular* if the determinant $R$ in (74·12) is different from zero along it.

Every non-singular extremal $E$ is imbedded in a $2n$-parameter family of such extremals. This can be seen most readily by introducing so-called *canonical variables* $(x, y, z)$ related to the variables $(x, y, y', l)$ by the equations

$$(75\cdot 3) \qquad z_i = F_{y_i'}(x, y, y', l), \qquad 0 = \phi_\beta(x, y, y').$$

The new variables $z$ here introduced should not be confused with the auxiliary variables $z_\gamma$ of Section 72. Along $E$ the equations (75·3) define functions $z_i(x)$ which have continuous derivatives on the interval $x_1x_2$. The functional determinant of the second members of equations (75·3) with respect to the variables $y'$, $l$ is the determinant $R$ in (74·12) and is different from zero along $E$. Hence, by the usual implicit function theorems there exists a neighborhood $S$ of the values $(x, y, z)$ belonging to $E$ in which equations (75·3) have a solution

$$(75\cdot 4) \qquad y_i' = P_i(x, y, z), \qquad l_\beta = L_\beta(x, y, z),$$

reducing to $y_i'(x)$, $l_\beta(x)$ at each point $[x, y(x), z(x)]$ belonging to $E$ and such that the functions $P_i$, $L_\beta$ have continuous partial derivatives of at least the second order, since the second members of equations (75·3) have this property. One can now readily verify the fact that in the neighborhood $S$ every solution of the differential equations

$$(75\cdot 5) \qquad y_i' = P_i(x, y, z), \qquad z_i' = f_{y_i}(x, y, P, L)$$

defines, by means of equations (75·4), functions $l_\beta(x)$ with which it satisfies equations (75·3) and therefore also equations (75·2).

Equations (75·5) are in the canonical form to which well-known existence theorems for differential equations apply. These theorems say that equations (75·5) have through each initial point $(x_0, y_0, z_0)$ in $S$ one and but one solution

$$(75\cdot 6) \qquad y_i = Y_i(x, x_0, y_0, z_0), \qquad z_i = Z_i(x, x_0, y_0, z_0).$$

The functions $Y_i$, $Y_{ix}$, $Z_i$, $Z_{ix}$ have continuous partial derivatives of at least the second order in a neighborhood of the set of $(2n + 2)$-dimensional points $(x,$

$x_0, y_0, z_0$) belonging to $E$, since the second members of equations (75·5) have such derivatives. None of the solutions (75·6) is lost if the value $x_0$ is fixed, say at $x_1$, since every one of them has an initial point with $x_0 = x_1$. With some further simple arguments it can now be concluded that for $x_0 = x_1$, and with the notations $a_i = y_{i0}$, $b_i = z_{i0}$ $(i = 1, \ldots, n)$, the functions (75·6) define a family of extremals with the properties described in the following theorem:

THEOREM 75·1. THE IMBEDDING THEOREM. *Every non-singular extremal* E *for a fixed value of the multiplier* $l_0$ *is imbedded for values*

$$x_1 \leqq x \leqq x_2\,, \qquad a_{10}, \ldots, a_{n0}\,, \qquad b_{10}, \ldots, b_{n0} \tag{75·7}$$

*in a* 2n-*parameter family of extremals defined by functions of the form*

$$y_i(x, a, b)\,, \qquad z_i(x, a, b)\,, \tag{75·8}$$

*in which* a, b *are symbols for* n-*dimensional sets* $(a_1, \ldots, a_n)$, $(b_1, \ldots, b_n)$. *The functions* $y_i$, $y_{ix}$, $z_i$, $z_{ix}$ *have continuous partial derivatives of at least the second order in a neighborhood of the values* (x, a, b) *defining* E, *and the determinant*

$$\begin{vmatrix} y_{ia_k} & y_{ib_k} \\ z_{ia_k} & z_{ib_k} \end{vmatrix} \tag{75·9}$$

*is different from zero along* E. *In terms of the original variables* x, y, y′, l *the extremals (75·8) are defined by functions*

$$y_i(x, a, b)\,, \qquad l_\beta(x, a, b)\,, \tag{75·10}$$

*related to the functions (75·8) by equations (75·4) and (75·3) and such that* $y_i$, $y_{ix}$, $l_\beta$ *have continuous partial derivatives of at least the second order.*

The first part of the theorem has been proved except for the statement concerning the determinant (75·9). By differentiating the identities

$$y_{i0} = Y_i(x_1, x_1, y_0, z_0)\,, \qquad z_{i0} = Z_i(x_1, x_1, y_0, z_0)$$

with respect to the variables $a_i = y_{i0}$, $b_i = b_{i0}$ it follows that the determinant (75·9) is equal to 1 at the value $x_1$. In the next paragraph it will be shown that if this determinant is different from zero at one value of $x$, it is different from zero everywhere on $E$. The properties of the functions (75·10) follow at once from preceding paragraphs.

In the neighborhood $S$ of points $(x, y, z)$ described above, a function $H(x, y, z)$ may be defined by the equation

$$\begin{aligned} H(x, y, z) &= [y_i' F_{y_i'} - F]^{y'=P,\ l=L} \\ &= z_i P_i(x, y, z) - F(x, y, P, L)\,. \end{aligned} \tag{75·11}$$

From equations (75·3) and simple calculations it follows that the partial derivatives of this function have the values

$$H_x = -F_x\,, \qquad H_{y_i} = -F_{y_i}\,, \qquad H_{z_i} = P\,. \tag{75·12}$$

These equations show that the function $H$ has continuous partial derivatives of at least the third order and that equations (75·5) are equivalent to the system

$$(75\cdot 13) \qquad y_i' = H_{z_i}, \qquad z_i' = -H_{y_i}.$$

These are called the *canonical equations of the extremals*. The functions (75·8) satisfy equations (75·13) identically in $x$, $a$, $b$. When they are substituted and the equations are differentiated with respect to $a_k$, it is found that the derivatives $y_{ia_k}$, $z_{ia_k}$ $(i = 1, \ldots, n)$, when substituted for $\eta_i$ and $\zeta_i$, are solutions of the linear equations

$$(75\cdot 14) \qquad \begin{aligned} \eta_i' &= H_{z_i y_k}\eta_k + H_{z_i z_k}\zeta_k, \\ \zeta_i' &= -H_{y_i y_k}\eta_k - H_{y_i z_k}\zeta_k. \end{aligned}$$

Similarly, every other column of the determinant (75·9) is a solution of these equations. But it is well known from the theory of linear differential equations[7] that a determinant of $2n$ solutions of the equations (75·14) is either identically zero or everywhere different from zero. Hence Theorem 75·1 is proved in its entirety.

The function $H$ and the canonical equations (75·13) of the extremals have many applications besides that of the last paragraph. Let $S$ be a region of points $(x, y, z)$ so related to $R_1$ that to every point $(x, y, z)$ interior to $S$ there corresponds a unique solution $(x, y, y', l)$ of equations (75·3) with $(x, y, y')$ in $R_1$ and the determinant (74·12) different from zero. Equations (75·3) then have, as before, single-valued solutions (75·4) with continuous second derivatives over the interior of $S$; and every solution $y(x)$, $z(x)$ of equations (75·13) in this region defines an extremal. Furthermore, if the region $S$ contains all the points $(x, y, z)$ corresponding to sets $(x, y, y', l)$ with $(x, y, y')$ interior to $R_1$ and satisfying the equations $\phi_\beta = 0$, and with arbitrary values of the multipliers $l_\beta$, then every extremal defines a solution of the canonical equations (75·13); and equations (75·2) and (75·13) are equivalent.

It should perhaps be remarked in closing this discussion of the extremals that the imbedding theorem can also be proved by applying the existence theorems for differential equations to the system

$$(75\cdot 15) \qquad \begin{gathered} \frac{d}{dx} F_{y_i'} = F_{y_i}, \qquad \phi_{\beta x} + \phi_{\beta y_k} y_k' + \phi_{\beta y_k'} y_k'' = 0, \\ \phi_\beta[x_1, y(x_1), y'(x_1)] = 0, \end{gathered}$$

equivalent to equations (75·2). The first two of the equations (75·15), solved for $y_i''$ and $l_\beta'$, define a $(2n + m)$-parameter family of solutions which reduces to a $2n$-parameter family when the last $m$ conditions at $x = x_1$ are imposed.

[7] See, e.g., Goursat-Hedrick, *A Course in Mathematical Analysis*, II, Part II, 153–54.

**76. Abnormality for minima of functions of a finite number of variables.**[8] The significance of the notion of abnormality in the calculus of variations can be indicated by a study of the theory of the simpler problem of finding, in the set of points $y = (y_1, \ldots, y_n)$ satisfying a system of equations of the form

$$\phi_\beta(y) = 0 \qquad (\beta = 1, \ldots, m < n),$$

one which minimizes a function $f(y)$. For a point $y^0 = (y_1^0, \ldots, y_n^0)$ near which the functions $f$ and $\phi_\beta$ have continuous partial derivatives of at least the second order, and which satisfies the equations $\phi_\beta = 0$, we have the following theorems, some of which are, of course, well known.

THEOREM 76·1. *A first necessary condition for* $f(y^0)$ *to be a minimum is that there exist constants* $l_0, l_\beta$, *not all zero, such that the derivatives* $F_{y_i}$ *of the function*

$$F = l_0 f + l_\beta \phi_\beta$$

*all vanish at* $y^0$.

To prove this we have only to note that the determinants of the matrix

$$\left\| \begin{matrix} f_{y_i}(y^0) \\ \phi_{\beta y_i}(y^0) \end{matrix} \right\|$$

must all vanish. Otherwise, according to well-known implicit function theorems, the equations $f(y) = f(y^0) + u$, $\phi_\beta(y) = 0$ would have solutions $y$ for negative values of $u$, and $f(y^0)$ could not be a minimum.

A point $y^0$ has, by definition, *order of abnormality equal to* $q$ if there exist $q$ linearly independent sets of multipliers of the form $l_0 = 0$, $l_\beta$ having the property of the theorem. When $q = 0$, the point $y^0$ is said to be *normal*. A necessary and sufficient condition for abnormality of order $q$ is evidently that the matrix $\|\phi_{\beta y_i}(y^0)\|$ have rank $m - q$. At a normal point $y^0$ the multipliers $l_0, l_\beta$ of the theorem can be divided by $l_0$ and put into the form $l_0 = 1, l_\beta$. In this form they are unique, since the non-vanishing difference of two such sets would be a set of multipliers implying abnormality.

LEMMA 76·1. *If a point* $y^0$ *is normal, then for every set of constants* $\eta_i$ $(i = 1, \ldots, n)$ *satisfying the equations*

$$(76{\cdot}1) \qquad \phi_{\beta y_i}(y^0)\eta_i = 0$$

*there exists a set of functions* $y_i(b)$ *having continuous second derivatives near* $b = 0$, *satisfying the equations* $\phi_\beta = 0$, *and such that*

$$y_i(0) = y_i^0, \quad y_i'(0) = \eta_i .$$

The proof can be made by considering the equations

$$(76{\cdot}2) \qquad \phi_\beta(y) = 0, \qquad \phi_\gamma(y) = \phi_\gamma(y^0) + b\zeta_\gamma$$
$$(\beta = 1, \ldots, m;\ \gamma = m+1, \ldots, n),$$

[8] For the arguments of Secs. 76 and 77 see Bliss [56].

in which the auxiliary functions $\phi_\gamma(y)$ are selected so that they have continuous second derivatives near $y^0$ and make the functional determinant $|\phi_{iy_k}(y^0)|$ different from zero, and in which the constants $\zeta_\gamma$ are defined by the equations

$$\phi_{\gamma y_i}(y^0)\,\eta_i = \zeta_\gamma\,. \tag{76·3}$$

Equations (76·2) then have solutions $y_i(b)$ with continuous derivatives of at least the second order near $b = 0$ and such that $y_i(0) = y_i^0$. By differentiating with respect to $b$ equations (76·2) with these solutions substituted, we find the equations

$$\phi_{\beta y_i}(y^0)\,y_i'(0) = 0\,,$$

$$\phi_{\gamma y_i}(y^0)\,y_i'(0) = \zeta_\gamma\,.$$

With equations (76·1) and (76·3) these show that $y_i'(0) = \eta_i$.

THEOREM 76·2. *If* $y^0$ *is a normal point and* $f(y^0)$ *a minimum, then the condition*

$$F_{y_iy_k}(y^0)\,\eta_i\eta_k \geqq 0$$

*must hold for every set* $\eta_i$ *satisfying equations (76·1), where* $F = f + l_\beta\phi_\beta$ *is the function formed with the unique set of multipliers* $l_0 = 1$, $l_\beta$ *belonging to* $y^0$.

The conclusion of the theorem is due to the fact that the function $g(b) = f[y(b)]$, formed with the functions $y_i(b)$ of the lemma, must have a minimum at $b = 0$. Since

$$\phi_{\beta y_i}[y(b)]\,y_i'(b) = 0$$

the derivatives of $g(b)$ are seen to have the values

$$g'(b) = f_{y_i}[y(b)]\,y_i'(b) = F_{y_i}[y(b)]\,y_i'(b)$$

$$g''(0) = F_{y_iy_k}(y^0)\,\eta_i\eta_k\,;$$

and for $g(0)$ to be a minimum we must have $g''(0) \geqq 0$.

THEOREM 76·3. *If a point* $y^0$ *has a set of multipliers* $l_0 = 1$, $l_\beta$ *for which the function* $F = f + l_\beta\phi_\beta$ *satisfies the conditions*

$$F_{y_i}(y^0) = 0 \qquad F_{y_iy_k}(y^0)\,\eta_i\eta_k > 0 \tag{76·4}$$

*for all sets* $\eta_i$ *satisfying the equations*

$$\phi_{\beta y_i}(y^0)\,\eta_i = 0 \tag{76·5}$$

*then* $f(y^0)$ *is a minimum.*

This can be proved with the help of Taylor's formula with integral form of remainder. For every point $y$ near $y^0$ satisfying the equations $\phi_\beta = 0$ we have the equations

$$(76\cdot 6)\qquad \begin{aligned} f(y) - f(y^0) &= f_{y_i}(y^0)\,\eta_i + \int_0^1 (1-\theta)\, f_{y_i y_k}(y')\,\eta_i\eta_k d\theta\,, \\ 0 &= \phi_{\beta y_i}(y^0)\,\eta_i + \int_0^1 (1-\theta)\,\phi_{\beta y_i y_k}(y')\,\eta_i\eta_k d\theta\,, \\ 0 &= \int_0^1 \phi_{\beta y_i}(y')\,\eta_i d\theta\,, \end{aligned}$$

where the sets $y'$ and $\eta$ are defined by the equations $y'_i = y^0_i + \theta(y_i - y^0_i)$, $\eta_i = y_i - y^0_i$. From these we find readily

$$f(y) - f(y^0) = \int_0^1 (1-\theta)\,F_{y_i y_k}(y')\,\eta_i\eta_k d\theta\,.$$

Since the quadratic form in the integrand of the last integral, thought of as a function of independent variables $y'$ and $\eta$, is positive for $y' = y^0$ and all sets $\eta$ satisfying the equations (76·5), it will remain positive for $y' = y^0 + \theta(y - y^0)$ and all sets $\eta$, including $\eta = y - y^0$, satisfying the third set of equations (76·6), provided that $y$ lies in a sufficiently small neighborhood $N$ of the point $y^0$. Thus we see that for all points $y$ in $N$ satisfying the equations $\phi_\beta = 0$ the difference $f(y) - f(y^0)$ is positive.

Theorem 76·1 has the multiplier rule as its analogue in the calculus of variations; an analogue of Lemma 76·1 is Theorem 77·1 of the next section; and theorems for the problem of Bolza corresponding to Theorems 76·2 and 76·3 are proved in Section 80 and Chapter IX. Theorems 76·1 and 76·2 give necessary conditions for a minimum at a normal point $y^0$, and Theorem 76·3 gives sufficient conditions. Since at a normal point the multipliers are unique, the sufficient conditions (76·4) are obtained from the necessary conditions merely by excluding the equality sign in the condition of Theorem 76·2. Near a normal point the minimum problem is never trivial, since Lemma 76·1 shows that near such a point there is always an infinity of other points $y$ satisfying the equations $\phi_\beta(y) = 0$. The normal points are the non-singular points of the manifold defined by these equations.

Abnormal points $y^0$ are the singular points of this manifold. Near one of them the minimum problem may be completely trivial, as, for example, in the case of a point $y^0$ which makes $\phi_1 = 0$ and minimizes $\phi_1$ in the class of points $y$ satisfying $\phi_2 = \ldots = \phi_m = 0$. A simple case is the point $(y_1, y_2) = (0, 0)$ for the problem of minimizing $f(y_1, y_2)$ in the class of points $(y_1, y_2)$ satisfying the equation $\phi = y_1^2 + y_2^2 = 0$.

An idea of the great variety of types of abnormal points may be gained by considering the problem of minimizing a function $f(y_1, y_2)$ in the class of points $(y_1, y_2)$ satisfying a single equation $\phi(y_1, y_2) = 0$, where $\phi$ is arbitrary. It is then evident that the variety of abnormal points is at least as great as the variety of singular points of an algebraic curve. At an abnormal point the condition of

Theorem 76·2 is not necessary for a minimum for all sets of multipliers satisfying the condition of Theorem 76·1, as is shown by the example $f = 2y_1^2 - y_2^2 =$ minimum, $\phi = y_1^2 y_2 - y_2^3 = 0$, and the minimizing point (0, 0). Theorem 76·3 does give sufficient conditions for a minimum at an abnormal point, but its conclusions for the abnormal points to which it applies can readily be established by the consideration of normal points only, as is shown by Theorem 76·4 below. In the statement of the theorem, $y^0$ is a point which has abnormality of order $q$, $\nu$ is a variable which ranges over a subset of the numbers $1, \ldots, m$ such that the matrix $\|\phi_{\nu y_i}(y^0)\|$ has rank $m - q$, and $\rho$ is a variable ranging over the complementary subset.

THEOREM 76·4. *Let* $y^0$ *be a point which satisfies the hypotheses of Theorem 76·3 with a set of multipliers* $l_0 = 1, l_\beta$, *and let* $\nu$ *and* $\rho$ *be variables having the ranges described in the last paragraph. Then* $y^0$ *is normal for the modified problem of minimizing the function* $g = f + l_\rho \phi_\rho$ *in the class of points* $y$ *satisfying the reduced system of equations* $\phi_\nu = 0$, *and* $y^0$ *satisfies the hypotheses of Theorem 76·3 for the modified problem with the multipliers* $l_0 = 1, l_\nu$. *Furthermore, if* $g(y^0)$ *is a minimum for the normal modified problem, then* $f(y^0)$ *is a minimum for the original one.*

We see that the point $y^0$ is normal for the modified problem, since the matrix $\|\phi_{\nu y_i}(y^0)\|$ has rank $m - q$. For the function $F = g + l_\nu \phi_\nu = f + l_\beta \phi_\beta$ of the modified problem the conditions (76·4) are satisfied for all sets $\eta$ satisfying the equations

$$\phi_{\nu y_i}(y^0)\,\eta_i = 0\,, \tag{76·7}$$

since equations (76·5) are linear and have a matrix of coefficients of rank $m - q$ and hence are consequences of equations (76·7). The set of points $y$ satisfying the equations $\phi_\nu = 0$ includes the points satisfying the complete system $\phi_\beta = 0$ as a subclass in which $g = f$. Hence, if $g(y^0)$ is a minimum for the modified problem, the value $f(y^0) = g(y^0)$ must have the same property for the original problem.

From the last theorem it is evident that generality is not lost by proving Theorem 76·3 only for points $y^0$ which are normal. Such points are, in fact, the non-singular points of the class which satisfy the equations $\phi_\beta = 0$, as we have seen. Theorem 76·4 has Theorem 92·2, below, as its analogue for the problem of Bolza.

**77. Normality for the problem of Bolza.** For the problem of Bolza the class $\mathfrak{M}$ of arcs $C$ of the form

$$y_i(x) \qquad (i = 1, \ldots, n;\ x_1 \leqq x \leqq x_2)$$

is defined, as in Section 70, to be the class of admissible arcs $C$ satisfying the differential equations $\phi_\beta = 0$ and the end-conditions $\psi_\mu = 0$. A particular arc $E$ of $\mathfrak{M}$ is said to have *abnormality of order* $q$ if it satisfies the multiplier rule in Theorem 74·1 with $q$ and only $q$ linearly independent sets of multipliers of the form $l_{0\sigma} = 0, l_{\beta\sigma}(x)$ $(\sigma = 1, \ldots, q)$. If $q = 0$, the arc $E$ is said to be *normal;* otherwise it is *abnormal.* A set of multipliers $l_0, l_\beta(x)$ with $l_0 = 0$ will be called an *abnormal set of multipliers.* If a normal arc $E$ has a set of multipliers, then the set can always be made over into a set of the form $l_0 = 1, l_\beta(x)$ by dividing by a suitable constant. A normal arc $E$ can have at most one set of multipliers of the form $l_0 = 1, l_\beta(x)$, since if there were two such sets their difference would also be a set of multipliers for $E$ and it would be an abnormal set.

THEOREM 77·1. *If an arc* E *of the set* $\mathfrak{M}$ *is normal, then there exists an admissible one-parameter family of arcs of the form (71·2) in* $\mathfrak{M}$ *including the arc* E *for the parameter value* b $= 0$ *and including in every neighborhood of* E *arcs of* $\mathfrak{M}$ *not identical with* E.

This theorem shows that for a normal arc $E$ the problem of proving that $J(E)$ is or is not a minimum is never trivial, since there are always other arcs of $\mathfrak{M}$ near $E$. A normal arc $E$ in $\mathfrak{M}$ may be thought of as in a sense a non-singular arc of $\mathfrak{M}$. Abnormal arcs $E$ are singular arcs of $\mathfrak{M}$. It is possible to construct examples to show that near an abnormal arc of $\mathfrak{M}$ there may be no other arc of $\mathfrak{M}$ whatsoever.

To prove the theorem one may make use of the first part of the proof of the multiplier rule in Section 74. The normal arc $E$ may be imbedded in admissible $(p + 1)$-parameter families of arcs (74·2), and for such families the maximum rank attainable for the last $p$ rows of the matrix (74·4) must be $p$. Otherwise there would be a set of constants $l_0 = 0, e_\mu$, not all zero, effective as in equation (74·5) and determining, as in Section 74, a non-vanishing set of multipliers $l_0 = 0, l_\beta(x)$ for $E$. This is impossible, since $E$ is normal. Suppose, then, that the variations (74·1) have been chosen so that the determinant of the first $p$ columns of the last $p$ rows of the matrix (74·4) is different from zero. Then the last $p$ equations in (74·3) have the form

$$\psi_\mu(b_1, \ldots, b_p, b) = 0 \tag{77·1}$$

if we now use $b$ in place of $b_{p+1}$. They have the solution $b_1 = \ldots = b_p = b = 0$ at which their functional determinant with respect to $b_1, \ldots, b_p$ is different from zero. From the usual implicit function theorems they therefore have solutions $b_\mu = B_\mu(b)$ $(\mu = 1, \ldots, p)$ with continuous derivatives near $b = 0$ and with initial values $B_\mu(0) = 0$. The admissible one-parameter family of arcs obtained from the family (74·2) by the substitution $b_\mu = B_\mu(b)$ contains the arc $E$ for $b = 0$ and consists of arcs in $\mathfrak{M}$ when $b$ is sufficiently small. With the set $\xi_{1,p+1}$, $\xi_{2,p+1}$, $\eta_{i,p+1}(x)$ of Section 74 replaced by $\xi_1, \xi_2, \eta_i(x)$ the variations along $E$ of the one-parameter family just determined are the functions

$$\xi_{1\mu}B_\mu'(0) + \xi_1, \qquad \xi_{2\mu}B_\mu'(0) + \xi_2, \qquad \eta_{i\mu}(x)B_\mu'(0) + \eta_i(x) . \tag{77·2}$$

If the last $n$ of these are not all identically zero, the family will surely contain arcs not identical with $E$. But when the functions $\eta_{i\mu}$ have been chosen to secure rank $p$ for the determinant of the matrix (74·4) specified above, the variations

$\eta_i$ can always be selected linearly independent of them, so that the last $n$ variations (77·2) are not identically zero. This selection can be made by determining the functions $\zeta_{i\mu}(x)$ corresponding to the variations $\eta_{i\mu}(x)$ by means of equations (72·2), selecting a set of functions $\zeta_i(x)$ linearly independent of the $p$ sets $\zeta_{i\mu}(x)$ $(\mu = 1, \ldots, p)$, and choosing for the variations $\eta_i(x)$ solutions of the equations (72·2) with the functions $\zeta_i(x)$ substituted. Thus the theorem is proved.

COROLLARY 77·1. *If* $\xi_1, \xi_2, \eta_i(x)$ *is a set of admissible variations satisfying the equations of variation* $\Phi_\beta = \Psi_\mu = 0$ *along a normal arc* E *of the class* $\mathfrak{M}$, *then the one-parameter family of arcs in* $\mathfrak{M}$ *imbedding* E, *described in Theorem 77·1, can be so chosen that it has the set* $\xi_1, \xi_2, \eta_i(x)$ *as its variations along* E.

The one-parameter family constructed for Theorem 77·1 will evidently have the variations required in the corollary if the derivatives $B_\mu'(0)$ in the variations (77·2) all vanish. The equations (77·1) with the functions $b_\mu = B_\mu(b)$ substituted have at $b = 0$ the derivatives

$$\Psi_\mu(\xi_\sigma, \eta_\sigma)B_\sigma'(0) + \Psi_\mu(\xi, \eta) = 0 \qquad (\mu, \sigma = 1, \ldots, p).$$

The last term in each of these equations vanishes because the set $\xi_1, \xi_2, \eta_i(x)$ satisfies the equations $\Psi_\mu = 0$, and the determinant $|\Psi_\mu(\xi_\sigma, \eta_\sigma)|$ is different from zero. Hence all of the values $B_\sigma'(0)$ are zero, and the corollary is proved.

The one-parameter family of arcs in $\mathfrak{M}$ in the corollary was constructed out of a sequence of elementary families of the form (71·1). Each of these elementary families contains a sub-arc of $E$ for values $(x, b)$ satisfying conditions of the form $x' \leqq x \leqq x''$, $b = 0$. The following corollary specifies some further properties of the elementary families which will be useful in Section 80, below.

COROLLARY 77·2. *Each of the sequence of elementary families (71·1), which together form the one-parameter family of arcs in* $\mathfrak{M}$ *described in Theorem 77·1 and Corollary 77·1, is defined by functions*

$$y_i(x, b) \qquad (x' \leqq x \leqq x'', \ |b| < \epsilon)$$

*for which the derivatives* $y_{ib}, y'_{ib}$ *exist and are continuous in a neighborhood of the values* $(x, b)$ *satisfying the conditions* $x' \leqq x \leqq x'', b = 0$. *If the imbedded arc* E *is an extremal, so that the functions* $y_i(x)$ *defining it have continuous second derivatives, then the derivatives* $y_{ibb}, y'_{ibb}, (y_{ibb})'$ *also exist at the values* $(x, b)$ *satisfying* $x' \leqq x \leqq x''$, $b = 0$, *and the last two derivatives are equal. On each elementary family the differentials appearing in equations (71·3) exist and satisfy these equations.*

The continuity of the functions $y_{ib}, y'_{ib}$ is a consequence of the already established continuity near $b = 0$ of the solutions $B_\mu(b)$ of equations (77·1). The existence of the derivatives $y_{ibb}, y'_{ibb}$ as stated would follow from the existence of the second derivatives $B_\mu''(0)$. To show that these second derivatives exist, we need the following lemma:

LEMMA 77·1. *Let* $\varphi(x, b)$ *be a function which with its derivative* $\varphi_b$ *is continuous in a neighborhood of the set of values* $(x, b)$ *satisfying the conditions* $x' \leqq x \leqq x''$, b = 0 *and which has its derivative* $\varphi_x$ *continuous on this set itself. Let* x(b) *be a function having values on the interval* x′x″ *and having a continuous derivative near* b = 0. *Then at* b = 0

$$\frac{d\varphi[x(b),\ b]}{db} = \varphi_x x' + \varphi_b \, .$$

This is readily provable by applying the mean-value theorem to the two differences in the second member of the equation

$$\varphi[x(b),\ b] - \varphi[x(0),\ 0] = \varphi[x(b),\ b] - \varphi[x(b),\ 0] + \varphi[x(b),\ 0] - \varphi[x(0),\ 0] \, .$$

An application of the lemma to the function $y_i'(x, b)$ of one of the elementary families is the formula, at $b = 0$,

$$dy'[x(b),\ b] = y''x' + y_b' \, . \tag{77·3}$$

The equations for the first derivatives $B_\mu'(b)$, found by differentiating the equations (77·1) with the functions $B_\mu(b)$ substituted, are

$$\psi_{\mu\rho} B_\rho'(b) + \psi_{\mu b} = 0 \, ,$$

where $\psi_{\mu\rho} = \partial\psi_\mu/\partial b_\rho$. If the coefficients in these equations have derivatives at $b = 0$, the same will be true of the solutions $B_\rho'(b)$. But the existence of the derivatives at $b = 0$ of the coefficients can be established by examining the functions which occur in them. It is found that all the functions involved are known to have derivatives at $b = 0$ except $y'[x_s(b), b]$, and the derivative of this is given by formula (77·3).

The existence of the derivative $(y_{ib})'$ and its equality with $(y_i')_b$ can be established by an application of the well-known theorem that a function $\varphi(x, y)$ which with its derivatives $\varphi_x$, $\varphi_y$, $\varphi_{xy}$ is continuous near a point $(x, y)$ has a derivative $\varphi_{yx}$ equal to $\varphi_{xy}$ at that point.[9] Similarly, by successive applications of the same theorem it can be shown that $(y_{ibb})'$ exists and is equal to $(y_i')_{bb}$.

To complete the proof of Corollary 77·2 it remains to prove the formulas (71·3) for differentials. This is simple except in the case of the last one, which depends again upon the formula (77·3). We have, in fact,

$$\begin{aligned} dy &= y'dx + \delta y \, , \\ d^2y &= dy'dx + y'd^2x + \delta y'dx + d^2y \\ &= (y''dx + \delta y')\,dx + y'd^2x + \delta y'dx + \delta^2 y \, , \end{aligned}$$

and this reduces at once to the last formula (71·3).

Besides the theorem and corollaries above, which show that a normal arc $E$ of the class $\mathfrak{M}$ is always imbedded in one-parameter families of arcs of $\mathfrak{M}$, there are a number of other theorems concerning normality which have useful applications.

[9] See, e.g., Pierpont, *op. cit.*

THEOREM 77·2. *The order of abnormality of an arc* E *of the class* $\mathfrak{M}$ *is always less than, or equal to, the numbers* m *and* p, *where* m *is the number of the equations* $\phi_\beta = 0$ *and* p *is the number of end-conditions* $\psi_\mu = 0$.

For, suppose that $l_{0\sigma} = 0, l_{\beta\sigma}(x)$ $(\sigma = 1, \ldots, q)$ are the $q$ linearly independent abnormal sets of multipliers with which the arc $E$ satisfies the multiplier rule. If $q > m$, there would be at least one linear combination $k_\sigma l_{0\sigma}, k_\sigma l_{\beta\sigma}(x)$ whose elements would all vanish at $x_1$. But in that case the elements of this set of multipliers would vanish identically, as indicated in the second paragraph following Theorem 74·1; and the $q$ sets of multipliers could not be linearly independent, as supposed.

If $q > p$, there would similarly be a linear combination $k_\sigma l_{0\sigma}, k_\sigma l_{\beta\sigma}(x)$ for which an arbitrarily selected set of $p$ of the coefficients of the $2n + 2$ differentials $dx_1, dy_{i1}, dx_2, dy_{i2}$ in the square bracket of (74·9) would be zero. This set could be selected so that the determinant of the corresponding terms in the expression for $d\psi_\mu$ would be different from zero. Since the expression (74·9) is identically zero in the differentials $dx_1, dy_{i1}, dx_2, dy_{i2}$, it follows that the constants $e_\mu$ would all be zero and, consequently, that the remaining terms in the square bracket of (74·9) would also have coefficients equal to zero. But in that case the derivatives $F_{y_i'}$ would all vanish at $x_1$; and it follows that the linear combinations $k_\sigma l_{0\sigma}$, $k_\sigma l_{\beta\sigma}(x)$ would vanish identically, contrary to the hypothesis originally made on the abnormal sets of multipliers. We can see this since the functions $v_i \equiv 0$ are the only ones which can vanish at $x_1$ and satisfy equations (73·8) with $l_0 = 0$, and therefore the multipliers $l_\beta(x) \equiv 0$ are the only ones which can make the derivatives $F_{y_i'}$ vanish at $x_1$ and satisfy equations (73·5) with $l_0 = 0$.

THEOREM 77·3. *If an admissible arc* E *is a solution of the first* n *equations in (74·8) with an abnormal set of multipliers* $l_0 = 0, l_\beta(x)$, *then the condition*

$$F_{y_i'}\eta_i = \text{constant} \tag{77·4}$$

*is true along the arc* E *for every set of admissible variations* $\eta_i(x)$ *satisfying the equations of variation* $\Phi_\beta = 0$ *along* E.

The equation

$$F_{y_i}\eta_i + F_{y_i'}\eta_i' = l_\beta\Phi_\beta = 0 \tag{77·5}$$

is evidently true under the circumstances described in the theorem. With the help of the first $n$ equations (74·8) it follows that the first member of (77·4) is continuous everywhere on the interval $x_1x_2$ belonging to the arc $E$ and has the first member of (77·5) as its derivative at all values $x$ on $x_1x_2$ not corresponding to the corners of the admissible arc $E$ or discontinuities of the functions $\eta_i'$. The conclusion of the theorem follows readily.

THEOREM 77·4. *A necessary and sufficient condition for an admissible arc* E *to have abnormality of order* q *is that for admissible sets of variations* $\xi_{1\sigma}, \xi_{2\sigma}, \eta_{i\sigma}(x)$

($\sigma = 1, \ldots, p$) *satisfying the equations of variation* $\Phi_\beta = 0$ *along* E *the maximum rank attainable for the matrix*

$$(77\cdot 6) \qquad \|\Psi_\mu(\xi_\sigma, \eta_\sigma)\|$$

*is* $p - q$.

To prove this we first note, as in Section 74, that a set $l_0, l_\beta(x), e_\mu$ with which the multiplier rule along the arc $E$ is satisfied will have its elements all identically zero if the elements of the set $l_0, l_\beta(x)$, or of the set $l_0, e_\mu$, vanish simultaneously. Consequently, the sets of a collection $l_{0\sigma}, l_{\beta\sigma}(x), e_{\mu\sigma}$ ($\sigma = 1, \ldots, s$) will be linearly independent if, and only if, the sets $l_{0\sigma}, l_{\beta\sigma}$ or the sets $l_{0\sigma}, e_{\mu\sigma}$ are linearly independent.

For each abnormal set $l_0 = 0, l_\beta(x), e_\mu$ the constants $e_\mu$ are such that the equation

$$(77\cdot 7) \qquad e_\mu \Psi_\mu(\xi, \eta) = 0$$

holds for every admissible set $\xi_1, \xi_2, \eta_i(x)$ for which the equations $\Phi_\beta = 0$ are satisfied along the arc $E$. This follows from the identical vanishing of the expression (74·6) and Theorem 77·3 for such an abnormal set of multipliers. It was seen in the paragraph following Theorem 74·1 that the identical vanishing of (74·6) in the variables $\xi_1, \eta_{i1}, \xi_2, \eta_{i2}$ is equivalent to the identical vanishing of (74·9) in the differentials $dx_1, dy_{i1}, dx_2, dy_{i2}$.

The number $q$ defined by the maximum rank $p - q$ of the matrix (77·6) is the number of linearly independent sets $e_\mu$ for which condition (77·7) holds. With each such set there is associated an abnormal set $l_0 = 0, l_\beta(x), e_\mu$ with which the multiplier rule is satisfied, by the argument applied to (74·5) in Section 74. Thus we see that there are at least $q$ linearly independent abnormal sets of multipliers $l_0 = 0, l_\beta(x)$ with which the arc $E$ satisfies the multiplier rule. There cannot be more, since otherwise there would be more than $q$ linearly independent sets $e_\mu$ for which the condition (77·7) holds, which is impossible. Thus Theorem 77·4 is proved.

The problem of Bolza with fixed end-points is the problem described in Section 69 when the number of independent end-conditions $\psi_\mu = 0$ in (69·3) is $2n + 2$, the same as the number of end-values of the variables $x, y_i$. The arcs satisfying the end-conditions in this case, in particular those of the class $\mathfrak{M}$, all have the same end-values at $x_1$ and $x_2$.

The multiplier rule of Theorem 74·1 must, of course, be satisfied by a minimizing arc $E$ for a problem with fixed end-points, just as for a problem with variable end-points. The transversality condition (74·9) can now, however, be omitted from the multiplier rule, since the constants $e_\mu$ are $2n + 2$ in number and can always be determined so that the equation (74·9) is an identity in the differentials $dx_1, dy_{i1}, dx_2, dy_{i2}$. The transversality condition therefore imposes no restriction upon a minimizing arc $E$ when the end-points are fixed.

An arc $E$ is said to have *normality*, or *abnormality of order* $q$, on an interval $x'x''$ for a problem of Bolza if it has normality, or abnormality of order $a$, for the corresponding problem with fixed end-points on that interval. From what has been said above, it is evident that an arc $E$ has this property if and only if on the interval $x'x''$ it satisfies equations (74·8) with $q$ and only $q$ linearly independent abnormal sets of multipliers $l_0 = 0,\ l_\beta(x)$.

With this definition of normality on an interval in mind, the remarks in the introduction (Sec. 68) have more meaning. The distinction between normal and abnormal arcs for the problem of Lagrange was mentioned by A. Mayer in 1886[10] and was emphasized explicitly by Von Escherich in 1899.[11] Since that time many proofs of fundamental theorems for the problem of Lagrange have depended upon the assumption that the arc $E$ under consideration was normal on every subinterval $x'x''$ or upon the slightly stronger assumption that $E$ had an extension normal on every subinterval.[12] As a result of papers by Bliss [17], Morse and Myers [24], Graves [29], and McShane [64], one can now prove, without any assumption whatsoever concerning normality, that the multiplier rule and the conditions of Weierstrass and Clebsch, to be proved in the next chapter, are necessary conditions on a minimizing arc. In his papers concerning sufficient conditions for a minimum, Morse [19, 23, 22] was the first to avoid the use of a hypothesis on an extension of the interval of the minimizing arc. Hestenes [38], Morse [41], and Reid [51] have proved sufficiency theorems applicable to arcs which are normal but not necessarily normal on every subinterval, and to abnormal arcs of a special type.

[10] "Begründung der Lagrangeschen Multiplicatorenmethode in der Variationsrechnung," *Mathematische Annalen*, XXVI (1886), 74.

[11] "Die Zweite Variation der einfachen Integrale (IV Mittheilung)," *Sitzungsberichten der kaiserlichen Akademie der Wissenschaften in Wien*, CVIII (1899), 1290.

[12] See, e.g., Bolza, *Vorlesungen über Variationsrechnung*, p. 603; Hahn, "Bemerkungen zur Variationsrechnung," *Mathematische Annalen*, LVIII (1904), 152; Bliss [17], pp. 718, 735, 737.

## CHAPTER VIII

## FURTHER NECESSARY CONDITIONS FOR A MINIMUM

**78. The necessary conditions of Weierstrass and Clebsch.** In this section the method of Graves is to be applied to prove the necessary condition of Weierstrass for a normal minimizing arc $E$ for the problem of Bolza. Such an arc satisfies the multiplier rule with one and but one set of multipliers $l_0 = 1$, $l_\beta(x)$, $e_\mu$, since the difference of two such sets would have the form $l_0 = 0$, $l_\beta(x)$, $e_\mu$ and be identically zero because $E$ is normal. According to Theorem 77·4, there is a set of admissible variations $\xi_{1\sigma}$, $\xi_{2\sigma}$, $\eta_{i\sigma}(x)$ $(\sigma = 1, \ldots, p)$ satisfying the equations of variation $\Phi_\beta = 0$ along $E$ and giving the determinant $|\Psi_\mu(\xi_\sigma, \eta_\sigma)|$ a value different from zero.

At an arbitrarily selected point *3* between corners on $E$ let $Y'_i$ $(i = 1, \ldots, n)$ be a set of values such that the element $[x_3, y(x_3), Y']$ is admissible and satisfies the equations $\phi_\beta = 0$. It is then possible to select the enlarged system of equations (72·1) with the continuity properties described in Section 72 near the element $[x_3, y(x_3), Y']$ as well as near the arc $E$, and so that the functional determinant $|\phi_{iy'_k}|$ is different from zero at $[x_3, y(x_3), Y']$ as well as on $E$. This will be proved in the next section. Equations (72·1) now define a set of functions $z_\gamma(x)$ associated with the functions $y_i(x)$ defining $E$, and a set of constants $Z_\nu$ to go with the set $[x_3, y(x_3), Y']$. Furthermore, the equations of variation (72·2) define functions $\zeta_{\gamma\sigma}(x)$ $(\sigma = 1, \ldots, p)$ corresponding to each of the sets of admissible variations $\xi_{1\sigma}$, $\xi_{2\sigma}$, $\eta_{i\sigma}(x)$ of the preceding paragraph. By the methods of Section 72 we may now infer the existence of three families of admissible arcs

$$\begin{aligned} &y_i(x, b) && (x_1 - \delta < x < x_3, \ |b| < \epsilon), \\ (78\cdot1) \quad &Y_i(x, b) && (x_3 \leqq x \leqq x_3 + e, \ |b| < \epsilon, \ |e| < \epsilon), \\ &y_i(x, b, e) && (x_3 + e \leqq x \leqq x_2 + \delta, \ |b| < \epsilon, \ |e| < \epsilon) \end{aligned}$$

satisfying on the first and third intervals the differential equations

$$(78\cdot2) \qquad y'_i = \chi_i[x, y, z(x) + b_\sigma \zeta_\sigma]$$

from (72·3), and on the second interval the equations

$$(78\cdot3) \qquad y'_i = \chi_i(x, y, z),$$

and having the initial values

$$\begin{aligned} y_i(x_1, b) &= y_i(x_1) + b_\sigma \eta_{i\sigma}(x_1) \\ (78\cdot4) \qquad Y_i(x_3, b) &= y_i(x_3, b), \\ y_i(x_3 + e, b, e) &= Y_i(x_3 + e, b). \end{aligned}$$

The systems (78·2) and (78·3) are equivalent, respectively, to the systems

$$(78\cdot 5)\qquad \begin{aligned} &\phi_\beta = 0\,, \qquad \phi_\gamma = z_\gamma(x) + b_\sigma\,\eta_{i\sigma}(x) \\ &\phi_\beta = 0\,, \qquad \phi_\gamma = Z_\gamma\,, \end{aligned}$$

and $Y'$ is the value of (78·3) for the arguments $(x_3, y_3, Z)$. For values $e > 0$ the three families (78·1), taken together, form a single admissible $(p+1)$-parameter family of arcs consisting of a finite sequence of adjacent elementary families. The functions defining these elementary families and their derivatives with respect to $x$ have continuous partial derivatives with respect to the parameters $b$, as one sees by the arguments used in proving Lemmas 72·1 and 72·2. They also have continuous derivatives with respect to the parameter $e$, since from the existence theorems for differential equations it is known that the solutions (72·4) of the equations (72·3) have continuous derivatives with respect to $x_0$, as well as the derivatives with respect to the variables $y_{i0}$, $b$ mentioned in the text following equations (72·4).[1]

When $b = e = 0$ the first and third sets of functions (78·1) reduce to the functions $y_i(x)$ defining the arc $E$. For, like the sets $y_i(x)$, they satisfy equations (78·5) with $b = 0$ and, from (78·4), are continuous and have the initial values $y_i(x_1)$. The solutions of equations (78·5) having given initial values are unique. The variations along $E$ with respect to $b_\sigma$ of the first and third families (78·1) satisfy the equations of variation (72·2) with the functions $\zeta_{i\sigma}(x)$ belonging to the variations $\eta_{i\sigma}(x)$. Furthermore, differentiation of the relations (78·4) shows that these variations form continuous solutions of equations (72·2) with the initial values $\eta_{i\sigma}(x_1)$, and hence they must be identically equal to the solutions $\eta_{i\sigma}(x)$. If we denote by $\eta_i(x)$ the variations along the arc $E$ of the first and third families (78·1) with respect to the parameter $e$, we find that they satisfy the equations $\Phi_\beta = 0$ and the relations

$$(78\cdot 6)\qquad \begin{aligned} &\eta_i(x) \equiv 0 \qquad\qquad (x_1 - \delta < x \leqq x_3) \\ &y_i'(x_3) + \eta_i(x_3) = Y_i'\,. \end{aligned}$$

The latter are found by differentiating the first and third equations (78·4) with respect to $e$. They show that the functions $\eta_i(x)$ are, in general, discontinuous at the value $x_3$; but this does not affect the validity of the arguments in the following paragraph. The notation $\xi_1, \xi_2, \eta_i(x)$ will be used for the set $\xi_1 = 0$, $\xi_2 = 0$, $\eta_i(x)$.

When the functions

$$(78\cdot 7)\qquad x_s(b) = x_s + b_\sigma \xi_{s\sigma} \qquad (s = 1,\ 2)$$

are used to define end-points on the arcs (78·1) and the corresponding end-values of these arcs are substituted in the functions $\psi_\mu$, the latter become func-

[1] See Appen., Part II, esp. Sec. 6.

tions $\psi_\mu(b, e)$ of the parameters $b$, $e$. At the values $(b, e) = (0, 0)$ these functions have the derivatives

$$\frac{\partial \psi_\mu}{\partial b_\sigma} = \Psi_\mu(\xi_\sigma, \eta_\sigma), \qquad \frac{\partial \psi_\mu}{\partial e} = \Psi_\mu(\xi, \eta).$$

Since the minimizing arc $E$ satisfies the conditions $\psi_\mu = 0$, the equations

$$\psi_\mu(b, e) = 0 \tag{78·8}$$

have the initial solution $(b, e) = (0, 0)$ at which the functional determinant

$$\left| \frac{\partial \psi_\mu}{\partial b_\sigma} \right| = |\Psi_\mu(\xi_\sigma, \eta_\sigma)|$$

is different from zero. Hence equations (78·8) have solutions $b_\sigma = B_\sigma(e)$ which vanish at $e = 0$ and have continuous derivatives near that value. At $e = 0$ these derivatives satisfy the equations

$$\Psi_\mu(\xi_\sigma, \eta_\sigma) B'_\sigma(0) + \Psi_\mu(\xi, \eta) = 0. \tag{78·9}$$

When the substitution $b_\sigma = B_\sigma(e)$ is made in the functions (78·1) and (78·7), a one-parameter family of arcs is determined which contains the minimizing arc $E$ for the parameter value $e = 0$. The arcs of the family are admissible for sufficiently small positive values of $e$ and satisfy the conditions $\phi_\beta = \psi_\mu = 0$. They are thus in the class $\mathfrak{M}$.

When the functions (78·1) and (78·7) are substituted in the sum $J$, it becomes a function of the variables $b$, $e$ whose value is

$$\begin{aligned} J(b, e) = g\{&x_1(b), y[x_1(b), b], x_2(b), y[x_2(b), b, e]\} \\ &+ \int_{x_1(b)}^{x_3} f[x, y(x, b), y'(x, b)]\,dx + \int_{x_3}^{x_3+e} f(x, Y, Y')\,dx \\ &+ \int_{x_3+e}^{x_2(b)} f[x, y(x, b, e), y'(x, b, e)]\,dx. \end{aligned}$$

With the help of the equations $\phi_\beta = 0$, the multiplier rule of Theorem 74·1 with the transversality condition in the form of the identity (74·6), the usual integration by parts, and equations (78·6), it is provable that at the values $(b, e) = (0, 0)$ the derivatives of $J$ have the values defined by the equations

$$\begin{aligned} &\frac{\partial J}{\partial b_\sigma} + e_\mu \Psi_\mu(\xi_\sigma, \eta_\sigma) = 0, \\ &\frac{\partial J}{\partial e} + e_\mu \Psi_\mu(\xi, \eta) = [E(x, y, y', l, Y')]^3, \end{aligned} \tag{78·10}$$

where

$$\begin{aligned} E(x, y, y', l, Y') = F(x, y, Y', l) &- F(x, y, y', l) \\ &- (Y'_i - y'_i) F_{y'_i}(x, y, y', l) \end{aligned}$$

is the well-known Weierstrass $E$-function.

For small negative values of $e$ the arcs defined by the functions (78·1) are not admissible. Each of them has, in fact, three points on each ordinate of the interval $x_3 + e < x < x_3$. For small positive values of $e$, on the other hand, they are admissible; and the same is true of the arcs of the one-parameter family defined by substituting $b_\mu = B_\mu(e)$ in the functions (78·1) and the end-values (78·7). If $J(E)$ is to be a minimum, the values of the sum $J$ on the arcs of this one-parameter family must be non-decreasing as $e$ increases from the value zero. The derivative at $e = 0$ of the function $J[B(u), u]$ is

$$J_{b_\mu}(0,\ 0)B_\mu'(0) + J_e(0,\ 0).$$

It must be non-negative. From (78·10) and (78·9) the value of this derivative is found to be the value of $E(x, y, y', l, Y')$ at the point *3*, and the following theorem is proved:

THEOREM 78·1. THE NECESSARY CONDITION OF WEIERSTRASS. *An admissible arc* E *satisfying the equations* $\phi_\beta = 0$ *and the multiplier rule, with multipliers* $l_0 = 1$, $l_\beta(x)$, *is said to satisfy the necessary condition of Weierstrass with these multipliers if the condition*

$$E(x,\ y,\ y',\ l,\ Y') \geqq 0 \tag{78·11}$$

*is valid at every element* $(x, y, y', l)$ *of* E *for all admissible sets* $(x, y, Y') \neq (x, y, y')$ *satisfying the equations* $\phi_\beta = 0$. *Every normal minimizing arc* E *for the problem of Bolza must satisfy this condition.*

The necessity of the condition for a minimizing arc $E$ has been proved above only at elements $(x, y, y', l)$ between corners of $E$. But it is evident by simple continuity considerations that for a minimizing arc the condition (78·11) must also hold at corner elements.

It should be noted here that the proof in the text of the necessary condition of Weierstrass is for a normal arc. Quite recently McShane [60] has proved that for a minimizing arc $E$, whether normal or not, there always exists a set of multipliers $l_0$, $l_\beta(x)$ with which $E$ satisfies both the multiplier rule and the necessary conditions of Weierstrass and Clebsch.

Let $\pi_i$ $(i = 1, \ldots, n)$ be a set of values satisfying the equations

$$\phi_{\beta y_i'}\pi_i = 0 \tag{78·12}$$

at an element $(x, y, y', l)$ of a normal minimizing arc $E$. By means of the equations

$$\phi_{\gamma y_i'}\pi_i = \kappa_\gamma \tag{78·13}$$

these numbers $\pi_i$ define $n - m$ further quantities $\kappa_\gamma$. The equations

$$\phi_\beta(x,\ y,\ p) = 0\,, \qquad \phi_\gamma(x,\ y,\ p) = z_\gamma + \epsilon\kappa_\gamma$$

have the initial solution $(\epsilon, p) = (0, y')$ and determine a set of solutions $p_i(\epsilon)$ with initial values $p_i(0) = y_i'$, and with derivatives $p_i'(0) = \pi_i$, since these derivatives satisfy the equations (78·12) and (78·13) when inserted in place of the numbers $\pi_i$. The sets $[x, y, p(\epsilon)]$ are all interior to $R_1$ for sufficiently small values of $\epsilon$ and, according to the last theorem, must satisfy the condition

$$E[x, y, y', l, p(\epsilon)] \geqq 0 .$$

By simple calculations one readily verifies, with the help of the definition of the $E$-function following (78·10), that the first member of this last inequality and its first derivative with respect to $\epsilon$ both vanish at $\epsilon = 0$. Its second derivative at $\epsilon = 0$ is the quadratic form $F_{y'_i y'_k}\pi_i\pi_k$, and this must not be negative. Consequently, we have the following theorem:

THEOREM 78·2. THE NECESSARY CONDITION OF CLEBSCH. *An admissible arc* E *satisfying the equations* $\phi_\beta = 0$ *and the multiplier rule with multipliers* $l_0 = 1$, $l_\beta(x)$ *is said to satisfy the necessary condition of Clebsch with these multipliers if the condition*

$$F_{y'_i y'_k}(x, y, y', l)\, \pi_i \pi_k \geqq 0$$

*is valid at every element* $(x, y, y', l)$ *of* E *for all sets* $(\pi_1, \ldots, \pi_n) \neq (0, \ldots, 0)$ *satisfying the equations*

$$\phi_{\beta y'_i}(x, y, y')\, \pi_i = 0 .$$

*Every normal minimizing arc for the problem of Bolza must satisfy this condition.*

**79. A lemma and corollary.** In Sections 72 and 78 frequent use has been made of an enlarged system of equations $\phi_\beta = 0$, $\phi_\gamma = z_\gamma$ for which the functional determinant $|\phi_{iy'_k}|$ is different from zero. The existence of such an extension of the system $\phi_\beta = 0$ can doubtless be proved in many ways, but in particular with the help of the following lemma and its corollary:

LEMMA 79·1. *Let* $\|a_{\beta k}(x)\|$ $(k = 1, \ldots, n;\ \beta = 1, \ldots, m < n)$ *be a matrix of functions with well-defined forward and backward limits at each point of an interval* $x_1 \leqq x \leqq x_2$ *and continuous except at a finite number of points of this interval. If the matrix has rank* m *at every point of the interval* $x_1x_2$, *then there exists an enlarged matrix* $\|a_{ik}(x)\|$ $(i, k = 1, \ldots, n)$, *with each* $a_{\gamma k}(x)$ $(\gamma = m + 1, \ldots, n;$ $k = 1, \ldots, n)$ *a polynomial, and such that the determinant* $|a_{ik}(x)|$ *is different from zero on* $x_1x_2$.

To prove this it will first be shown that there exists one row of continuous functions $a_k(x)$ such that the matrix

$$\begin{Vmatrix} a_{\beta k}(x) \\ a_k(x) \end{Vmatrix}$$

is of rank $m + 1$ on $x_1x_2$. Evidently there exists such a row of functions $a_k(x)$ on an interval $x_1 \leqq x \leqq x'$ so short that on it one of the determinants of order $m$ of the matrix $\|a_{\beta k}(x)\|$ remains different from zero. Let $\xi$ be the least upper bound on $x_1x_2$ for the end-values $x'$ of such intervals, and let $\lambda$ and $\mu$ range over two sets of $m$ values each for which the determinants

$$|a_{\beta\lambda}(\xi - 0)|, \qquad |a_{\beta\mu}(\xi + 0)|$$

are different from zero. Then for a sufficiently small $\epsilon$

$$|a_{\beta\lambda}(x)| \neq 0 \qquad (\xi - \epsilon < x < \xi),$$

$$|a_{\beta\mu}(x)| \neq 0 \qquad (\xi < x < \xi + \epsilon).$$

Let $x_1x'$ be an interval with $\xi - \epsilon < x' < \xi$ for which the functions $a_k(x)$ exist, and let $j$ be a value not on the range of $\lambda$. For all values $i \neq j$ on the range $1, \ldots, n$ the definitions of the functions $a_i(x)$ may be extended so that

$$a_i(x) = a_i(x') \qquad (x' < x \leqq \xi),$$

and the definition of $a_j(x)$ may be extended continuously on the same interval so that

$$\begin{vmatrix} a_{\beta\lambda}(x) & a_{\beta j}(x) \\ a_\lambda(x) & a_j(x) \end{vmatrix} \neq 0 \qquad (x' < x \leqq \xi).$$

If the subscript $j$ is next selected to be a value not on the range of the subscript $\mu$, then by a similar process the definitions of the functions $a_k(x)$ may be extended continuously over the interval $\xi < x \leqq \xi + \epsilon$; and it is evident that $\xi$ cannot be the upper bound described unless it is at $x_2$. By continuing this process, additional rows may be added until a matrix $\|a_{ik}(x)\|$ is reached whose determinant is different from zero. If the continuous functions $a_{\gamma k}(x)$ are replaced by polynomials approximating them sufficiently closely, the result stated in the lemma is attained.

COROLLARY 79·1. *The polynomials* $a_{\gamma k}(x)$ *of the lemma can be so chosen that at a finite number of points* $\xi$ *on the interval* $x_1x_2$, *each having associated with it a matrix of constants* $\|b_{\beta k}\|$ *of rank* m, *the inequalities*

$$(79\cdot1) \qquad \begin{vmatrix} b_{\beta k} \\ a_{\gamma k}(\xi) \end{vmatrix} \neq 0$$

$$(\beta = 1, \ldots, m;\ \gamma = m+1, \ldots, n;\ k = 1, \ldots, n)$$

*are satisfied.*

Let $\lambda$ range over a set of $m$ values such that the determinant $|b_{\beta\lambda}|$ is different from zero, and let $j$ be a value not on the range of $\lambda$. The definition of $a_{m+1,j}(x)$ can be changed slightly near $\xi$ if necessary, so that it remains continuous, makes

$$\begin{vmatrix} b_{\beta\lambda} & b_{\beta j} \\ a_{m+1,\lambda}(\xi) & a_{m+1,j}(\xi) \end{vmatrix} \neq 0,$$

and leaves the determinant $|a_{ik}(x)|$ different from zero on $x_1x_2$. The same process can be repeated for the other points $\xi$ so that the matrices (79·1) all have rank $m + 1$. Similar modifications for succeeding rows and the subsequent approximation to the continuous functions $a_{\gamma k}(x)$ by polynomials lead to a matrix $\|a_{ik}(x)\|$ with the properties described in the corollary.

In order to construct the functions $\phi_\gamma(x, y, y')$ of equations (72·1), let the functions $a_{\beta k}(x)$ of Lemma 79·1 be the values of the derivatives $\phi_{\beta y'_k}$ along the arc $E$. The functions

$$\phi_\gamma(x, y, y') = a_{\gamma k}(x)\, y'_k, \tag{79·2}$$

formed with the functions $a_{\gamma k}(x)$ of the lemma, then have the properties described in Section 72. The constants $\phi_{\beta y'_k}[x_3, y(x_3), Y'(x_3)]$ in the second paragraph of Section 78 may be denoted by $b_{\beta k}$, and the value $x_3$ by $\xi$. The functions (79·2) formed with the functions $a_{\gamma k}(x)$ of Corollary 79·1 satisfy the requirements for equations (72·1) prescribed in Section 72.

**80. The second variation and a fourth necessary condition for a minimum.** In this section we shall consider an arc $E$ of the class $\mathfrak{M}$ which is an extremal and satisfies the multiplier rule of Theorem 74·1 with a set of multipliers of the form $l_0 = 1$, $l_\beta(x)$. We suppose, furthermore, that $E$ is defined, as usual, by functions of the form

$$y_i(x) \qquad (i = 1, \ldots, n;\ x_1 \leqq x \leqq x_2) \tag{80·1}$$

and that $E$ is imbedded in a one-parameter admissible family of arcs in $\mathfrak{M}$,

$$y_i = y_i(x, b) \qquad [x_1(b) \leqq x \leqq x_2(b);\ |b| < \epsilon], \tag{80·2}$$

having the continuity properties of Corollary 77·2 which are sufficient to justify the deduction of the second variation in the following paragraphs. The variations of the family (80·2) along the arc $E$ will, as before, be denoted by $\xi_1$, $\xi_2$, $\eta_i(x)$.

If the arc $E$ is a normal non-singular minimizing arc without corners, it will certainly have the properties just described, as we shall see in the paragraph following Theorem 80·1. But the second variation turns out to be well defined on every extremal arc $E$ of the class $\mathfrak{M}$ with multipliers of the form $l_0 = 1$, $l_\beta(x)$.

The value of the sum $J$ on the arc (80·2) is a function $J(b)$ with a first differential (73·1), which can easily be put into the more convenient form

$$\delta J = dg + e_\mu\, d\psi_\mu + [F\, dx]_1^2 + \int_{x_1}^{x_2} (F_{y_i}\, \delta y_i + F_{y'_i}\, \delta y'_i)\, dx$$

by adding to (73·1) terms which vanish. This formula holds along every arc of the family (80·2). Along the particular arc $E$ where $b = 0$ the usual integration by parts shows that the value of $dJ$ is zero, since $E$ satisfies the multiplier rule in Theorem 74·1.

With the help of Lemma 77·1 applied to the function

$$F[x, y(x, b), y'(x, b), l(x)],$$

thought of as a function of $x$ and $b$, the second differential $d^2J = J''(0)db^2$, taken along the arc $E$, has the value

$$d^2J = [F\, d^2x + F'\, dx^2 + 2F_{y_i}\, \delta y_i\, dx + 2F_{y'_i}\, \delta y'_i\, dx]_1^2 + d^2g + e_\mu d^2\psi_\mu$$
$$+ \int_{x_1}^{x_2} [F_{y_i}\, \delta^2 y_i + F_{y'_i}\, \delta^2 y'_i + 2\omega(x, \delta y, \delta y')]\, dx,$$

where $2\omega$ is the quadratic form

$$2\omega(x, \eta, \eta') = F_{y_iy_k}\eta_i\eta_k + 2F_{y_iy'_k}\eta_i\eta'_k + F_{y'_iy'_k}\eta'_i\eta'_k .$$

The symbol $F'$ stands for the derivative of $F$ with respect to the $x$ which occurs in all of its arguments. After calculating this, applying the usual integration by parts to the first two terms under the integral sign in the expression for $d^2J$, and eliminating the $\delta$-differentials outside the integral sign by means of the equations (71·3), it turns out that

$$d^2J = [F\,d^2x + (d^2y_i - y'_i\,d^2x)F_{y'_i}]_1^2 + d^2g + e_\mu\,d^2\psi_\mu$$
$$+ [(F_x - y'_iF_{y_i})\,dx^2 + 2F_{y_i}\,dy_i\,dx]_1^2 + \int_{x_1}^{x_2} 2\omega\,dx .$$

In this expression the coefficients of the terms in $d^2x_1$, $d^2y_{i1}$, $d^2x_2$, $d^2y_{i2}$ are zero, on account of the transversality condition (74·9); and a final value for $d^2J$ is therefore

$$d^2J = [(F_x - y'_iF_{y_i})\,dx^2 + 2F_{y_i}\,dy_i\,dx]_1^2 + 2q + e_\mu 2q_\mu$$
$$(80\cdot 3) \qquad + \int_{x_1}^{x_2} 2\omega(x, \delta y, \delta y')\,dx ,$$

where $2q$ is the quadratic form in $dx_1$, $dy_{i1}$, $dx_2$, $dy_{i2}$ whose coefficients are the second derivatives of $g$ and where $2q_\mu$ is the similar form for the function $\psi_\mu$. In terms of the variations

$$(80\cdot 4) \qquad \xi_1 = x'_1(0), \qquad \xi_2 = x'_2(0), \qquad \eta_i(x) = y_{ib}(x, 0)$$

the last equation is equivalent to the equation

$$d^2J = J_2(\xi, \eta)\,db^2 ,$$

with

$$J_2(\xi, \eta) = 2\gamma[\xi_1, \eta_i(x_1), \xi_2, \eta_i(x_2)]$$
$$(80\cdot 5) \qquad + \int_{x_1}^{x_2} 2\omega(x, \eta, \eta')\,dx ,$$

where $2\gamma[dx_1, \delta y_{i1}, dx_2, \delta y_{i2}]$ stands for the terms outside the integral sign in (80·3) with the differentials $dx_1$, $dy_{i1}$, $dx_2$, $dy_{i2}$ expressed in terms of $dx_1$, $\delta y_{i1}$, $dx_2$, $\delta y_{i2}$ by means of the equations (71·3).

The expression $J_2(\xi, \eta)$ is called the *second variation* of the sum $J$ along the arc $E$. It is well defined for admissible sets $\xi_1$, $\xi_2$, $\eta_i(x)$ along every extremal arc with multipliers of the form $l_0 = 1$, $l_\beta(x)$. It is said to be *non-negative* if it is positive or zero for every admissible set of variations $\xi_1$, $\xi_2$, $\eta_i(x)$ satisfying along $E$ the conditions $\Phi_\beta = \Psi_\mu = 0$. It is *positive definite* if it is non-negative and vanishes only when the elements of the set $\xi_1$, $\xi_2$, $\eta_i(x)$ vanish identically. With the help of the results of the preceding paragraphs the following fourth necessary condition for a minimum can now be easily justified:

THEOREM 80·1. A FOURTH NECESSARY CONDITION FOR A MINIMUM. *An extremal arc* E *with multipliers* $l_0 = 1$, $l_\beta(x)$ *is said to satisfy the fourth necessary condition for a minimum if the second variation* $J_2(\xi, \eta)$ *along* E *is non-negative. Every normal non-singular minimizing arc* E *without corners for the problem of Bolza must satisfy this fourth necessary condition.*

To prove this, we note first that a minimizing arc $E$ must satisfy the multiplier rule of Theorem 74·1. If $E$ is normal, its multipliers can be taken in the form $l_0 = 1$, $l_\beta(x)$; and in that form they are unique, by the remark in the first paragraph of Section 77. If $E$ is non-singular and has no corners, it is an extremal, according to Corollary 74·3 and the definition of an extremal in Section 75. Thus with the help of Theorem 77·1 and Corollaries 77·1 and 77·2 it is seen that a minimizing arc $E$ of the type described in the theorem can be imbedded in a one-parameter family of arcs in $\mathfrak{M}$ of the form (80·2). Since $E$ is a minimizing arc, the function $J(b)$ described above for this family must have a minimum $J(0)$ and must have

$$J'(0) = 0, \qquad J''(0) = J_2(\xi, \eta) \geqq 0.$$

The first derivative vanishes, as has already been proved, and the second derivative must be non-negative for every set of admissible variations $\xi_1$, $\xi_2$, $\eta_i(x)$ satisfying the conditions $\Phi_\beta = \Psi_\mu = 0$ along $E$, since every such set is the set of variations along $E$ of an imbedding family of the form (80·2), according to Theorem 77·1 and its corollaries. Thus the proof of Theorem 80·1 is complete.

**81. The accessory minimum problem.** The fact that the second variation must be positive or zero along a normal non-singular minimizing arc $E$ without corners, as stated in Theorem 80·1, suggests, as usual, an auxiliary minimum problem called the *accessory minimum problem*. This is the problem of finding, in the class of admissible sets of variations $\xi_1$, $\xi_2$, $\eta_i(x)$ satisfying the equations of variation $\Phi_\beta = 0$, $\Psi_\mu = 0$ along $E$, one which minimizes the second variation $J_2(\xi, \eta)$ for $E$ in equation (80·5). That this problem is equivalent, with slight changes, to one of precisely the Bolza type will be seen in the proof of Lemma 81·3. There is an accessory minimum problem on every extremal arc $E$ with multipliers of the form $l_0 = 1$, $l_\beta(x)$, since on every such arc the second variation (80·5) is well defined. We shall assume in this section that the extremal arcs $E$ considered have multipliers of this form and are non-singular unless otherwise expressly stated.

The equations of the extremals for an accessory minimum problem, analogous to equations (74·11) and $\phi_\beta = 0$, are the equations

$$(81\cdot1) \qquad \frac{d\Omega_{\eta'_i}}{dx} - \Omega_{\eta_i} = 0 \qquad \Phi_\beta = 0$$

where $\Omega$, defined by the equation

$$(81\cdot2) \qquad \Omega(x, \eta, \eta', \lambda) = \omega + \lambda_\beta(x)\Phi_\beta,$$

is seen to be a homogeneous quadratic form in the variables $\eta_i, \eta_i', \lambda_\beta$. The equations (81·1) are called *accessory differential equations.*[2] Canonical variables $x$, $\eta_i, \zeta_i$ may be defined for them in terms of $x, \eta_i, \eta_i', \lambda_\beta$ by means of the equations

$$(81\cdot 3) \qquad \zeta_i = \Omega_{\eta_i'}(x, \eta, \eta', \lambda), \qquad 0 = \Phi_\beta(x, \eta, \eta'),$$

whose second members are linear in $\eta_i, \eta_i', \lambda_\beta$ and have the determinant

$$\begin{vmatrix} \Omega_{\eta_i'\eta_k'} & \Omega_{\eta_i'\mu_\gamma} \\ \Phi_{\beta\eta_k'} & 0 \end{vmatrix} = \begin{vmatrix} F_{y_i'y_k'} & \phi_{\gamma y_i'} \\ \phi_{\beta y_k'} & 0 \end{vmatrix}$$

of coefficients of $\eta_i', \lambda_\beta$. Since the arc $E$ is, by hypothesis, non-singular, this determinant is everywhere different from zero; and the linear equations (81·3) have solutions

$$(81\cdot 4) \qquad \eta_i' = \Pi_i(x, \eta, \zeta), \qquad \lambda_\beta = \Lambda_\beta(x, \eta, \zeta)$$

linear and homogeneous in the variables $\eta_i, \zeta_i$. The Hamiltonian function $\mathfrak{h}$ for the second variation, analogous to the function (75·11), is defined by the formula

$$\begin{aligned} \mathfrak{H}(x, \eta, \zeta) &= [\eta_i'\Omega_{\eta_i'} - \Omega]^{\eta' = \Pi,\, \lambda = \Lambda} \\ &= \zeta_i \Pi_i - \Omega(x, \eta, \Pi, \Lambda). \end{aligned}$$

It is a homogeneous quadratic form in the variables $\eta_i, \zeta_i$ with coefficients which are functions of $x$ having continuous derivatives on the interval $x_1x_2$ on which the arc $E$ is defined. By an argument similar to that of Section 75 it follows that equations (81·1) are equivalent to the *canonical accessory equations*

$$(81\cdot 5) \qquad \eta_i' = \mathfrak{H}_{\zeta_i}, \qquad \zeta_i' = -\mathfrak{H}_{\eta_i},$$

analogous to equations (75·13).

The systems (81·1) and (81·5) are, in a sense, the equations of variation along $E$ of the Euler-Lagrange equations

$$(81\cdot 6) \qquad \frac{dF_{y_i'}}{dx} - F_{y_i} = 0 \qquad \phi_\beta = 0$$

and the canonical equations (75·13) of the original problem, respectively. Equations (81·6) are, in fact, satisfied identically in $x$ and the constants $a_i, b_i$ by the functions (75·10) defining the family of extremals in which the non-singular arc $E$ is imbedded for values $x_1 \leqq x \leqq x_2, a_{i0}, b_{i0}$. When these functions are substituted in (81·6) and the result is differentiated with respect to one of the constants $a$ of the set $a_i, b_i$, it is found that the functions $\eta_i = y_{ia}(x, a_0, b_0)$,

[2] Von Escherich, "Die zweite Variation der einfachen Integrale (I. Mittheilung)," *Sitzungsberichten der kaiserlichen Akademie der Wissenschaften in Wien*, CVII (1898), 1236; Bolza, *Vorlesungen über Variationsrechnung*, p. 622.

$\lambda_\beta = l_{\beta a}(x, a_0, b_0)$ satisfy the equations (81·1). Similar differentiations of the equations

$$z_i(x, a, b) = F_{y_i'}[x, y(x, a, b), y'(x, a, b), l(x, a, b)]$$

$$0 = \phi_\beta[x, y(x, a, b), y'(x, a, b)]$$

show that the derivatives $\zeta_i = z_{ia}$ are related to the derivatives $\eta_i = y_{ia}$, $\lambda_\beta = l_{\beta a}$ along $E$ by means of equations (81·3) and, hence, that $\eta_i = y_{ia}$, $\zeta_i = z_{ia}$ satisfy the canonical accessory equations (81·5). Thus the columns of the matrix (75·9) are $2n$ independent solutions of the equations (81·5). Since they are also solutions of equations (75·14), it follows readily that the systems (75·14) and (81·5) are identical and that

(81·7) $$2\mathfrak{H} = H_{y_i y_k}\eta_i\eta_k + 2H_{y_i z_k}\eta_i\zeta_k + H_{z_i z_k}\zeta_i\zeta_k\,.$$

One verifies by means of the properties of the family of extremals (75·8) and the remark following equations (75·12) that the coefficients of the quadratic form $\mathfrak{h}$ calculated for the arc $E$ are functions of $x$ with continuous derivatives of at least the first order in a neighborhood of the interval $x_1x_2$.

By a solution of the equations (81·5) is meant a pair of functions $\eta_i(x)$, $\zeta_i(x)$ having continuous derivatives on a neighborhood of the interval $x_1x_2$ and satisfying the equations. By differentiating equations (81·5) it follows that such a solution will also have continuous second derivatives. The existence theorems for differential equations tell us that through each initial element $(x_0, \eta_{i0}, \zeta_{i0})$ with $x_0$ on $x_1x_2$ the equations have a unique solution $\eta_i(x)$, $\zeta_i(x)$, and, in particular, that a solution $\eta_i$, $\zeta_i$ whose elements all vanish at a point $x_0$ is identically zero. Every solution $\eta_i$, $\zeta_i$ is linearly expressible with constant coefficients in terms of a fundamental system consisting of an arbitrarily selected set of $2n$ linearly independent solutions. The $2n$ columns of the determinant (75·9) form such a fundamental system.

A set $\xi_1$, $\xi_2$, $\eta_i(x)$ is said to satisfy the *accessory multiplier rule* if there exists a set of functions $\zeta_i(x)$ and constants $\epsilon_\mu$ such that the set $\eta_i$, $\zeta_i$ is a solution of the canonical accessory equations and such that the equation

(81·8) $$[\zeta_i\, d\eta_i]_1^2 + d\gamma + \epsilon_\mu\, d\Psi_\mu = 0$$

is an identity in the differentials $d\xi_1$, $d\eta_{i1}$, $d\xi_2$, $d\eta_{i2}$. The form of this multiplier rule is suggested by the multiplier rule for the problem of Bolza used in the proof of Lemma 81·3. The *accessory minimum problem is said to have abnormality of order q* if there exist $q$ linearly independent sets of constants and solutions of the canonical accessory equations of the form $\eta_i \equiv 0$, $\zeta_i(x)$, $\epsilon_\mu$ for each of which the equation

(81·9) $$[\zeta_i\, d\eta_i]_1^2 + \epsilon_\mu\, d\Psi_\mu = 0$$

is an identity in $d\xi_1$, $d\eta_{i1}$, $d\xi_2$, $d\eta_{i2}$. By an argument similar to that in the paragraphs just preceding Corollary 74·1 it follows that the $q$ sets $\zeta_i(x)$ and the $q$ sets $\epsilon_\mu$ are separately linearly independent.

LEMMA 81·1. *The original problem of Bolza and the accessory minimum problem have the same order of abnormality.*

According to the definition of abnormality in Section 77, above, there will exist exactly $q$ linearly independent abnormal sets of multipliers of the form $l_0 = 0$, $l_\beta(x)$, $e_\mu$ for which the multiplier rule in Theorem 74·1 is satisfied, provided that the arc $E$ has abnormality of order $q$. It is seen, upon examination, that for one of these sets the equations (74·8) and (74·9) imply the equations

$$(81\cdot 10) \qquad \Omega_{\eta'_i} = \int_{x_1}^{x} \Omega_{\eta_i}\, dx + c_i\,, \qquad \Phi_\beta = 0\,,$$

$$(81\cdot 11) \qquad [\Omega_{\eta'_i}(dy_i - y'_i\, dx)]_1^2 + e_\mu\, d\psi_\mu = 0$$

where the arguments of the derivatives of $\Omega$ and $\Phi_\beta$ are $x$, $\eta_i \equiv 0$, $\lambda_\beta = l_\beta$. Near every value $x$ there is a set of $m$ of the equations (81·10) which can be solved for the multipliers $l_\beta$ occurring in their first members, from which it follows that these multipliers are continuous and have continuous first derivatives, since the arc $E$ is an extremal and therefore has no corners and has continuous second derivatives. Equations (81·10) are now seen to be equivalent to (81·1) with $\eta_i \equiv 0$, $\lambda_\beta = l_\beta$, and the identity (81·11) in $dx_1$, $dy_{i1}$, $dx_2$, $dy_{i2}$ is equivalent to the identity (81·9) in $\xi_1$, $\eta_{i1}$, $\xi_2$, $\eta_{i2}$. Consequently, every set of $q$ linearly independent multipliers $l_0 = 0$, $l_\beta$, $e_\mu$ satisfying along $E$ the equations (74·8) and (74·9) defines, by means of equations

$$(81\cdot 12) \quad \eta_i \equiv 0\,, \qquad \zeta_i = \Omega_{\eta'_i}(x,\ 0,\ 0,\ l) = F_{y'_i}(x,\ y,\ y',\ l)\,,\ \epsilon_\mu = e_\mu\,,$$

$q$ linearly independent sets $\eta_i \equiv 0$, $\zeta_i(x)$, $\epsilon_\mu$ satisfying the conditions (81·5) and (81·9), and conversely. The original and the accessory problems, therefore, have the same order of abnormality.

LEMMA 81·2. *The accessory minimum problem is equivalent to a normal problem of similar type obtained by deleting a suitably selected subset of its end-conditions.*

If the accessory minimum problem has order of abnormality equal to $q$, there exist $q$ linearly independent sets $\eta_{i\sigma} \equiv 0$, $\zeta_{i\sigma}(x)$, $\epsilon_{\mu\sigma}$ ($\sigma = 1, \ldots, q$) satisfying the canonical accessory equations and making the equations

$$(81\cdot 13) \qquad [\zeta_{i\sigma}\eta_i]_1^2 + \epsilon_{\mu\sigma}\Psi_\mu = 0 \qquad (\sigma = 1,\ \ldots,\ q)$$

identities in $\xi_1$, $\eta_{i1}$, $\xi_2$, $\eta_{i2}$, as one sees with the help of equation (81·9). Since the $q$ sets $\epsilon_{\mu\sigma}$ are linearly independent, the matrix $\|\epsilon_{\mu\sigma}\|$ has a determinant $|\epsilon_{\rho\sigma}|$ of order $q$ which is different from zero. Consequently, equations (81·13) are equivalent to identities of the form

$$(81\cdot 14) \qquad \Psi_\rho = c_{\rho\nu}\Psi_\nu + d_{\rho\sigma}[\zeta_{i\sigma}\, \eta_i]_1^2\,,$$

where the range of $\nu$ is complementary to the range of $\rho$ on the set $\mu = 1, \ldots, p$. From Theorem 77·3, equations (81·12) showing that $\zeta_i$ and $F_{y'_i}$ are equal, and the last equations it follows that every set of admissible variations $\xi_1$, $\xi_2$, $\eta_i(x)$

which satisfies the equations $\Phi_\beta = 0$, $\Psi_\nu = 0$ will also satisfy the equations $\Phi_\beta = 0$, $\Psi_\mu = 0$, and conversely. Hence the accessory minimum problem with the reduced system of equations $\Phi_\beta = 0$, $\Psi_\nu = 0$ is equivalent to the original one. The reduced problem is normal, since a non-vanishing set $\eta_i \equiv 0$, $\zeta_i(x)$, $\epsilon_\nu$, satisfying the canonical accessory equations and making the equation

$$[\zeta_i \, \eta_i]_1^2 + \epsilon_\nu \Psi_\nu = 0$$

an identity, would be a part of a similar set $\eta_i \equiv 0$, $\zeta_i(x)$, $\epsilon_\nu$, $\epsilon_\rho = 0$ making (81·9) an identity. This last set would then be linearly expressible in terms of the sets $\eta_{i\sigma} \equiv 0$, $\zeta_{i\sigma}$, $\epsilon_{\nu\sigma}$, $\epsilon_{\rho\sigma}$, which is evidently impossible, since the determinant $|\epsilon_{\rho\sigma}|$ is different from zero.

COROLLARY 81·1. *If the matrix $\|\Psi_{\mu,1}\Psi_{\mu,2}\|$ of coefficients of $\xi_1$ and $\xi_2$ in the functions $\Psi_\mu$ is of rank two, then the corresponding matrix for the reduced problem has the same property.*

This is a consequence of the fact that the system $\Psi_\mu = 0$ and the system $\Psi_\nu = 0$, $[\zeta_{i\sigma}\eta_i]_1^2 = 0$ are equivalent by means of the relation (81·14). If one of them has no non-vanishing solution $\xi_1$, $\eta_{i1} = 0$, $\xi_2$, $\eta_{i2} = 0$, the same must be true of the other.

LEMMA 81·3. *Every minimizing set $\xi_1$, $\xi_2$, $\eta_i(x)$ for the accessory minimum problem must satisfy the accessory multiplier rule with at least one set $\zeta_i(x)$, $\epsilon_\mu$.*

To prove this, one may replace the accessory minimum problem by one which is precisely of the Bolza type. An admissible set $\xi_1(x)$, $\xi_2(x)$, $\eta_i(x)$ may be defined as one determining in the space of points $(x, \xi_1, \xi_2, \eta_i)$ a continuous curve consisting of a finite number of arcs with continuous derivatives. The problem of finding, in the class of admissible sets of this sort satisfying the conditions

$$\Phi_\beta = 0\,, \qquad \xi_1' = 0\,, \qquad \xi_2' = 0\,,$$

$$\Psi_\nu\,[\,\xi_1(x_1),\ \eta(x_1),\ \xi_2(x_2),\ \eta(x_2)\,] = 0$$

$$x_1 - x_{10} = 0 \qquad x_2 - x_{20} = 0\,,$$

one which minimizes the sum

$$2\gamma\,[\,\xi_1(x_1),\ \eta(x_1),\ \xi_2(x_2),\ \eta(x_2)\,] + \int_{x_1}^{x_2} 2\omega(x,\ \eta,\ \eta')\,dx$$

is an auxiliary problem of Bolza equivalent to the original accessory problem. When the multiplier rule of Theorem 74·1 is applied, it is found that every admissible arc for the auxiliary problem is normal and non-singular, since the reduced accessory problem of Lemma 81·2 is normal and since the arc $E$ is non-singular. The equations analogous to (74·8) and (74·9) for a minimizing arc of the auxiliary problem imply the multiplier rule for a minimizing arc of the accessory minimum problem.

Attention should be called, at this point, to the notions of conjugate solutions and conjugate systems of solutions of the canonical accessory equations. For an arbitrarily selected pair of solutions, $\eta_i$, $\zeta_i$ and $\bar{\eta}_i$, $\bar{\zeta}_i$, of these equations the expression $\eta_i \bar{\zeta}_i - \bar{\eta}_i \zeta_i$ is a constant, as one sees by differentiating this expression, applying the equations (81·5), and using a simple property of quadratic forms. If this constant is zero, the two solutions are said to be *conjugate solutions*. A *conjugate system of solutions* of the canonical accessory equations is a system of $n$ linearly independent solutions $\eta_{ik}$, $\zeta_{ik}$ $(k = 1, \ldots, n)$, every pair of which are conjugate. If a solution $\eta_i$, $\zeta_i$ is conjugate to every one of a system of conjugate solutions, it is linearly expressible in terms of the solutions of the system. The initial values $\eta_i(x_1)$, $\zeta_i(x_1)$ of such a solution are, in fact, solutions at $x = x_1$ of the $n$ linearly independent equations

$$\zeta_{ik}\eta_i - \eta_{ik}\zeta_i = 0 \qquad (k = 1, \ldots, n).$$

The $n$ linearly independent sets $\eta_{ij}(x_1)$, $\zeta_{ij}(x_1)$ $(j = 1, \ldots, n)$ are, however, also solutions, since the system $\eta_{ij}$, $\zeta_{ij}$ is a conjugate system. Hence, at $x = x_1$ there are relations of the form

$$\eta_i - \eta_{ij}c_j = 0\,, \qquad \zeta_i - \zeta_{ij}c_j = 0$$

which also hold at every value of $x$, since a solution $\eta_i - \eta_{ij}c_j$, $\zeta_i - \zeta_{ij}c_j$ of the canonical accessory equations with elements vanishing at one point vanishes identically. Thus the maximum number of linearly independent conjugate solutions is $n$.

It is easy to construct special cases of conjugate systems of solutions of the accessory equations. A necessary and sufficient condition that a system $\eta_{ij}$, $\zeta_{ij}$ form a conjugate system is that its matrix $\|A_{ij}\ B_{ij}\|$ of initial values at $x = x_0$, for example, shall be of rank $n$ and have the property that the product matrix whose elements are the sums $A_{ij}B_{ik}$ shall be symmetric. The conditions for this symmetry are the equations

$$A_{ij}B_{ik} - A_{ik}B_{ij} = 0 \qquad (j,\ k = 1, \ldots, n),$$

and these are the conditions for conjugacy of the pairs of solutions $\eta_{ij}$, $\zeta_{ij}$ and $\eta_{ik}$, $\zeta_{ik}$. Two types of conjugate systems which are sometimes useful are those which have matrices of initial values of the form $\|\delta_{ij}\ 0\|$ or $\|0\ \delta_{ij}\|$ at a point $x = x_0$, where $\|\delta_{ij}\|$ is the identity matrix. Evidently, for an arbitrarily selected value $x_0$ there exists a conjugate system $\eta_{ik}$, $\zeta_{ik}$ $(k = 1, \ldots, n)$ whose determinant $|\eta_{ik}(x_0)|$ is different from zero.

The following lemma will be useful in Section 90, below.

LEMMA 81·4. *If the end-values* $x_1$ *and* $x_2$ *for a non-singular extremal arc* E *are not conjugate, then for every admissible set of variations* $\eta_i(x)$ *satisfying the equations of variation* $\Phi_\beta = 0$ *along* E *there exists an accessory extremal* $u_i(x)$, $v_i(x)$ *such that* $u_i(x_1) = \eta_i(x_1)$, $u_i(x_2) = \eta_i(x_2)$.

The end-values $x_1$ and $x_2$ of $E$ are said to be *conjugate* if there is an accessory extremal for $E$ with elements vanishing at $x_1$ and $x_2$ but not identically zero between $x_1$ and $x_2$. Otherwise $x_1$ and $x_2$ are said to be *non-conjugate*.

If the order of abnormality of the arc $E$ on the interval $x_1x_2$ for the problem with fixed end-points is equal to $q$, there are $q$ and only $q$ linearly independent sets of multipliers $l_{0\sigma} = 0, l_{\beta\sigma}(x)$ $(\sigma = 1, \ldots, q)$ with which $E$ satisfies equations of the form (74·8), according to the definition of the order of abnormality for fixed end-points in Section 77. If $F_\sigma = l_{\beta\sigma}\phi_\beta$, then the equations

$$(81\cdot 15) \qquad [F_{\sigma y_i'}\eta_i]_1^2 = 0$$

are satisfied by every admissible set of variations $\eta_i(x)$ satisfying the equations $\Phi_\beta = 0$, as stated in Theorem 77·3. Equations (81·15) are linear in the end-values $\eta_i(x_1), \eta_i(x_2)$ and, furthermore, are independent. To see this, one can first readily verify the fact that the equations (74·8) with abnormal multipliers $l_{0\sigma} = 0, l_{\beta\sigma}$ are equivalent to equations (81·10) with arguments $x, \eta_{i\sigma} \equiv 0, \lambda_\beta = l_\beta$ in the derivatives of $\Omega$; and this in turn implies that the functions $\eta_{i\sigma} \equiv 0$, $\zeta_{i\sigma} = F_{\sigma y_i'} = \Omega_{\eta_i'}(x, 0, 0, l)$ are solutions of the canonical accessory equations. Linear dependence of the equations (81·15) would imply conditions of the form $c_\sigma\zeta_{i\sigma}(x_1) = 0$, and these would in turn imply that the solution $c_\sigma\eta_{i\sigma}, c_\sigma\zeta_{i\sigma}$ of the canonical accessory equations has all of its functions zero at $x_1$ and hence is identically zero. Since the rank of the matrix $\|\phi_{\beta y_i'}\|$ is everywhere equal to $m$, the identities $c_\sigma\zeta_{i\sigma} \equiv c_\sigma l_{\beta\sigma}\phi_{\beta y_i'} \equiv 0$ would imply that $c_\sigma l_{\beta\sigma} \equiv 0$, which contradicts the linear independence of the multipliers. Equations (81·15) are therefore independent.

It can now be verified further that, for a non-singular extremal arc $E$ with ends not conjugate and order of abnormality equal to $q$ with respect to the fixed end-point problem, the rank of a matrix

$$(81\cdot 16) \qquad \left\| \begin{matrix} u_{is}(x_1) \\ u_{is}(x_2) \end{matrix} \right\|,$$

formed with a fundamental system $u_{is}(x), v_{is}(x)$ $(s = 1, \ldots, 2n)$ of accessory extremals belonging to $E$, is always $2n - q$. The rank cannot be more than $2n - q$, since the columns of the matrix satisfy the $q$ independent equations (81·15). If it were less than $2n - q$, there would be more than $q$ linearly independent accessory extremals $u_i = u_{is}c_s$, $v_i = v_{is}c_s$ with functions $u_i$ vanishing at $x_1$ and $x_2$. Since the order of abnormality of the accessory problem along $E$ is $q$, at least one of these would have its functions $u_i$ not identically zero between $x_1$ and $x_2$, and this is impossible when the ends of $E$ are not conjugate.

The conclusion of the lemma now follows easily. Every admissible set of functions $\eta_i(x)$ satisfying the equations $\Phi_\beta = 0$ has end-values $\eta_i(x_1), \eta_i(x_2)$ satisfying the equations (81·15). The columns of the matrix (81·16) have among them $2n - q$ linearly independent solutions of equations (81·15) in terms of which all other solutions are linearly expressible. In particular, we must have $\eta_i(x_1) = c_s u_{is}(x_1), \eta_i(x_2) = c_s u_{is}(x_2)$; and the functions $u_i(x)$ of the accessory extremal $u_i = c_s u_{is}$, $v_i = c_s v_{is}$ therefore have the same end-values as the functions $\eta_i(x)$.

## CHAPTER IX

## SUFFICIENT CONDITIONS FOR A MINIMUM

**82. Statement of the sufficiency theorem.** The proof of the sufficiency theorem to be given in this chapter is an outgrowth of arguments originally made by Hestenes [38] and depends essentially upon methods which he devised. His proofs have the great advantage that they establish sufficient conditions for a normal arc $E$ of the class $\mathfrak{M}$ to be a minimizing arc, even if $E$ is not normal on every subinterval, as was assumed by earlier writers.[1] The method of Hestenes is applicable also to some abnormal cases the proofs for which can be made to involve only normal ones, as we shall see in Section 92.

In order to state the sufficiency theorem later to be proved, it is necessary first to define the four conditions I, $\mathrm{II}'_N$, III′, IV′ which are the basis of the sufficiency proof. Conditions I, II, III, IV on an arc E of the class $\mathfrak{M}$ are, re spectively, the multiplier rule of Theorem 74·1, the condition of Weierstrass of Theorem 78·1, the condition of Clebsch of Theorem 78·2, and the condition IV of Theorem 80·1. It has been shown that all of these are necessary conditions for a minimum on a normal non-singular minimizing arc $E$ without corners. An arc $E$ is said to satisfy the *strengthened condition* $II'_N$ *of Weierstrass* if the inequality

$$E(x,\ y,\ y',\ l,\ Y') > 0$$

is satisfied for every set $(x, y, y', l)$ satisfying the equations $\phi_\beta = 0$ in a neighborhood $N$ of those belonging to $E$, and for all admissible sets $(x, y, Y') \neq (x, y, y')$ and satisfying the equations $\phi_\beta = 0$. The *strengthened condition of Clebsch*, designated by III′, is the condition of Theorem 78·2 with the equality sign excluded. The *condition IV′* is the positive definiteness of the second variation $J_2(\xi, \eta)$ along $E$, as described in Section 80. The theorem to be proved can now be stated as follows:

THEOREM 82·1. SUFFICIENT CONDITIONS FOR A STRONG RELATIVE MINIMUM. *Let* E *be a normal arc, without corners, belonging to the class* $\mathfrak{M}$ *which, by definition, consists of all admissible arcs satisfying the conditions* $\phi_\beta = \psi_\mu = 0$. *If* E *satisfies the conditions* $I, II'_N, III', IV'$, *it is a non-singular extremal and there exists in* (x, y)*-space a neighborhood* F *of the arc* E *such that* J (C) > J (E) *for every arc* C *of the class* $\mathfrak{M}$ *in* F *not identical with* E *and having its end-points sufficiently near to those of E.*

It is to be noted that the theorem does not involve the assumption that $E$ is normal on every subinterval but only that $E$ is normal for the problem of Bolza under consideration. The stronger assumption is now unnecessary, as a result of

[1] See remarks on pp. 187–88.

the relatively recent work of Graves, establishing the necessity of the conditions II and III, and the necessity and sufficiency proofs of Hestenes related to the condition IV. The calculus of variations theory for a normal arc of a problem of Bolza has thus been brought to a stage comparable with that of simpler problems of the calculus of variations, as far as conditions necessary for a minimum and conditions sufficient for a minimum are concerned.

The theory when the normality of the arc $E$ is not assumed is in a much less satisfactory state. McShane [64] has recently proved, with the help of the theory of convex sets, the necessity of the multiplier rule and the conditions of Weierstrass and Clebsch, with no assumption concerning normality whatsoever. The proof is, as yet, rather complicated. Once attained, the result is not surprising, since these conditions are closely related first-order conditions. The situation with respect to a second-order condition analogous to IV seems to the writer of these pages quite different. The variety of singular arcs $E$ in the class $\mathfrak{M}$ is very great, and examples involving only a finite number of variables indicate that a necessary condition of the type of the condition IV is not provable for all cases. McShane [71, p. 529] has given an example from the calculus of variations to substantiate this statement. It is possible that conditions analogous to IV can be proved for special types of abnormal arcs $E$. McShane has also considered such cases and has found results for abnormal arcs of order one.

In order to carry through the proof of the sufficiency theorem, a number of lemmas will be developed in Sections 83, 84, and 85, below.

**83. An auxiliary theorem.** Let us consider three functions $x_1(u)$, $x_2(u)$, $a(u)$ having continuous derivatives on an interval $u' \leqq u \leqq u''$, and a one-parameter family of extremals

$$y_i = y_i(x, a), \qquad l_\beta = l_\beta(x, a) \tag{83·1}$$

such that the functions $y_i(x, a)$, $y_{ix}(x, a)$, $l_\beta(x, a)$ have continuous first partial derivatives in a neighborhood of the sets $(x, a)$ defined by the conditions

$$x_1(u) \leqq x \leqq x_2(u), \qquad a = a(u) \qquad (u' \leqq u \leqq u'').$$

The end-points *1* and *2* of the extremal arc (83·1) describe two arcs $C$ and $D$ when the parameter $u$ varies, the equations of $C$, for example, being

$$x = x_1(u), \qquad y_i = y_i[x_1(u), a(u)] \qquad (u' \leqq u \leqq u'').$$

The equations of $D$ are found by replacing $x_1(u)$ by $x_2(u)$ in these formulas. The differentials $dx$, $dy_i$ along the arcs $C$ and $D$ are defined by the equations

$$dx = x'(u)\,du\,, \qquad dy_i = y_{ix}\,dx + y_{ia}\,da\,, \tag{83·2}$$

with $x(u)$ replaced, respectively, by $x_1(u)$ and $x_2(u)$.

Along the particular extremal arc defined by a value $u$ the integral $I$ has a value

$$I(u) = \int_{x_1}^{x_2} F[x, y(x, a), y'(x, a), l(x, a)]\,dx\,,$$

whose differential with respect to $u$ is

$$dI = [F\,dx]_1^2 + da \int_{x_1}^{x_2} [F_{y_i} y_{ia} + F_{y'_i} y'_{ia}]\,dx\,.$$

By the usual integration by parts of the calculus of variations one finds further

$$dI = [F\,dx + F_{y'_i} y_{ia}\,da]_1^2\,,$$

and finally, with the help of the relations (83·2), the formula of the following theorem:

THEOREM 83·1. *The value of the integral* I, *taken along a one-parameter family of extremal arcs whose end-points* 1 *and* 2 *describe two arcs* C *and* D, *as described above, has the differential*

$$dI = [\,(F - y'_i F_{y'_i})\,dx + F_{y'_i}\,dy_i]_1^2\,, \tag{83·3}$$

*in which the arguments of* F *and its derivatives are the values* $x$, $y_i$, $y'_i$, $l_\beta$ *belonging to the extremal arc, and the differentials* $dx$, $dy_i$ *are those of the arcs* C *and* D.

The symbol $I^*$ is customarily used for the integral

$$I^* = \int [\,(F - y'_i F_{y'_i})\,dx + F_{y'_i}\,dy_i]\,.$$

By integrating equation (83·3) from $u'$ to $u''$ one obtains, then, the following corollary:

COROLLARY 83·1. *If the extremal arcs of the family (83·1) corresponding to the values* $u'$ *and* $u''$ *are* $E_{34}$ *and* $E_{56}$, *respectively, as shown in Figure 83·1 then*

$$I(E_{56}) - I(E_{34}) = I^*(D_{46}) - I^*(C_{35})\,. \tag{83·4}$$

The theorem of this section and its corollary have many applications in the theory of the calculus of variations.[2]

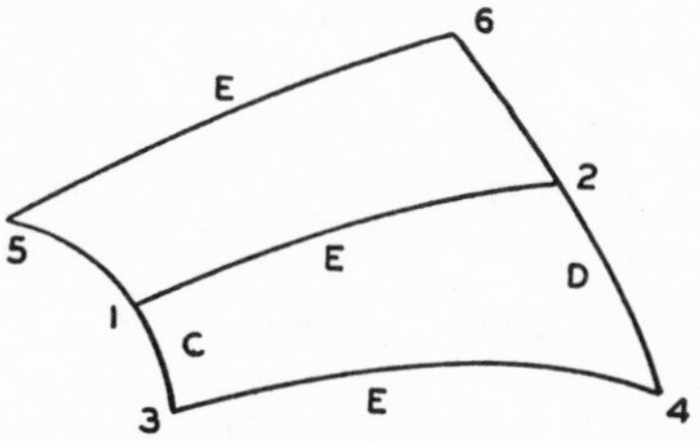


FIG. 83·1

**84. Fields and their construction.** The definition of a field to be given here is one frequently used before by Bliss[3] and others.

DEFINITION OF A FIELD. A *field* is a region $F$ of $xy$-space with which there is associated a set of slope functions and multipliers $p_i(x, y)$, $l_0 = 1$, $l_\beta(x, y)$ hav-

[2] See Bliss [17], pp. 714–23. [3] *Ibid.*, p. 730.

ing continuous first partial derivatives in F, defining elements $(x, y, p)$ which lie in the region $R_1$ and satisfy the equations $\phi_\beta = 0$ for every $(x, y)$ in F, and making the integral

$$I^* = \int [(F - p_i F_{y'_i})\, dx + F_{y'_i}\, dy_i] \tag{84·1}$$

independent of the path in F when the arguments of the function $F(x, y, y', l)$ and its derivatives are $x, y_i, p_i(x, y), l_0 = 1, l_\beta(x, y)$.

If the coefficients of the differentials in the integrand of the integral (84·1) are denoted by

$$A(x, y) = F - p_i F_{y'_i}, \qquad B_i(x, y) = F_{y'_i},$$

then one can readily prove that the equations

$$\begin{aligned} A_{y_i} - B_{ix} &= F_{y_i} - \frac{\partial}{\partial x} F_{y'_i} - p_k \frac{\partial}{\partial y_k} F_{y'_k} + p_k (B_{iy_k} - B_{ky_i}) \\ &= F_{y_i} - \frac{d}{dx} F_{y'_i} + p_k (B_{iy_k} - B_{ky_i}) \end{aligned} \tag{84·2}$$

are identities in the variables $x$ and $y$. The partial derivatives $\partial/\partial x$ and $\partial/\partial y_i$ are taken with respect to the variables $x, y_i$ which occur explicitly and in $p_i(x, y)$, $l_\beta(x, y)$, and the total derivative $d/dx = \partial/\partial x + p_i \partial/\partial y_i$ is taken in the direction satisfying the equations

$$\frac{dy_i}{dx} = p_i(x, y). \tag{84·3}$$

The conditions

$$A_{y_i} = B_{ix}, \qquad B_{iy_k} = B_{ky_i}$$

are well known to be necessary for the integral $I^*$ to be independent of the path. From these conditions it follows, with the help of the identities (84·2), that the solutions of the differential equations (84·3) are extremals, with multipliers $l_0 = 1, l_\beta(x)$ identical along them with the multipliers $l_0 = 1, l_\beta(x, y)$ of the field. The extremals so defined form an $n$-parameter family, since one and only one of them passes through each point $(x, y)$. They are called the *extremals of the field*. Since the integrand of $I^*$ reduces simply to $F$ along an extremal of the field, we find the following lemma:

LEMMA 84·1. *Every field* F *is simply covered by an* n*-parameter family of extremals defined by the differential equations (84·3). On an extremal arc of the field* $I^*(E) = I(E)$.

There are a number of methods of constructing fields, only one of which is needed for the sufficiency proofs of this chapter. It is justified by the proof of the following lemma:

LEMMA 84·2. *Let* E *be a non-singular extremal arc having a conjugate system of solutions* $U_{ik}(x), V_{ik}(x)$ $(k = 1, \ldots, n)$ *of the accessory equations along* E *with determinant* $|U_{ik}|$ *different from zero on* E. *Then* E *is an extremal of a field* F *having an* n-*parameter family of extremals*

$$y_i = Y_i(x, a_1, \ldots, a_n), \qquad z_i = Z_i(x, a_1, \ldots, a_n)$$

*containing* E *for values* (x, α) *satisfying conditions of the form*

$$x_1 \leqq x \leqq x_2, \qquad a_k = 0 \qquad (k = 1, \ldots, n).$$

*The functions* $Y_i$, $Y_{ix}$, $Z_i$, $Z_{ix}$ *have continuous first partial derivatives in a neighborhood of the values* (x, α) *belonging to* E, *and the variations of the family along* E *have the values*

$$(84\cdot4) \qquad Y_{ia_k}(x, 0) = U_{ik}(x), \qquad Z_{ia_k}(x, 0) = V_{ik}(x).$$

To prove this consider first the $2n$-parameter family of extremals

$$(84\cdot5) \qquad y_i = y_i(x, a, b), \qquad z_i = z_i(x, a, b)$$

in which the extremal arc $E$ is imbedded for values

$$x_{10} \leqq x \leqq x_{20}, \qquad a_i = a_{i0}, \qquad b_i = b_{i0} \quad (i = 1, \ldots, n)$$

and whose properties are described in Theorem 75·1. Without loss of generality it may be assumed that the constants $a_i$, $b_i$ are the initial values

$$(84\cdot6) \qquad a_i = y_i(x_0, a, b), \qquad b_i = z_i(x_0, a, b)$$

at some value $x_0$ on the $x$-interval belonging to $E$. From equations (84·6) one finds

$$(84\cdot7) \qquad \begin{aligned} \delta_{ik} &= y_{ia_k}(x_0, a, b), & 0 &= z_{ia_k}(x_0, a, b), \\ 0 &= y_{ib_k}(x_0, a, b), & \delta_{ik} &= z_{ib_k}(x_0, a, b), \end{aligned}$$

where $\delta_{ii} = 1$, $\delta_{ik} = 0$ for $i \neq k$. If we define two functions $A(\alpha)$, $B(\alpha)$ by the equations

$$(84\cdot8) \qquad \begin{aligned} 2A(\alpha) &= 2a_{i0}\alpha_i + U_{ik}(x_0)\alpha_i\alpha_k, \\ 2B(\alpha) &= 2b_{i0}\alpha_i + V_{ik}(x_0)\alpha_i\alpha_k, \end{aligned}$$

the family (84·5) with $a_i = A_{\alpha_i}$, $b_i = B_{\alpha_i}$ becomes an $n$-parameter family of extremals

$$(84\cdot9) \qquad \begin{aligned} y_i &= y_i(x, A_\alpha, B_\alpha) = Y_i(x, \alpha_1, \ldots, \alpha_n), \\ z_i &= z_i(x, A_\alpha, B_\alpha) = Z_i(x, \alpha_1, \ldots, \alpha_n) \end{aligned}$$

containing the arc $E$ for $(\alpha_1, \ldots, \alpha_n) = (0, \ldots, 0)$ and having, with respect to the parameter $\alpha_k$, the variations

$$\begin{aligned} Y_{i\alpha_k} &= y_{ia_j}U_{jk}(x_0) + y_{ib_j}V_{jk}(x_0), \\ Z_{i\alpha_k} &= z_{ia_j}U_{jk}(x_0) + z_{ib_j}V_{jk}(x_0) \end{aligned} \qquad (i = 1, \ldots, n).$$

For the arc $E$ these variations have at $x_0$ the initial values $U_{ik}(x_0)$, $V_{ik}(x_0)$ $(i = 1, \ldots, n)$, on account of the relations (84·7); and they satisfy the canonical accessory equations (75·14), as was seen in Section 75. Hence, along the arc $E$ they are identically equal to $U_{ik}(x)$, $V_{ik}(x)$ $(i = 1, \ldots, n)$, as stated in the lemma.

Since the determinant $|Y_{i\alpha_k}| = |U_{ik}(x)|$ is different from zero along $E$, the existence theorems for implicit functions tell us that there is a neighborhood $\mathfrak{F}$ of the arc $E$ in $xy$-space in which the first $n$ equations (84·9) have unique solutions $\alpha_k(x, y)$ vanishing on the arc $E$ and having continuous first partial derivatives in $\mathfrak{F}$. If the multipliers of the family (84·9) are denoted by $L_\beta(x, \alpha_1, \ldots, \alpha_n)$, then the functions

$$
\begin{aligned}
p_i(x, y) &= Y_{ix}[x, \alpha(x, y)], \\
l_\beta(x, y) &= L_\beta\,[x, \alpha(x, y)]
\end{aligned}
\tag{84·10}
$$

have continuous first partial derivatives in $\mathfrak{F}$.

It remains to show that in a sufficiently small neighborhood $\mathfrak{F}$ the integral $I^*$ formed with the slope functions and multipliers (84·9) is independent of the path, and hence that $\mathfrak{F}$ is a field. On the hyperplane $x = x_0$

$$I^* = \int F_{y_i'}\, dy_i = \int Z_i\,[x_0, \alpha(x_0, y)]\, d\,Y_i\,[x_0, \alpha(x_0, y)]\,.$$

From (84·6), (84·7), and (84·9) it follows, further, that on this hyperplane

$$
\begin{aligned}
I^* &= \int [b_{i0} + V_{ij}(x_0)\,\alpha_j]\, U_{ik}(x_0)\, d\alpha_k \\
&= \int d\,[b_{i0}U_{ik}(x_0)\,\alpha_k + \tfrac{1}{2} V_{ij}(x_0)\, U_{ik}(x_0)\,\alpha_j\alpha_k]\,.
\end{aligned}
$$

The last expression is justified by the fact that for the conjugate system $U_{ik}$, $V_{ik}$ the equations $U_{ij}V_{ik} - V_{ij}U_{ik} = 0$ are identities and the matrix $\|V_{ij}U_{ik}\|$ is, therefore, symmetric. Hence $I^*$ is independent of the path on the hyperplane $x = x_0$. An arbitrary arc $D_{46}$ in a sufficiently small neighborhood $\mathfrak{F}$ of $E$ determines a one-parameter family of extremals which cuts the hyperplane $x = x_0$ in an arc $C_{35}$, forming a configuration similar to that pictured in Figure 83·1. From Corollary 83·1 we see that

$$I^*(D_{46}) = I^*(C_{35}) + I(E_{56}) - I(E_{34})\,.$$

Each term on the right is completely determined by the end-points *4* and *6*, since $I^*$ is independent of the path on the hyperplane $x = x_0$. The integral $I^*$ is therefore independent of the path in the whole neighborhood $\mathfrak{F}$, and $\mathfrak{F}$ is a field with the slope functions and multipliers (84·10).

**85. A fundamental sufficiency theorem.** In a field the integral $I^*$ taken along an arc $C$ in $(x, y)$-space is a function of the coordinates $x_1, y_{i1}, x_2, x_{i2}$ of the end-points of $C$ only, so that the same is true of the function $w$ defined by the equation

$$w(x_1, y_{i1}, x_2, y_{i2}) = I^*(C) + g\,[x_1, y(x_1), x_2, y(x_2)]\,. \tag{85·1}$$

The sufficiency proofs to be given in later sections are based upon the following theorem:

THEOREM 85·1. A FUNDAMENTAL SUFFICIENCY THEOREM. *If an arc* E *is an extremal of a field* F *in* (x, y)*-space and satisfies the condition* $II'_N$ *of Weierstrass, and if the function* $w(x_1, y_{i1}, x_2, y_{i2})$ *defined by equation (85·1) has a proper minimum at the ends of* E *in the class of sets* $(x_1, y_{i1}, x_2, y_{i2})$ *satisfying the equations* $\psi_\mu = 0$, *then* J(E) *is a minimum in the sense described in Theorem 82·1.*

The proof of this theorem is simple. On account of the assumption that the arc $E$ satisfies the condition $II'_N$, the field $F$ can be restricted to be a neighborhood of $E$ so small that all the elements $[x, y, p(x, y), l(x, y)]$ belonging to $F$ lie in the neighborhood $N$. Then at every point $(x, y)$ of $F$ the inequality

$$E[x, y, p(x, y), l(x, y), Y'] > 0$$

holds for every admissible set $(x, y, Y') \neq (x, y, p)$ which satisfies the equations $\phi_\beta = 0$. Furthermore, we can choose a neighborhood $N$ of the ends of $E$ in the space of points $(x_1, y_{i1}, x_2, y_{i2})$ so small that $w(x_1, y_{i1}, x_2, y_{i2}) > w(E)$ for every set $(x_1, y_{i1}, x_2, y_{i2})$ in $N$ and not at the ends of $E$, where $w(E)$ represents the value of $w$ at those ends. Then, since $I^*(E) = I(E)$, by Lemma 84·1, it follows that for every arc $C$ with the properties described in Theorem 82·1

$$\begin{aligned} J(C) - J(E) &= I(C) + g(C) - I(E) - g(E) \\ &= I(C) - I^*(C) + w(C) - w(E) \\ &= \int_C E[x, y, p(x, y), l(x, y), y']\, dx \\ &\qquad\qquad + [w(C) - w(E)]\,. \end{aligned}$$

Both terms on the right are positive or zero. The integral vanishes only when $y'_i = p_i(x, y)$ everywhere on the arc $C$, in which case $C$ is an extremal of the field. When the ends of $C$ are sufficiently near to the ends of $E$ the difference $w(C) - w(E)$ is always positive unless the ends of $C$ coincide with those of $E$. The difference $J(C) - J(E)$ is, therefore, positive unless $C$ coincides with $E$, since there is one and but one solution of the equations (84·3) through an end-point of $E$. Thus the theorem is proved.

In order to determine whether or not the value $w(E)$ has the minimum property described in the theorem, one may make use of the criteria for a minimum of a function of a finite number of variables in Section 76, above. The auxiliary function analogous to the function $F$ of that section has the form $W = w + e_\mu \psi_\mu$; and its first two differentials with respect to $x_1, y_{i1}, x_2, y_{i2}$ as independent variables are

$$(85\cdot 2) \qquad dW = [(F - p_i F_{y'_i})\, dx + F_{y'_i}\, dy_i]_1^2 + dg + e_\mu d\psi_\mu\,,$$

$$(85\cdot 3) \qquad d^2W = 2\gamma[dx_1,\ \delta y(x_1),\ dx_2,\ \delta y(x_2)] + [\delta y_i \delta z_i]_1^2\,,$$

where $\delta y_i$ and $\delta z_i$ are now simply symbols for the expressions

$$(85\cdot 4) \qquad \delta y_i = dy_i - p_i dx\,, \qquad \delta z_i = dF_{y'_i} - F_{y_i} dx\,.$$

The value for $dW$ is an immediate consequence of the definitions of the invariant integral $I^*$ in (84·1) and of the function $w$ in equation (85·1). The formula for $d^2W$ can be verified with the help of the definitions of $\delta y_i$ and $\delta z_i$ in equations (85·4), the definition of the quadratic form $2\gamma$ following equation (80·5), and the easily provable equation

$$d(F - p_i F_{y'_i}) = F_x dx + F_{y_i} dy_i - p_i dF_{y'_i},$$

in which the arguments of $F$ and its derivatives are $x, y, p(x, y), l(x, y)$.

In a field such as is described in Lemma 84·2 the values of the functions $\delta y_i$, $\delta z_i$ in the formula (85·3) for $d^2W$ taken along the arc $E$ will presently be seen to be

$$\delta y_i = U_{ik}(x)\, da_k, \qquad \delta z_i = V_{ik}(x)\, da_k, \tag{85·5}$$

where the differentials

$$da_k = a_{kx} dx + a_{ky_l} dy_l \tag{85·6}$$

are the differentials of the solutions $a_k(x, y)$ of the first $n$ equations in Lemma 84·2. The first $n$ of the equations (85·5) are immediate consequences of the definition of $\delta y_i$ in (85·4) and the equations

$$y_i = Y_i[x,\ a(x,\ y)],$$

$$dy_i = Y_{ix} dx + Y_{ia_k} da_k = p_i dx + U_{ik} da_k$$

deduced with the help of equations (84·10) and (84·4). The last $n$ equations (85·5) follow from the second equation (85·4) and the identities

$$Z_i(x,\ a) = F_{y'_i}[x,\ Y(x,\ a),\ Y'(x,\ a),\ L(x,\ a)],$$

$$Z_{ix}(x,\ a) = F_{y_i}[x,\ Y(x,\ a),\ Y'(x,\ a),\ L(x,\ a)],$$

$$Z_{ix} dx + Z_{ia_k} da_k = dF_{y'_i},$$

when use is made of equations (84·4) and (84·10).

With the help of these results the following lemma can now be proved:

LEMMA 85·1. *Let* F *be a field simply covered by an* n*-parameter family of extremals*

$$y_i = Y_i(x,\ a_1,\ \ldots,\ a_n), \qquad z_i = Z_i(x,\ a_1,\ \ldots,\ a_n)$$

*containing a particular extremal arc* E *for values* $x_1 \leqq x \leqq x_2$, $a_i = 0$ *and having the variations*

$$Y_i(x,\ 0) = U_{ik}(x), \qquad Z_i(x,\ 0) = V_{ik}(x)$$

*along* E, *as described in Lemma 84·2. Then the value* w(E) *will be a proper minimum if* E *satisfies the multiplier rule of Theorem 74·1 with constants* $e_\mu$ *and if, further, at the ends of* E *and with the constants* $e_\mu$ *the condition*

$$\begin{aligned} 2\gamma[\xi,\ U_{ik}(x_1)\, a_k,\ \xi_2,\ U_{ik}(x_2)\, b_k] + U_{ij}(x_2)\, b_j V_{ik}(x_2)\, b_k \\ - U_{ij}(x_1)\, a_j V_{ik}(x_1)\, a_k > 0 \end{aligned} \tag{85.7}$$

*is satisfied for all sets* $(\xi_1, a_k, \xi_2, b_k) \neq (0, 0, 0, 0)$ *satisfying the equations*

$$\Psi_\mu[\xi_1,\ U_{ik}(x_1)a_k,\ \xi_2,\ U_{ik}(x_2)b_k] = 0\ . \tag{85·8}$$

This follows with the help of the theorems of Section 76. The expression (85·2) for $dW$ vanishes identically in $dx_1, dy_{i1}, dx_2, dy_{i2}$ when $E$ satisfies the multiplier rule with the constants $e_\mu$. The value (85·3) of the differential $d^2W$ is the expression in the first member of the inequality (85·7) when

$$\xi_1 = dx_1, \qquad a_k = [da_k]^1, \qquad \xi_2 = dx_2, \qquad b_k = [da_k]^2, \tag{85·9}$$

as one sees from equations (85·5) and (85·6). With these same substitutions the equations (85·8) become the equations $d\psi_\mu = 0$. Since the determinant $|U_{ik}(x)|$ is different from zero along $E$, the same is true of the determinant $|a_{k\gamma l}|$ for the solutions $a_k$ of the first equations (84·9). It follows that by means of equations (85·9) each set $dx_1, dy_{i1}, dx_2, dy_{i2}$ determines uniquely a set $\xi_1, a_k, \xi_2, b_k$, and conversely. From the hypotheses of the lemma it follows, then, that the quadratic form $d^2W$ is positive for all sets $(dx_1, dy_{i1}, dx_2, dy_{i2}) \neq (0, 0, 0, 0)$ satisfying the equations $d\psi_\mu = 0$, and therefore that $w(E)$ is a proper minimum.

**86. The second variation for problems with separated end-conditions satisfying also the non-tangency condition.** According to the definition in Section 69, the function $g$ and the end-conditions $\psi_\mu = 0$ for problems with separated end-conditions have the forms

$$g = g_1[x_1,\ y(x_1)] - g_2[x_2,\ y(x_2)]\,,$$

$$\psi_\rho[x_1,\ y(x_1)] = 0\,, \qquad \psi_\sigma[x_2,\ y(x_2)] = 0$$

$$(\rho = 1, \ldots, r;\ \sigma = r+1, \ldots, p)\,.$$

The arc $E$ to be considered in this section is supposed (1) to be an extremal of the class $\mathfrak{M}$ with multipliers of the form $l_0 = 1, l_\beta(x)$; (2) to satisfy the non-tangency condition; and (3) to be non-singular. The properties (1) insure the existence of the second variation along $E$. Assumption (2), concerning the non-tangency condition, implies that at the ends of $E$ the matrix

$$\|\psi_{\mu,1} + \psi_{\mu,i1}\, y_i'(x_1),\ \psi_{\mu,2} + \psi_{\mu,i2}\, y_i'(x_2)\| = \|\Psi_{\mu,1},\ \Psi_{\mu,2}\| \tag{86·1}$$

is of rank two, according to the definition in Section 69. When the end-conditions are separated, this is equivalent to saying that each of the matrices

$$\|\Psi_{\rho,1}\|, \qquad \|\Psi_{\sigma,2}\|$$

is of rank one. On account of assumption (3) concerning the non-singularity of $E$, the accessory canonical variables and equations are well defined.

The second variation is now found, without difficulty, to have the form

$$J_2(\xi,\ \eta) = 2\gamma_1[\xi_1,\ \eta(x_1)] - 2\gamma_2[\xi_2,\ \eta(x_2)] + \int_{x_1}^{x_2} 2\omega\, dx\,,$$

where $2\gamma_1$ and $2\gamma_2$ are homogeneous quadratic forms in their arguments. The accessory minimum problem has end-conditions of the form

$$\Psi_\rho[\xi_1,\ \eta(x_1)] = 0 \qquad (\rho = 1, \ldots, r),$$
$$\Psi_\sigma[\xi_2,\ \eta(x_2)] = 0 \qquad (\sigma = r+1, \ldots, p);$$

and the accessory transversality conditions are also separated into the following two groups of identities in $d\xi_1$, $d\eta_{i1}$, $d\xi_2$, $d\eta_{i2}$

$$(86\cdot 2) \qquad -\zeta_i(x_1)\, d\eta_{i1} + d\gamma_1 + \epsilon_\rho d\Psi_\rho = 0\ ,$$

$$(86\cdot 3) \qquad -\zeta_i(x_2)\, d\eta_{i2} + d\gamma_2 + \epsilon_\sigma d\Psi_\sigma = 0\ ,$$

where $\rho$ and $\sigma$ have the ranges indicated above.

It is not, in general, possible to find solutions $\eta_i$, $\zeta_i$ of the canonical accessory equations and constants $\xi_1$, $\xi_2$ which satisfy simultaneously the end-conditions $\Psi_\rho = \Psi_\sigma = 0$ and the conditions imposed by the transversality conditions (86·2) and (86·3). But we may now prove that there is a family of solutions which satisfy the end and transversality conditions at the initial point *1* of $E$, and a second family which similarly satisfies the conditions at the end-point *2* of $E$.

If derivatives with respect to the variables $\xi_1$ and $\eta_{i1}$ are indicated by subscripts 1 and $i1$, respectively, the conditions $\Psi_\rho = 0$ and (86·2) are equivalent to the $n + r + 1$ linear equations

$$\gamma_{1,1} + \epsilon_\rho \Psi_{\rho,1} = 0\ ,$$
$$(86\cdot 4) \qquad -\zeta_i(x_1) + \gamma_{1,i1} + \epsilon_\rho \Psi_{\rho,i1} = 0\ ,$$
$$\Psi_\rho = 0$$

in the $2n + r + 1$ variables $\xi_1$, $\eta_i(x_1)$, $\zeta_i(x_1)$, $\epsilon_\rho$. Equations (86·4) are independent, because the rank of the matrix of coefficients of the functions $\Psi_\rho$ is $r$ and the non-tangency condition requires at least one of the coefficients $\Psi_{\rho,1}$ to be different from zero. Hence there are exactly $n$ linearly independent sets of solutions of equations (86·4) of the form

$$\xi_{1k},\ \eta_{ik}(x_1),\ \zeta_{ik}(x_1),\ \epsilon_{\rho k} \qquad (k = 1, \ldots, n).$$

One may verify, with the help of the non-tangency condition and the independence of the functions $\Psi_\rho$, that no non-vanishing set of the form $(\xi_1, \eta_i, \zeta_i, \epsilon_\rho) = (\xi_1, 0, 0, \epsilon_\rho)$ can satisfy the equations (86·4), and hence that the sets $\eta_{ik}(x_1)$, $\zeta_{ik}(x_1)$ $(k = 1, \ldots, n)$ are linearly independent. As initial values they define a system of $n$ linearly independent solutions $\eta_{ik}(x)$, $\zeta_{ik}(x)$ of the accessory canonical equations. These solutions form a conjugate system, since, when $(\xi_1, \eta_i, \zeta_i, \epsilon_\rho)$ and $(\bar\xi_1, \bar\eta_i, \bar\zeta_i, \bar\epsilon_\rho)$ are two solutions of equations (86·4), it follows from those equations that at $x = x_1$

$$-\bar\eta_i\zeta_i + \bar\xi_1\gamma_{1,1} + \bar\eta_i\gamma_{1,i1} = 0\ ,$$
$$-\eta_i\bar\zeta_i + \xi_1\bar\gamma_{1,1} + \eta_i\bar\gamma_{1,i1} = 0$$

in which strokes indicate always stroked arguments. But with the help of a well-known property of quadratic forms it is evident that these relations imply the equation $-\bar{\eta}_i \zeta_i + \bar{\zeta}_i \eta_i = 0$, which shows that the two solutions $\eta_i, \zeta_i$ and $\bar{\eta}_i, \bar{\zeta}_i$ are conjugate.

In the same manner, one may determine a second conjugate system of solutions $u_{ik}(x)$, $v_{ik}(x)$ $(k = 1, \ldots, n)$ of the canonical accessory equations, corresponding to a set

$$\xi_{2k}, \; u_{ik}(x_2), \; v_{ik}(x_2), \; \epsilon_{\sigma k} \qquad (k = 1, \ldots, n)$$

of $n$ linearly independent solutions of the set of conditions found by taking the equations $\Psi_\sigma = 0$ with the further conditions implied by the identity (86·3).

If in the expressions

$$(86{\cdot}5) \qquad \begin{aligned} \xi_1 &= \xi_{1j}\, a_j, \quad \eta_i(x) = a_j\, \eta_{ij}(x) & (x_1 \leqq x \leqq x_3), \\ \xi_2 &= \xi_{2k}\, b_k, \quad u_i(x) = b_k\, u_{ik}(x) & (x_3 \leqq x \leqq x_2) \end{aligned}$$

the constants $a$, $b$ satisfy the conditions

$$(86{\cdot}6) \qquad a_j\, \eta_{ij}(x_3) = b_k\, u_{ik}(x_3)$$

at an arbitrarily selected value $x_3$ on the interval $x_1x_2$, then the set $\xi_1$, $\xi_2$, $\eta_i(x)$ defined by the equations (86·5) on the whole interval $x_1x_2$ is a set of admissible variations along $E$. The value of $J_2(\xi, \eta)$ on this set is

$$(86{\cdot}7) \qquad \begin{aligned} &2\gamma_1[\xi_1, \eta(x_1)] + \int_{x_1}^{x_3} 2\omega(x, \eta, \eta')\, dx \\ &- 2\gamma_2[\xi_2, u(x_2)] + \int_{x_3}^{x_2} 2\omega(x\;\; u, u')\, dx . \end{aligned}$$

In order to evaluate the sum of the first two terms, it should first be noted that by means of equations (81·4) the functions $\eta_i, \zeta_i$ determine multipliers $\lambda_\beta(x)$ with which the functions $\eta_i$ satisfy the accessory equations (81·1) and that the integrand of the first integral in the last expression can therefore be changed to $2\Omega(x, \eta, \eta', \lambda)$ by adding the sum $\lambda_\beta \Phi_\beta$. By means of the relation

$$(86{\cdot}8) \qquad 2\Omega = \eta_i \Omega_{\eta_i} + \eta_i' \Omega_{\eta_i'} + \lambda_\beta \Omega_{\lambda_\beta},$$

in which $\Omega_{\lambda_\beta} = \Phi_\beta = 0$, and with the help of the usual integration by parts, the first two terms in the expression (86·7) are then seen to have the value

$$(86{\cdot}9) \qquad -\zeta_i(x_1)\,\eta_i(x_1) + 2\gamma_1 + \epsilon_\rho \Psi_\rho + \zeta_i(x_3)\,\eta_i(x_3),$$

in which the terms $\epsilon_\rho \Psi_\rho$, vanishing by (86·4), have been arbitrarily added. The first equation (86·2) is an identity in the variables $d\xi_1$, $d\eta_{i1}$ and will continue to be true if these differentials are replaced by $\xi_1$, $\eta_{i1}$. It follows that the first three terms in (86·9) add up to be zero, so that the value of the first two terms in the expression (86·7) for $J_2$ is the sum $\eta_i(x_3)\zeta_i(x_3)$. Similarly, it can be shown that the last two terms in (86·7) have the value $-v_i(x_3)\,u_i(x_3)$, so that

$$(86\cdot10)\qquad \begin{aligned} J_2 &= \eta_i(x_3)\,\zeta_i(x_3) - u_i(x_3)\,v_i(x_3) \\ &= \zeta_i(x_3)\,u_i(x_3) - \eta_i(x_3)\,v_i(x_3), \end{aligned}$$

since equations (86·6) at $x = x_3$ imply that $\eta_i(x_3) = u_i(x_3)$. The last expression is the value of the second variation along the set of admissible variations $\xi_1, \xi_2, \eta_i(x)$ defined on the whole interval $x_1x_2$ by the equations (86·5) and (86·6). The value (86·10) of $J_2$ must therefore be $\geqq 0$ when $J_2$ is non-negative. We can now state the following theorem:

THEOREM 86·1. *Consider a problem of Bolza with separated end-conditions, and let* E *be an extremal arc of the class* $\mathfrak{M}$ *for the problem, with multipliers of the form* $l_0 = 1, l_\beta(x)$. *Furthermore, suppose that* E *satisfies the non-tangency condition and is non-singular. Then there exist two conjugate systems of solutions of the accessory canonical equations,* $\eta_{ij}, \zeta_{ij}$ *and* $u_{ik}, v_{ik}$, *determined by the end and transversality conditions at the end-points* 1 *and* 2 *of* E, *respectively. If the second variation* $J_2(\xi, \eta)$ *along* E *is non-negative, the bilinear form*

$$(86\cdot11)\qquad a_j(\zeta_{ij}u_{ik} - \eta_{ij}v_{ik})\,b_k$$

*is non-negative for all non-vanishing sets of constants* $a_j, b_k$ *which satisfy the equations*

$$(86\cdot12)\qquad a_j\,\eta_{ij}(x_3) = b_k\,u_{ik}(x_3)$$

*at an arbitrarily selected value* $x_3$ *on the interval* $x_1x_2$.

The theorem is an immediate consequence of the arguments in the preceding paragraphs, and in particular of the value (86·10) of the second variation.

COROLLARY 86·1. *If in Theorem 86·1 the second variation is positive definite and the arc* E *normal, then the two conjugate systems of the theorem can be chosen so that the matrix of the bilinear form (86·11) is the identity matrix, and the bilinear form* $a_ib_i$ *will be non-negative for all non-vanishing sets* $a_i, b_i$ *satisfying conditions the form (86·12).*

To prove this we note first that the elements of the matrix in (86·11) are all constants, as was shown in the second paragraph following Lemma 81·3. Furthermore, the determinant of the matrix is not zero under the hypotheses of the corollary. Otherwise there would be a set of constants $a_j$, not all zero, such that the solution $\eta_i = a_j\eta_{ij}$, $\zeta_i = a_j\zeta_{ij}$ of the accessory canonical equations would be conjugate to each of the $n$ solutions $u_{ik}, v_{ik}$ and would therefore be linearly expressible in terms of them in the form $b_ku_{ik}, b_kv_{ik}$. Thus the solution $\eta_i, \zeta_i$ would satisfy all the accessory end and transversality conditions; and with suitable constants $\xi_1, \xi_2$, the set $\xi_1, \xi_2, \eta_i(x)$ would make $J_2$ vanish. From the positive definiteness of $J_2$ it would follow that $\eta_i \equiv 0$, which is impossible, since the assumption that the arc $E$ is normal implies that there is no non-vanishing solution $\eta_i$, $\zeta_i$ of the canonical accessory equations satisfying the accessory end and transversality conditions and having $\eta_i \equiv 0$.

Since the determinant of the matrix in (86·11) is different from zero, the conjugate system $\eta_{ij}$, $\zeta_{ij}$ can be transformed by a linear transformation with constant coefficients into a new system which with $u_{ik}$, $v_{ik}$ has the identity matrix as the matrix in (86·11). The value $a_i b_i$ of the bilinear form in (86·11) must be non-negative for all non-vanishing sets of constants $a_i$, $b_i$ satisfying conditions of the form (86·12), on account of the positive definiteness of the second variation.

**87. The sufficiency theorem for problems with separated end-conditions satisfying also the non-tangency condition.** To the hypotheses of the sufficiency theorem, Theorem 82·1, we now add the assumptions that the problem of Bolza under consideration has separated end-conditions and that the arc $E$ to be studied satisfies the non-tangency condition. These restrictions will be removed in later sections. The first of the lemmas of this section gives a simple algebraic result. The essential remaining step in the proof of the sufficiency theorem is contained in the Lemma 87·2 due to Hestenes.

LEMMA 87·1. *If an admissible arc* E *satisfies the strengthened Clebsch condition III′ with a set of multipliers* $l_0$, $l_\beta(x)$, *then the determinant (74·12) formed with these multipliers is different from zero at every point of* E.

Otherwise at some value $x$ there would be constants $\pi_k$, $\lambda_\gamma$, not all zero, satisfying the linear equations

$$F_{y_i' y_k'}\pi_k + \lambda_\gamma \phi_{\gamma y_i'} = 0 \ ,$$

$$\phi_{\beta y_k'}\pi_k = 0 \ .$$

The constants $\pi_k$ could not all be zero, since the matrix $\|\phi_{\gamma y_i'}\|$ has rank $m$ and the equations therefore imply that all the numbers $\lambda_\gamma$ are zero when the constants $\pi_k$ all vanish. The equations also have as consequences

$$F_{y_i' y_k'}\pi_i \pi_k = 0 \ , \qquad \phi_{\beta y_k'}\pi_k = 0 \ ,$$

which is impossible when the condition III′ is satisfied along $E$.

LEMMA 87·2. *Let* E *be an arc satisfying the hypotheses of Theorem 86·1 and Corollary 86·1. Then there exists a conjugate system of solutions* $U_{ik}(x)$, $V_{ik}(x)$ $(k = 1, \ldots, n)$ *of the canonical accessory equations along* E, *with determinant* $|U_{ik}(x)| \neq 0$ *on the interval* $x_1x_2$ *belonging to* E, *and such that the inequalities*

$$(87\cdot1)\qquad \begin{aligned} 2\gamma_1[\xi_1,\ U_{ij}(x_1)a_j] - U_{ij}(x_1)a_j V_{ik}(x_1)a_k > 0\ , \\ -2\gamma_2[\xi_2,\ U_{ij}(x_2)b_j] + U_{ij}(x_2)b_j V_{ik}(x_2)b_k > 0 \end{aligned}$$

*hold for all non-vanishing sets* $(\xi_1, a)$, $(\xi_2, b)$ *satisfying the equations*

$$(87\cdot2)\qquad \begin{aligned} \Psi_\rho[\xi_1,\ U_{ij}(x_1)a_j] = 0\ , \\ \Psi_\sigma[\xi_2,\ U_{ij}(x_2)b_j] = 0\ , \end{aligned}$$

*the notations being those in (80·5) and (71·7).*

To prove the lemma consider the conjugate systems $\eta_{ij}$, $\zeta_{ij}$ and $u_{ik}$, $v_{ik}$ in Corollary 86·1, which have the property

$$\zeta_{ij}u_{ik} - \eta_{ij}v_{ik} = \delta_{jk} . \tag{87·3}$$

Then the system which will be proved to have the properties of the lemma is

$$U_{ik} = \eta_{ik} + u_{ik} , \qquad V_{ik} = \zeta_{ik} + v_{ik} . \tag{87·4}$$

This system is evidently a conjugate system, since

$$V_{ij}U_{ik} - U_{ij}V_{ik} = (\zeta_{ij}\eta_{ik} - \eta_{ij}\zeta_{ik}) + (\zeta_{ij}u_{ik} - \eta_{ij}v_{ik}) + (v_{ij}\eta_{ik} - u_{ij}\zeta_{ik}) + (v_{ij}u_{ik} - u_{ij}v_{ik}) .$$

The first and fourth terms on the right are zero because $\eta_{ij}$, $\zeta_{ij}$ and $u_{ik}$, $v_{ik}$ are conjugate systems, and the second and third cancel because the matrix in (86·11) is now the identity matrix.

The determinant $|U_{ik}(x)|$ is different from zero on the interval $x_1x_2$. Otherwise there would be a value $x_3$ and a set of constants $a_j$, not all zero, such that

$$U_{ij}(x_3)\, a_j = \eta_{ij}(x_3)\, a_j + u_{ij}(x_3)\, a_j = 0 .$$

The set $(a_j, b_k) = (a_j, -a_k)$ would then satisfy the equations (86·12) at $x = x_3$ and would give the bilinear form (86·11) the negative value $-a_ja_j$, contrary to the property of this form described in Corollary 86·1.

It remains to show that the conditions (87·1) are satisfied. It is only necessary to prove the first of these inequalities, subject to the first condition (87·2), since the proof of the second is similar. To do this we use the notations

$$\eta_i = \eta_{ik}a_k , \qquad \zeta_i = \zeta_{ik}a_k ,$$

$$u_i = u_{ik}a_k , \qquad v_i = v_{ik}a_k ,$$

$$U_i = U_{ik}a_k , \qquad V_i = V_{ik}a_k .$$

The values $\xi_1$, $U_i(x_1)$ satisfy the first set of equations (87·2) by hypothesis. Because of the non-tangency condition it is possible to find auxiliary constants $(\zeta_{i1}, \epsilon_\rho)$ which with $(\xi_1, \eta_{i1}) = [\xi_1, U_i(x_1)]$ satisfy equations (86·4). For convenience in making the proof we may use the notations $\zeta_{i1} = \overline{V}_i(x_1)$ for the first $n$ of these new constants. Let $\bar{\eta}_i(x)$, $\bar{\zeta}_i(x)$ be the solution of the canonical accessory equations which has initial values at $x_1$ defined by the equations

$$\begin{aligned} \eta_i(x_1) + \bar{\eta}_i(x_1) &= U_i(x_1) , \\ \zeta_i(x_1) + \bar{\zeta}_i(x_1) &= \overline{V}_i(x_1) . \end{aligned} \tag{87·5}$$

Then $\bar{\eta}_i$, $\bar{\zeta}_i$ also satisfy equations (86·4) with suitable constants $\bar{\xi}_1$, $\bar{\epsilon}_\rho$, since these equations are linear. It follows that there are constants $\bar{a}_k$ such that

$$\bar{\eta}_i(x) = \eta_{ik}(x)\,\bar{a}_k , \qquad \bar{\zeta}_i(x) = \zeta_{ik}(x)\,\bar{a}_k .$$

From the homogeneity of $2\gamma_1$, equations (86·4) with $[\xi_1, \eta_i(x_1), \zeta_i(x_1)] = [\xi_1, U_i(x_1), \overline{V}_i(x_1)]$ and suitable values of the constants $\epsilon_\rho$, and further from equations (87·4) and (87·5), we find that the first member of the first inequality (87·1) has the value

$$\xi_1\gamma_{1,1} + U_i(x_1)\gamma_{1,i1} - U_i(x_1)V_i(x_1) = \overline{V}_i(x_1)U_i(x_1) - U_i(x_1)V_i(x_1)$$
$$= (\zeta_i + \overline{\zeta}_i)(\eta_i + \overline{\eta}_i) - (\eta_i + \overline{\eta}_i)(\zeta_i + v_i),$$

in which $x = x_1$ everywhere. From equations (87·4) and (87·5) it is clear that $\overline{\eta}_i(x_1) = u_i(x_1)$, so that the last expression is equal to

$$(\zeta_i u_i - \eta_i v_i) + (\overline{\zeta}_i u_i - \overline{\eta}_i v_i) + (\overline{\zeta}_i \eta_i - \overline{\eta}_i \zeta_i) = a_i a_i + \bar{a}_i a_i \, .$$

The two terms on the right are the values of the first two parentheses, by equations (87·3); and the third parenthesis vanishes since the solutions $\eta_i$, $\zeta_i$ and $\overline{\eta}_i$, $\overline{\zeta}_i$ are members of the same conjugate system. The sum $\bar{a}_i a_i$ is positive or zero because of the equations

$$\eta_{ij}(x_1)\bar{a}_j = \overline{\eta}_i(x_1) = u_i(x_1) = u_{ik}(x_1)a_k$$

and the property of the quadratic form (86·11) stated in Corollary 86·1. The constants $a_i$ are not all zero, since otherwise the first equations (87·2) and the non-tangency condition would imply also $\xi_1 = 0$, contrary to hypothesis. Consequently, the first inequality (87·1) is valid, and the proof of Lemma 87·2 may be regarded as complete.

It is now possible to conclude the proof that the hypotheses of the sufficiency theorem, Theorem 82·1, justify its conclusion for the case when the end-conditions of the problem of Bolza are separated and the non-tangency condition is satisfied. An admissible arc without corners which satisfies conditions I and III′ with a set of multipliers $l_0 = 1$, $l_\beta(x)$, $e_\mu$ must be a non-singular extremal arc, according to Lemma 87·1, Corollary 74·3, and the definition of an extremal in Section 75. The condition IV′ and the non-tangency condition, in addition to the others, imply the existence of a conjugate system of solutions $U_{ik}(x)$, $V_{ik}(x)$ $(k = 1, \dots, n)$ of the canonical accessory equations along $E$ with determinant $|U_{ik}(x)|$ different from zero on the interval $x_1x_2$ belonging to $E$, and satisfying the inequalities (87·1) under the conditions (87·2), according to Lemma 87·2. In the field constructed with this conjugate system and imbedding the non-singular extremal arc $E$, as described in Lemma 84·2, the function $w(x_1, y_{i1}, x_2, y_{i2})$ defined in (85·1) has a minimum at the ends of $E$. This follows from Lemmas 85·1 and 87·2, since for the case of separated end-conditions the quadratic form in the condition (85·7) is the sum of the first members of the inequalities (87·1) and the conditions (85·8) are equivalent to the conditions (87·2). From these results and the condition $\text{II}'_N$, assumed in Theorem 82·1 to hold along $E$, it is clear that all of the hypotheses of Theorem 85·1, the fundamental sufficiency theorem, are satisfied by the arc $E$; and the conclusion of Theorem 82·1 is therefore justified.

**88. Sufficiency theorems for problems with end-conditions unrestricted.** It was shown in Section 69 that every problem of Bolza with differential equations, end-conditions, and sum $J$ in the usual forms (69·2), (69·3), and (69·4) is equivalent to another similar problem of Bolza having separated end-conditions and satisfying the non-tangency condition. The differential and end-conditions for this second problem are shown in (69·10). We may designate these two problems by the letters $P$ and $Q$, respectively. The purpose of this section is to show that the two problems are equivalent and that, if the hypotheses of the sufficiency theorem, Theorem 82·1, hold for problem $P$, they will also hold for problem $Q$. Thus the sufficiency theorem which was found in the last section for a problem like $Q$, having separated end-conditions and satisfying the non-tangency condition, will also be proved for problem $P$.

The arcs involved in problem $Q$ are defined by functions

$$y_i(x), \; y_{n+\alpha}(x) \qquad (x_1 \leqq x \leqq x_2;\; i = 1, \ldots, n;\; \alpha = 1, \ldots, n+2).$$

The region for $Q$ analogous to $R_1$ for $P$ is the totality of $(4n + 5)$-dimensional sets

$$(x,\; y_i,\; y_{n+\alpha},\; y_i',\; y_{n+\alpha}')$$

for which $(x, y, y')$ is in $R_1$ and the $(2n + 2)$-dimensional set $(y_{2n+1}, y_i, y_{2n+2}, y_{n+i})$ is in the region $R_2$ for $P$. The region for $Q$ analogous to $R_2$ for $P$ is the totality of $(4n + 6)$-dimensional sets

$$[x_1,\; y_i(x_1),\; y_{n+\alpha}(x_1),\; x_2,\; y_i(x_2),\; y_{n+\alpha}(x_2)]$$

for which the sets

$$[y_{2n+1}(x_1),\; y_i(x_1),\; y_{2n+2}(x_1),\; y_{n+i}(x_1)]$$

are in $R_1$. With this understanding about regions it is provable that every admissible arc $C$ satisfying the conditions $\phi_\beta = \psi_\mu = 0$ for the problem $P$ defines uniquely an admissible arc $D$ satisfying the corresponding conditions for the problem $Q$, and conversely. Furthermore, the sums $J$ for the two problems have equal values on corresponding arcs, so that the two minimum problems are clearly equivalent.

It remains to show that on an arc $C$ of the class $\mathfrak{M}$ the hypotheses of the sufficiency theorem of Section 82 for problem $P$ imply the analogous hypotheses on the corresponding arc $D$ for the problem $Q$, and vice versa. The functions involved in the multiplier rules for the two problems have the forms

$$F = l_0 f + l_\beta \phi_\beta ,$$

$$G = l_0 f + l_\beta \phi_\beta + l_{m+\alpha}\, y_{n+\alpha}' , \tag{88·1}$$

$$(\beta = 1, \ldots, m;\; \alpha = 1, \ldots, n+2),$$

respectively. When the multiplier rules themselves are formulated with these functions, it is found that, if an arc $D$ for the problem $Q$ satisfies the multiplier rule for that problem, then a set of multipliers is uniquely determined with which the corresponding arc $C$ satisfies the multiplier rule for the problem $P$, and conversely. Furthermore, if the multipliers are abnormal in one case, they are so in the other. Thus the hypothesis $I$ and normality for an arc $C$ imply the analogous properties for the corresponding arc $D$.

The Weierstrass $E$-functions and the quadratic forms involved in the Clebsch conditions for the two problems can easily be proved identical, so that the conditions $II'_N$ and III′ for one problem imply the analogous conditions for the other.

The second variations along corresponding arcs $C$ and $D$ for the two problems are equal. This can be seen from the formula (80·3). The terms in parenthesis and the integrand function $2\omega$ for the problem $Q$ reduce to those for problem $P$ with the help of equations (69·10) and the expressions (88·1). For the problem $Q$ the quadratic form $2q$ has the arguments $dy_{2n+1}(x_1)$, $dy_i(x_1)$, $dy_{2n+2}(x_1)$, $dy_{n+i}(x_1)$. With the help of equations (69·10) these are seen to be equal, respectively, to the arguments $dx_1$, $dy_i(x_1)$, $dx_2$, $dy_i(x_2)$ for the problem $P$. A similar remark holds for the quadratic form $2q_\mu$. Finally, the equations of variation for the problem $Q$ are

$$\Phi_\beta = 0\,, \qquad \eta'_{n+a} = 0\,,$$

$$\psi_{\mu,1}\eta_{2n+1}(x_1) + \psi_{\mu,i1}[y'_{i1}\xi_1 + \eta_i(x_1)] + \psi_{\mu,2}\eta_{2n+2}(x_1) + \psi_{\mu,i2}\,\eta_{n+i}(x_1) = 0\,,$$

$$\eta_{2n+1}(x_1) - \xi_1 = 0\,, \qquad \eta_{2n+2}(x_2) - \xi_2 = 0\,,$$

$$\eta_{n+i}(x_2) - \eta_i(x_2) - y'_{i2}\xi_2 = 0\,.$$

These are formed from equations (69·10) as the functions $\Phi_\beta$ and $\Psi_\mu$ in (71·5) and (71·7) are formed from $\phi_\beta$ and $\psi_\mu$. They are equivalent to the equations of variation $\Phi_\beta = \Psi_\mu = 0$ for the problem $P$. Thus the condition IV′ for the problem $P$ implies the analogous condition for the problem $Q$, and vice versa. The sufficiency theorem of Section 82 is therefore proved.

The first three sufficiency theorems indicated in the table of Section 17 are also applicable to the problems of Bolza discussed in the present section, provided that they are applied to arcs $E$ which are normal and without corners. The theorem in the third row has just been established. The theorem in the second row, which states that the conditions I, $\mathrm{II}_N$, IV′, $E$ non-singular are sufficient for a minimum, is a consequence of the following lemma:

LEMMA 88·1. *The conditions $II'_N$ and $III'$ are equivalent to the conditions $II_N$ and* E *non-singular.*

It is evident, as a result of the arguments in the first paragraphs of Section 87, that the conditions $\mathrm{II}'_N$ and III′ imply $\mathrm{II}_N$ and $E$ non-singular. We can prove[4] that the conditions $\mathrm{II}_N$ and $E$ non-singular imply $\mathrm{II}'_N$ by showing that at a set $(x, y, y', l, Y')_0$, where

$$\phi_\beta(x,\ y,\ y') = 0\,, \qquad \phi_\beta(x,\ y,\ Y') = 0 \qquad E(x,\ y,\ y',\ l,\ Y') = 0\,,$$

[4] Hestenes and Reid [62].

we must have $Y_0' = y_0'$. At such a set the $E$-function with the arguments $(x_0, y_0, y', l, Y_0')$ must have a minimum at the values $y_0'$, $l_0$ relative to all the sets $y'$, $l$ which satisfy the equations $\phi_\beta(x_0, y_0, y') = 0$, on account of the condition $\mathrm{II}_N$. According to the results of Section 76, there must be a function $E + \lambda_\beta \phi_\beta$ whose derivatives with respect to $y_i'$ and $l_\beta$ all vanish at the point $(x, y, y', l, Y')_0$. At this point, therefore, we must have

$$-(Y_k' - y_k')F_{y_i'y_k'} + \lambda_\beta \phi_{\beta y_i'} = 0\ ,$$

$$-(Y_k' - y_k')\phi_{\alpha y_k'} = 0\ .$$

This is impossible unless $Y_0' = y_0'$, since the determinant of coefficients is different from zero on account of the presupposed non-singularity of the arc $E$.

To prove that $\mathrm{II}_N$ and the non-singularity of the arc $E$ imply III′, we note first that $\mathrm{II}_N$ implies III, as in Section 78. Let $\pi_0$ be a set of values $(\pi_{10}, \ldots, \pi_{n0})$ satisfying the equations

$$(88\cdot 2) \qquad \phi_{\beta y_i'}\pi_i = 0\ , \qquad F_{y_i'y_k'}\pi_i\pi_k = 0\ .$$

On account of the condition III it is evident that the quadratic form has a minimum at $\pi_0$ in the class of sets $\pi$ satisfying the first equations (88·2). Hence, by results of Section 76 again, there must be a set of multipliers $\lambda_\beta$ such that the function

$$F_{y_i'y_k'}\pi_i\pi_k + \lambda_\beta \phi_{\beta y_i'}\pi_i$$

has all of its derivatives zero at $\pi_0$. Hence at $\pi_0$

$$F_{y_i'y_k'}\pi_k + \lambda_\beta \phi_{\beta y_i'} = 0\ ,$$

$$\phi_{\alpha y_k'}\pi_k = 0\ ;$$

and we see, since the arc $E$ is non-singular, that the only set of values which can satisfy the equations (88·2) is $\pi_0 = 0$. This completes the proof of the lemma.

An arc $E$ of the class $\mathfrak{M}$ is said to make $J(E)$ a *weak relative minimum* if there is a neighborhood $\mathsf{N}$ of the sets

$$(88\cdot 3) \qquad (x,\ y,\ y')$$

belonging to $E$ such that $J(C) > J(E)$ for every arc $C$ of the class $\mathfrak{M}$ not identical with $E$, having all of its elements (88·3) in $\mathsf{N}$, and having its end points sufficiently near to those of $E$.

THEOREM 88·1. *For a normal arc* E *without corners in the class* $\mathfrak{M}$ *the conditions I, III′, IV′ imply that* J(E) *is a weak relative minimum.*

We may prove the theorem first for a problem with separated end-conditions, and this result may then be extended to the more general case by the arguments in the first three paragraphs of this section. The reasoning of Section 87 is effective with the addition of a proof that there is a neighborhood $\mathsf{N}$ of the sets $(x, y, y')$ on $E$ such that the condition

$$(88\cdot 4) \qquad E[x,\ y,\ p(x,\ y),\ l(x,\ y),\ Y'] > 0$$

holds for all admissible sets $(x, y, Y') \neq (x, y, p)$ in $N$ satisfying the equations $\phi_\beta(x, y, Y') = 0$, where $p(x, y)$ and $l(x, y)$ are the slope functions and multipliers of the field constructed in Section 87 with the conjugate system of Lemma 87·2. With the help of Taylor's formula with integral form of remainder the function (88·4) can be expressed in the form

$$(88\cdot5) \qquad \pi_i\pi_k\int_0^1 (1-\theta)F_{y_i'y_k'}[x,\ y,\ p+\theta(Y'-p),\ l]\,d\theta$$

with $\pi_i = Y_i' - p_i$; and, since the sets $(x, y, p)$ and $(x, y, Y')$ satisfy the equations $\phi_\beta = 0$, we have

$$(88\cdot6) \qquad 0 = \pi_i\int_0^1 \phi_{\beta y_i'}[x,\ y,\ p+\theta(Y'-p)]\,d\theta\,.$$

According to the condition III′, the quadratic form (88·5) is positive for all sets $(x, y, Y', \pi)$ with $(x, y, Y')$ on the arc $E$, satisfying the equations (88·6), and with $\pi_i\pi_i = 1$. As will be shown in the next paragraph, there is then a neighborhood $N$ of the sets $(x, y, Y')$ belonging to $E$ such that the quadratic form (88·5) is positive, and the condition (88·4) therefore satisfied for all sets $(x, y, Y')$ in $N$ and sets $\pi \neq 0$ satisfying equations (88·6).

To prove the existence of the neighborhood $N$ we note first that the totality of sets $(x, y, Y', \pi)$ with $(x, y, Y')$ on $E$, satisfying the equations (88·6) and having $\pi_i\pi_i = 1$, is a bounded and closed set $S$. There is therefore a neighborhood $S_\epsilon$ such that the expression (88·5) is still positive for all sets $(x, y, Y', \pi)$ in $S_\epsilon$ satisfying the equations (88·6) and with $\pi_i\pi_i = 1$. By an indirect proof it may be shown that there is a neighborhood $N$ of the sets $(x, y, Y')$ on $E$ such that the sets $(x, y, Y', \pi)$ with $(x, y, Y')$ in $N$, satisfying the equations (88·6) and having $\pi_i\pi_i = 1$, are all in $S_\epsilon$.

**89. The second variation for problems with fixed end-points.** In this section two lemmas will be established which will be of use in Section 90. The accessory problem of minimizing the second variation $J_2(\xi, \eta)$ along a normal non-singular minimizing arc $E$ without corners was formulated in Section 81. In the present section we shall study the analogous problem of minimizing the integral

$$I_2(\eta) = \int_{x_1}^{x_2} 2\omega(x,\ \eta,\ \eta')\,dx$$

of the second variation in the class $H$ of all admissible variations $\eta_i(x)$ satisfying the equations of variation $\Phi_\beta = 0$ and the end-conditions $\eta_i(x_1) = \eta_i(x_2) = 0$. The end-values $x_1$ and $x_2$ are now supposed fixed. The arc $E$, along which the integral $I_2$ is taken, is supposed to satisfy the conditions I and III′ with a set of multipliers of the form $l_0 = 1$, $l_\beta(x)$.

A value $x_3$ on the interval $x_1 < x_3 \leqq x_2$ is said to be *conjugate to* $x_1$ for this problem if there exists a solution $u_i(x)$, $v_i(x)$ of the accessory canonical equations (81·5) with elements $u_i(x)$ vanishing at $x_1$ and $x_3$ but not all identically zero on the interval $x_1x_3$.

LEMMA 89·1. *A necessary and sufficient condition for* $I_2(\eta)$ *to be positive definite in the class* H *of admissible variations* $\eta_i(x)$ *satisfying the conditions*

$$(89\cdot 1) \qquad \eta_i(x_1) = 0\,, \qquad \eta_i(x_2) = 0\,, \qquad \Phi_\beta = 0$$

*is that there exists a conjugate system* $U_{ik}(x), V_{ik}(x)$ $(k = 1, \ldots, n)$ *of solutions of the accessory equations with* $|U_{ik}(x)| \neq 0$ *on the interval* $x_1x_2$.

To prove the sufficiency of the condition one finds readily, in the first place, that the $E$-function for the integral $I_2(\eta)$ has the form

$$E_\omega(x,\ \eta,\ \pi,\ \lambda,\ \eta') = F_{y_i'y_k'}(\eta_i' - \pi_i)(\eta_k' - \pi_k)$$

with $(x, \eta, \eta')$ and $(x, \eta, \pi)$ satisfying the equations

$$0 = \Phi_\beta(x,\ \eta,\ \eta') - \Phi_\beta(x,\ \eta,\ \pi) = \phi_{\beta y_i'}(\eta_i' - \pi_i)\,.$$

Hence the function $E_\omega$ is positive for such sets when $(x, \eta, \eta') \neq (x, \eta, \pi)$, on account of the condition III′. The $n$-parameter family of accessory extremals $\eta_i = U_{ik}\, a_k$, $\zeta_i = V_{ik}\, a_k$, now assumed to exist, simply covers the region of $x\eta$-space between the hyperplanes $x = x_1$ and $x = x_2$; and in that region the slope functions and multipliers $\pi_i(x, \eta)$, $\lambda_\beta(x, \eta)$ of the family form a field for the integral $I_2(\eta)$, according to the proof of Lemma 84·2 applied to the problem of the present section. The fundamental sufficiency theorem, Theorem 85·1, applied to this field, justifies the sufficiency of the condition of the lemma.

The proof of the necessity of the condition in the lemma can be made by the method used by Hestenes in proving the first part of Lemma 87·2, but with some modifications, because of the fact that the minimum problem here considered is not necessarily normal. If the order of abnormality of the axis $\eta_i = 0$ for our present problem is $q$, then there will be a maximal set of $q$ linearly independent sets of multipliers $\lambda_{0\rho} = 0$, $\lambda_{\beta\rho}(x)$ $(\rho = 1, \ldots, q)$ with which it satisfies the accessory equations, or, what is equivalent, a maximal set of $q$ linearly independent solutions $\eta_{i\rho}$, $\zeta_{i\rho}$ of the accessory canonical equations having $\eta_i(x) \equiv 0$ on the interval $x_1x_2$. We consider now the two conjugate systems, $\eta_{ik}$, $\zeta_{ik}$ and $u_{ik}$, $v_{ik}$ $(k = 1, \ldots, n)$, with elements $\eta_{ik}$ and $u_{ik}$ all vanishing at $x_1$ and $x_2$, respectively, and so chosen that the solutions $\eta_{i\rho}$, $\zeta_{i\rho}$ $(\rho = 1, \ldots, q)$ are the first $q$ solutions of each system. Without loss of generality we may assume that the sets $\zeta_{i\rho}(x_1)$ $(\rho = 1, \ldots, q)$ are normed and orthogonalized and that we have the relations

$$(89\cdot 2) \qquad \zeta_{i\rho}(x_1)\,\zeta_{i\alpha}(x_1) = 0\,, \qquad \zeta_{i\rho}(x_1)\,v_{i\alpha}(x_1) = 0 \qquad (\rho = 1, \ldots, q;\ \alpha = q+1, \ldots, n)\,.$$

The presupposed positive definiteness of the integral $I_2(\eta)$ implies the non-negativeness of the bilinear form (86·11) for all sets $b_k$, $c_k$ satisfying equations (86·12). The matrix of constants in (86·11) has elements all zero in $q$ rows across the top and in $q$ columns on the left, since the solutions $\eta_{i\rho}$, $\zeta_{i\rho}$ $(\rho = 1, \ldots, q)$ are common to both conjugate systems. The remaining matrix

$$(89\cdot 3) \qquad \|\zeta_{i\alpha}\, u_{i\beta} - \eta_{i\alpha}\, v_{i\beta}\| \qquad (\alpha, \beta = q+1, \ldots, n)$$

has determinant different from zero. Otherwise there would be an accessory extremal $\eta_i = b_a \eta_{ia}$, $\zeta_i = b_a \zeta_{ia}$ conjugate to every one of the systems $u_{ik}$, $v_{ik}$ ($k = 1, \ldots, n$), and hence linearly expressible in terms of this latter conjugate system in the form $c_k u_{ik}$, $c_k v_{ik}$. The accessory extremal $\eta_i$, $\zeta_i$ so determined would belong to both conjugate systems and would therefore satisfy the conditions (89·1). The functions $\eta_i(x)$ could not all be identically zero, since the set $\eta_{i\rho}$, $\zeta_{i\rho}$ ($\rho = 1, \ldots, q$) is a maximal set of accessory extremals with elements $\eta_i$ vanishing identically on the interval $x_1x_2$. Taken along the arc $\eta_i(x)$, the integral $I_2(\eta)$ would vanish, as one sees by the usual integration by parts. But this is impossible since the integral $I_2(\eta)$ is positive definite. Since the determinant of the matrix (89·3) is different from zero, we may transform the system $u_{ia}$, $v_{ia}$ ($a = q + 1, \ldots, n$) linearly so that (89·3) is the identity matrix.

Let us now define a system $U_{ik}(x)$, $V_{ik}(x)$ ($k = 1, \ldots, n$) by the initial values

$$(89 \cdot 4) \quad \begin{aligned} U_{i\rho}(x_1) &= \zeta_{i\rho}(x_1), & V_{i\rho}(x_1) &= 0, \\ U_{ia}(x_1) &= \eta_{ia}(x_1) + u_{ia}(x_1), & V_{ia}(x_1) &= \zeta_{ia}(x_1) + v_{ia}(x_1). \end{aligned}$$

With the help of the relations (89·2) and the fact that the matrix of constants (89·3) is now the identity matrix, it is easy to see that the system $U_{ik}(x)$, $V_{ik}(x)$ ($k = 1, \ldots, n$) is a conjugate system. Furthermore, the determinant $|U_{ik}(x)|$ is different from zero on $x_1x_2$. Otherwise there would be a value $x_3$ and a set of constants $b_k$, not all zero, such that

$$(89 \cdot 5) \qquad b_k U_{ik}(x_3) = 0 \qquad (k = 1, \ldots, n).$$

The constants $b_\rho$ would all be zero, as one sees by multiplying the equations (89·4) by $\zeta_{i\sigma}(x_3)$ and adding, since from conjugacy relations and (89·2) and (89·4)

$$\begin{aligned} \zeta_{i\sigma}(x_3)\, U_{i\rho}(x_3) &= \zeta_{i\sigma}(x_1)\, \zeta_{i\rho}(x_1) = \delta_{\rho\sigma}, \\ \zeta_{i\sigma}(x_3)\, U_{ia}(x_3) &= 0. \end{aligned}$$

In deducing these relations one needs to remember that the functions $\eta_{i\rho}(x)$ are all identically zero on the interval $x_1x_2$. From (89·4) the constants $b_a$ ($a = q + 1, \ldots, n$) would then satisfy the relations

$$b_a\, \eta_{ia}(x_3) = -\, b_a\, u_{ia}(x_3)\,\cdot$$

and on the broken extremal

$$\begin{aligned} \eta_i(x) &= b_a\, \eta_{ia}(x) & &\text{on} \quad x_1 \leqq x \leqq x_3, \\ &= -\, b_a\, u_{ia}(x) & &\text{on} \quad x_3 \leqq x \leqq x_2 \end{aligned}$$

the value (86·11) of $I_2(\eta)$ would be $-b_a b_a$, which is impossible since $I_2(\eta)$ is positive definite. Thus Lemma 89·1 is proved.

LEMMA 89·2. *A necessary and sufficient condition for* $I_2(\eta)$ *to be positive definite in the class* H *is that there is no value* $x_3$ *conjugate to* $x_1$ *on the interval* $x_1 < x \leqq x_2$.

The necessity follows from the fact that if $x_3$ is conjugate to $x_1$ there is an accessory extremal $u_i(x)$, $v_i(x)$ with $u_i(x_1) = u_i(x_3) = 0$ but with $u_i(x)$ not identically zero on the interval $x_1x_3$. The composite arc $\eta_i(x)$ on $x_1x_2$ with $\eta_i(x) \equiv u_i(x)$ on $x_1x_3$ and $\eta_i(x) \equiv 0$ on $x_3x_2$ would then give to $I_2(\eta)$ the value zero, which is impossible since $I_2(\eta)$ is, by hypothesis, positive definite.

To prove the sufficiency of the condition in the lemma, let $\xi$ be the least upper bound of the end-values $x_3$ of the intervals $x_1x_3$ on which the integral $I_2(\eta)$, taken between the limits $x_1$ and $x_3$, is positive definite in the class of admissible variations $\eta_i(x)$ satisfying the equations $\Phi_\beta = 0$ and having the end-values $\eta_i(x_1) = \eta_i(x_3) = 0$. That there are such intervals is a consequence of Lemma 89·1 and of the fact that there exists a conjugate system $U_{ik}(x)$, $V_{ik}(x)$ $(k = 1, \ldots, n)$ of accessory extremals with initial values $U_{ik}(x_1) = \delta_{ik}$, $V_{ik}(x_1) = 0$ and a determinant $|U_{ik}|$ consequently different from zero near $x_1$.

On the interval $x_1\xi$ the integral $I_2(\eta)$ is at least non-negative. Otherwise there would be on this interval an admissible set of variations $\eta_i(x)$ satisfying the equations $\Phi_\beta = 0$ and $\eta_i(x_1) = \eta_i(\xi) = 0$ and having $I_2[\eta(x)] < 0$. It will be shown in the fourth paragraph below that there would then be a family of sets of variations $\eta_i(x_1, x_3)$ vanishing at $x_1$ and $x_3 < \xi$ and such that the inequality $I_2[\eta(x, x_3)] < 0$ would hold for values $x_3$ sufficiently near to $\xi$. This is, however, impossible, since on intervals $x_1x_3$ with such values $x_3$ the integral $I_2(\eta)$ is, by hypothesis, positive definite.

On the interval $x_1\xi$ the integral $I_2(\eta)$ is not only non-negative but is also positive definite. Otherwise there would be an admissible set of variations satisfying the equations $\Phi_\beta = 0$, vanishing at $x_1$ and $\xi$, but not identically zero between these values, and giving to the integral $I_2(\eta)$ its minimum value zero. Such a minimizing set would necessarily satisfy the accessory multiplier rule and be an accessory extremal, since the condition III′ implies that the arc $E$ is non-singular. This is, however, impossible since $\xi$, by hypothesis, is not conjugate to $x_1$.

The least upper bound $\xi$ must be at $x_2$. For the positive definiteness of the integral $I_2(\eta)$ on the interval $x_1\xi$ implies the existence of a conjugate system $U_{ik}(x)$, $V_{ik}(x)$ $(k = 1, \ldots, n)$ with determinant $|U_{ik}(x)|$ different from zero on the interval $x_1\xi$, by Lemma 89·1. This determinant will remain different from zero on a slightly larger interval; and by Lemma 89·1 again, it follows that $\xi$ cannot be the upper bound which it is supposed to be, unless it is at $x_2$. The proof of the lemma will now be complete when the postponed arguments of the next two paragraphs are supplied.

If the arc $E$ on which the second variation is taken has abnormality of order $q$ on an interval $x_1\xi$, then it has the same order of abnormality on every interval $x_1x_3$ with $x_3 < \xi$ and sufficiently near to $\xi$. For in the second paragraph of the proof of Lemma 81·4 it was seen that the matrix

$$\left\| \begin{matrix} u_{is}(x_1) \\ u_{is}(x_3) \end{matrix} \right\| \qquad (i = 1, \ldots, n;\ s = 1, \ldots, 2n) \tag{89·6}$$

of a fundamental system of accessory extremals must have rank $2n - q'$ if $q'$ is the order of abnormality of $E$ on the interval $x_1x_3$. When $x_3 = \xi$, this rank is $2n - q$; and for values $x_3$ sufficiently near to $\xi$ it is at least $2n - q$, because of the continuity of the elements of the matrix. But the number $q'$ of linearly independent accessory extremals $\eta_i, \zeta_i$ with $\eta_i \equiv 0$ on the subinterval $x_1x_3$ is at least as great as the corresponding number $q$ for the interval $x_1\xi$ itself. Hence $q' = q$.

To prove now the existence of the family of variations $\eta_i(x, x_3)$ used in the third paragraph following Lemma 89·2, let $\eta_i(x)$ be a set of admissible variations satisfying the equations $\Phi_\beta = 0$ along $E$ and having $\eta_i(x_1) = \eta_i(\xi) = 0$ for a value $\xi$ on the interval $x_1 < \xi \leqq x_2$. From Lemma 81·4 it follows that for every $x_3 < \xi$ there is an accessory extremal $u_i, v_i$ having $u_i(x_1) = \eta_i(x_1) = 0$, $u_i(x_3) = \eta_i(x_3)$. When $x_3$ is sufficiently near to $\xi$, this extremal can be determined by solving a suitably selected system of $2n - q$ of the equations

$$0 = c_s u_{is}(x_1), \qquad \eta_i(x_3) = c_s u_{is}(x_3)$$

for $2n - q$ of the coefficients $c_s$ while the other $q$ coefficients are chosen to be all equal to zero. The functions $c_s(x_3)$ so determined are continuous and approach zero as $x_3$ approaches $\xi$. The variations

$$\eta_i(x, x_3) = \eta_i(x) - c_s(x_3)u_{is}(x) \tag{89·7}$$

then vanish for $x = x_1$ and $x = x_3$; and $\eta_i(x, x_3)$ and $\eta_i'(x, x_3)$ approach $\eta_i(x)$ and $\eta_i'(x)$ uniformly for $x$ on the interval $x_1\xi$ as $x_3$ approaches $\xi$. The family (89·7) is the one used in the proof of Lemma 89·2.

**90. Conditions equivalent to the strengthened fourth condition.** It is not easy to test directly the positive definiteness of the second variation, which is the condition IV′ of Section 82. In this and the following section it is proposed to establish three equivalent conditions which, theoretically at least, can be more easily applied.

We shall use *the notation* $IV_1'$ to designate the condition that the second variation is positive definite on the class of all at most once-broken accessory extremals satisfying the accessory end-conditions. Similarly, *the notation* $IV_2'$ will stand for the condition that the second variation is positive definite on the class of all accessory extremals satisfying the accessory end-conditions and, further, that there is no conjugate point $x_3$ to $x_1$ on the interval $x_1 < x < x_2$. The definition of a conjugate point is given in Section 89.

THEOREM 90·1. *The conditions* $IV'$, $IV_1'$, $IV_2'$ *are equivalent to each other.*

It is easy to see that IV′ implies $IV_1'$, and that $IV_1'$ implies $IV_2'$. Hence the theorem will be proved if we can show that $IV_2'$ implies IV′.

To make this proof we note first that when $IV_2'$ is satisfied the value $x_2$ cannot be conjugate to $x_1$. With this remark in mind, let $\eta_i(x)$ be an arbitrarily selected admissible set of variations satisfying the equations $\Phi_\beta = 0$ and the accessory end-conditions. According to Lemma 81·4, there exists an accessory extremal $u_i(x), v_i(x)$ with $u_i(x_1) = \eta_i(x_1)$, $u_i(x_2) = \eta_i(x_2)$. If the second variation is formed with the integrand $\Omega$ having the multipliers of $u_i$, $v_i$ we may express it, with the help of Taylor's formula, in the form

$$J_2(\eta) = J_2(u) + I_2(\eta - u) + \int_{x_1}^{x_2} [(\eta_i - u_i)\Omega_{\eta_i}(u) + (\eta_i' - u_i')\Omega_{\eta_i'}(u)]\, dx .$$

The integral vanishes, as one sees by the usual integration by parts. The second term on the right is positive unless $\eta_i \equiv u_i$, by Lemma 89·2; and the first term is positive unless $u_i \equiv 0$, by the hypothesis $\mathrm{IV}_2'$. Hence the second variation is positive definite, and Theorem 90·1 is proved.

To test the condition $\mathrm{IV}_2'$ we may use the criteria which will be described in this and the following paragraphs. First of all, we assume that the order of abnormality of the arc $E$ on the interval $x_1x_2$ is $q$. A necessary and sufficient condition for this to be true is that there exists a maximal set of $q$ linearly independent secondary extremals $u_{i\rho}(x)$, $v_{i\rho}(x)$ $(\rho = 1, \ldots, q)$ with elements $u_{i\rho}$ all identically zero on $x_1x_2$. Let $u_{ia}(x)$, $v_{ia}(x)$ $(a = q + 1, \ldots, 2n)$ be $2n - q$ further accessory extremals forming with $u_{i\rho}$, $v_{i\rho}$ a fundamental system. The equations

$$(90\cdot 1) \qquad \Psi_\mu[\xi_1, \ c_a u_{ia}(x_1), \ \xi_2, \ c_a u_{ia}(x_2)] = 0$$

have a maximal set of $2n - q + 2 - r$ solutions $(\xi_1, \xi_2, c_a)$, where $r$ is the rank of the matrix of coefficients of these constants in the equations (90·1). Corresponding to the solutions so determined, there is then a maximal set of constants $\xi_1$, $\xi_2$ and accessory extremals

$$\xi_{1\gamma}, \ \xi_{2\gamma}, \ \eta_{i\gamma}(x), \ \zeta_{i\gamma}(x) \qquad (\gamma = 1, \ldots, 2n - q + 2 - r),$$

each of which satisfies the accessory end-conditions and has elements $\eta_{i\gamma}(x)$ not all identically zero on the interval $x_1x_2$. The value of the second variation, taken on the elements

$$\xi_1 = \xi_{1\gamma} z_\gamma, \qquad \xi_2 = \xi_{2\gamma} z_\gamma, \qquad \eta_i = \eta_{i\gamma} z_\gamma$$

of an arbitrary linear combination of these, is a quadratic form $Q(z)$ in the variables $z_\gamma$. The following result can then be readily verified:

THEOREM 90·2. *The condition* $\mathit{IV}_2'$ *is equivalent to the conditions that the quadratic form* $Q(z)$ *is positive definite and that there is no value* $x_3$ *conjugate to* $x_1$ *on the interval* $x_1 < x < x_2$.

If the original extremal arc $E$ is normal for the original problem of Bolza, then every accessory extremal arc satisfying the accessory end-conditions will be normal for the accessory minimum problem, as indicated in Lemma 81·1. According to Theorem 77·1, applied to the accessory minimum problem, there will then be an infinity of admissible sets $\xi_1$, $\xi_2$, $\eta_i(x)$ satisfying the accessory end-conditions. Both the condition $\mathrm{IV}_2'$ and the equivalent conditions of Theorem 90·2 imply that the values $x_1$ and $x_2$ are not conjugate. Hence, according to Lemma 81·4, there is an accessory extremal arc $u_i(x)$, $v_i(x)$ joining the ends of the arc defined by each set of functions $\eta_i(x)$, and the set $\xi_1$, $\xi_2$, $u_i(x)$ will also satisfy the accessory end-conditions. Thus the quadratic form $Q(z)$ must contain variables $z$.

To determine the values $x_3$ conjugate to $x_1$ on the interval $x_1x_2$, we may follow a procedure of Reid [44, p. 577]. On each interval $x_1x$ the arc $E$ has an order of abnormality, which we may denote by $q(x)$ and which is equal to the number of linearly independent accessory extremals $u_i$, $v_i$ with elements $u_i$ all vanishing identically on $x_1x$. The function $q(x)$ so defined is non-increasing and has only integral values $\leqq m$, according to Theorem 77·2. Hence it has only a finite number of discontinuities on the interval $x_1x_2$, which will be denoted by $t_a$ $(a = 1, \ldots, g-1)$ with $t_0 = x_1 < t_1 < \ldots < t_{g-1} < t_g = x_2$. The accessory extremals $u_i$, $v_i$ with elements $u_i$ all vanishing at $x_1$ form a conjugate system $u_{ik}(x)$, $v_{ik}(x)$ $(k = 1, \ldots, n)$ whose elements $v_{ik}(x_1)$ may be normed and orthogonalized so that

$$v_{ij}(x_1)\, v_{ik}(x_1) = \delta_{jk} \quad (\delta_{jj} = 1,\ \delta_{jk} = 0 \text{ if } j \neq k). \tag{90·2}$$

Furthermore, the order of the columns in the system may be so chosen that for each $a = 1, \ldots, g$ the first $q(t_a)$ of them are the ones whose elements $u_{i\rho}$ $[\rho = 1, \ldots, q(t_a)]$ vanish identically on the interval $x_1 \leqq x \leqq t_a$. A fundamental system of accessory extremals can be formed by adjoining $n$ new accessory extremals $u_{i,n+k}(x)$, $v_{i,n+k}(x)$ $(k = 1, \ldots, n)$ determined by the initial conditions

$$u_{i,n+k}(x_1) = v_{ik}(x_1), \qquad v_{i,n+k}(x_1) = 0\,. \tag{90·3}$$

Finally, for each value $a = 1, \ldots, q$ we may define a system $u_{ik}(x\,|\,a)$, $v_{ik}(x\,|\,a)$ by the equations

$$u_{i\rho}(x\,|\,a) = u_{i,n+\rho}(x), \qquad v_{i\rho}(x\,|\,a) = v_{i,n+\rho}(x) \qquad [\rho = 1, \ldots, q(t_a)]$$

$$u_{i\sigma}(x\,|\,a) = u_{i\sigma}(x), \qquad v_{i\sigma}(x\,|\,a) = v_{i\sigma}(x) \qquad [\sigma = q(t_a) + 1, \ldots, n].$$

The system so determined is a conjugate system, as one verifies with the help of the relations (90·2), (90·3), and $u_{i\rho}(x) \equiv 0$. With these definitions and notations agreed upon we may prove the following theorem:

THEOREM 90·3. *For each value $a = 1, \ldots, g$ the values $x_3$ conjugate to $x_1$ on the interval $x_1 < x \leqq t_a$ are the values $x_3$ when any one of the following conditions is satisfied:*

(1) *The matrix*

$$\begin{Vmatrix} u_{ik}(x_1) & u_{i,n+k}(x_1) \\ u_{ik}(x_3) & u_{i,n+k}(x_3) \end{Vmatrix}$$

*has rank less than* $2n - q(t_a)$;

(2) *The matrix* $\|u_{i\sigma}(x_3)\|$ $[\sigma = q(t_a) + 1, \ldots, n]$ *has rank less than* $n - q(t_a)$;

(3) *The determinant* $|u_{ik}(x_3\,|\,a)|$ *is equal to zero.*

Every accessory extremal $u_i$, $v_i$ is expressible linearly in terms of the fundamental system whose elements occur in the matrix in (1). The elements in the first $q(t_a)$ columns of this matrix are all zero. It can readily be seen, then, that an accessory extremal $u_i$, $v_i$ exists with $u_i(x_1) = u_i(x_3) = 0$ and $u_i(x) \not\equiv 0$ on $x_1x_3$ if, and only if, the matrix has rank less than $2n - q(t_a)$.

Every accessory extremal $u_i$, $v_i$ with elements $u_i$ all vanishing at $x_1$ is expressible linearly in terms of the conjugate system $u_{ik}$, $v_{ik}$ $(k = 1, \ldots, n)$. Its elements $u_i$ will vanish at $x_3$, and not all be identically zero on $x_1\, x_3$, if, and only if, the matrix in (2) has rank less than $n - q(t_a)$.

The determinant in (3) will vanish when $x_3$ is conjugate to $x_1$ by the criterion stated in (2). Conversely, if the determinant vanishes, there will be a set of constants $c_k$, not all zero, satisfying the equations

$$c_k\, u_{ik}(x_3 \mid a) = 0 .$$

If this equation is multiplied by $u_{i\rho}(x_3)$ $[\rho = 1, \ldots, q(t_a)]$ and summed for $i$, it follows from the construction of the conjugate systems $u_{ik}$, $v_{ik}$ and $u_{ik}(x \mid a)$, $v_{ik}(x \mid a)$ $(k=1, \ldots, n)$ that the first $q(t_a)$ of the constants $c_k$ are zero. It is clear, then, that the matrix in (2) has rank less than $n - q(t_a)$, and the theorem is proved.

**91. Boundary-value problems associated with the second variation.** Related to the second variation there are so-called "boundary-value problems" leading to still other conditions equivalent to the condition IV. One of these, analogous to similar boundary-value problems well known for simpler cases, will be exhibited here.[5] The details of the arguments of the following paragraphs go back to Hickson,[6] who applied them to problems of the calculus of variations having fixed end-points and no differential or other equations of condition. For the problem of Bolza a condition like that given in this section, equivalent to condition IV of Section 90, was formulated by Cope [16, p. 21], and an abbreviated discussion was given by Hestenes [38, p. 812]. A much more detailed account has been published by Reid [33, 44]. In the paragraphs below, the methods used hitherto are somewhat modified. The new condition equivalent to IV will be denoted by the symbol $\mathrm{IV}_3$.

In the developments of this section it is understood that the arc $E$ of the class $\mathfrak{M}$ on which the second variation is taken is normal, has no corners, and satisfies the multiplier rule I and the strengthened Clebsch condition III′. The arc $E$ is therefore a non-singular extremal, as one sees with the help of Lemma 87·1; and its multipliers taken in the form $l_0 = 1$, $l_\beta(x)$ are unique.

The boundary-value problem of the second variation along $E$, to be considered here, is related to the problem of finding, in the class of admissible sets $\eta_i(x)$ satisfying conditions of the form

$$(91\cdot1) \qquad \begin{gathered} \Phi_\beta(x, \eta, \eta') = 0 , \quad \Psi_\mu[\eta(x_1), \eta(x_2)] = 0 \\ x_1 = \text{const.}, x_2 = \text{const.}, \end{gathered}$$

[5] See Bliss [57].

[6] "An Application of the Calculus of Variations to Boundary Value Problems," *Transactions of the American Mathematical Society*, XXXI (1929), 563–79.

one which minimizes the sum

$$(91\cdot 2)\quad J_2(\eta,\ \sigma) = 2\gamma[\eta(x_1),\ \eta(x_2)] + \int_{x_1}^{x_2}(2\omega - \sigma\eta_i\eta_i)\,dx\ .$$

For the present the functions $2\gamma$, $\Psi_\mu$ are supposed not to depend upon the usual constants $\xi_1$ and $\xi_2$, a restriction which will be removed later. The symbol $\sigma$ is a constant.

The equations characterizing a minimizing set $\eta_i(x)$ for the problem just proposed are

$$(91\cdot 3)\quad \begin{aligned} &\frac{d\Omega_{\eta'_i}}{dx} - \Omega_{\eta_i} - \sigma\eta_i = 0\ , &\Phi_\beta = 0\ ,\\ &[\Omega_{\eta'_i} d\eta_i]_1^2 + d\gamma + \epsilon_\mu\, d\Psi_\mu \equiv 0\ , &\Psi_\mu = 0\ , \end{aligned}$$

where the next to last equation is, as usual, an identity in the differentials $d\eta_{i1}$, $d\eta_{i2}$. The boundary-value problem to be studied is that of finding the sets $\eta_i(x)$, $\lambda_\beta(x)$, $\epsilon_\mu$, $\sigma$ which satisfy the conditions (91·3). In accordance with established custom, a number $\sigma$ which belongs to a solution of the boundary-value problem is called a *characteristic number*, and a set $\eta_i(x)$, $\lambda_\beta(x)$, $\epsilon_\mu$ belonging to such a solution is called a *characteristic set*.

In terms of accessory canonical variables defined, as usual, by the equations (81·3) and with the function $\mathfrak{H}$ defined in the equation just preceding (81·5), the conditions (91·3) take the form

$$(91\cdot 4)\quad \begin{aligned} &\frac{d\eta_i}{dx} = \mathfrak{H}_{\zeta_i}\ , \qquad \frac{d\zeta_i}{dx} = -\mathfrak{H}_{\eta_i} - \sigma\eta_i\ ,\\ &[\zeta_i\, d\eta_i]_1^2 + d\gamma + \epsilon_\mu\, d\Psi_\mu \equiv 0\ , \qquad \Psi_\mu = 0\ . \end{aligned}$$

The end-conditions, written out more explicitly, have the form

$$(91\cdot 5)\quad \begin{aligned} -\zeta_{i1} + \gamma_{i1} + \epsilon_\mu \Psi_{\mu,\,i1} &= 0\ ,\\ \zeta_{i2} + \gamma_{i2} + \epsilon_\mu \Psi_{\mu,\,i2} &= 0\ ,\\ \Psi_\mu &= 0\ , \end{aligned}$$

where the subscripts $i1$ and $i2$ on $\gamma$ and $\Psi_\mu$ indicate partial derivatives with respect to $\eta_{i1}$ and $\eta_{i2}$, respectively. The quantities involved in equations (91·5) are $\eta_{i1}$, $\zeta_{i1}$, $\eta_{i2}$, $\zeta_{i2}$, $\epsilon_\mu$. If two such sets, the second indicated by strokes, satisfy these equations, then

$$(91\cdot 6)\quad -\bar{\eta}_{i1}\,\zeta_{i1} + \bar{\eta}_{i2}\,\zeta_{i2} + 2\gamma(\eta;\ \bar{\eta}) = 0\ ,$$

where the third term on the left is a symbol for the bilinear form associated with the quadratic form $2\gamma$. If the two sets are the same, we have

$$(91\cdot 7)\quad [\eta_i\,\zeta_i]_1^2 + 2\gamma = 0\ .$$

A fundamental property of characteristic numbers and sets is given in the following lemma:

LEMMA 91·1. *If $\eta_i(x)$, $\lambda_\beta(x)$, $\epsilon_\mu$, $\sigma$, or in canonical coordinates $\eta_i(x)$, $\zeta_i(x)$, $\epsilon_\mu$, $\sigma$, is a solution of the boundary-value problem above for the second variation, then*

$$J_2(\eta, \sigma) = 0\,, \tag{91·8}$$

*where $J_2(\eta, \sigma)$ is defined to be the sum in (91·2).*

To prove this we may replace $2\omega$ by

$$2\Omega = \eta_i\,\Omega_{\eta_i} + \eta_i'\,\Omega_{\eta_i'}$$

in the expression (91·2) and apply the usual integration by parts. With the help of the first equations (91·3) and equation (91·7) it is seen, then, that $J_2(\eta, \sigma)$ vanishes.

LEMMA 91·2. *If $\sigma$ is sufficiently large and negative, the sum $J_2(\eta, \sigma)$ is positive definite on the class of admissible sets $\eta_i(x)$ satisfying the conditions $\Phi_\beta = \Psi_\mu = 0$ in (91·1).*

In the proof of this lemma we use the fact that a quadratic form $a_{ik}\,\eta_i\,\eta_k$ in $n$ variables has a minimum $m$ on the set of points $(\eta_1, \ldots, \eta_n)$ for which $\eta_i\,\eta_i = 1$. Consequently, $a_{ik}\,\eta_i\,\eta_k + c\eta_i\,\eta_i$ is positive definite if $c$ is sufficiently large and positive.

Consider, then, the integral

$$\int_{x_1}^{x_2} (2\Omega - \sigma\eta_i\eta_i)\,dx \tag{91·9}$$

as a function of the sets $\eta_i$ specified in the lemma. From (81·7) and the equation just preceding (81·5) we have, in terms of canonical accessory variables,

$$\begin{aligned} 2\Omega(x,\ \eta,\ \Pi,\ \Lambda) &= 2\zeta_i\,\mathfrak{H}_{\zeta_i} - 2\mathfrak{H} \\ &= -H_{y_iy_k}\,\eta_i\eta_k + H_{z_iz_k}\zeta_i\zeta_k\,. \end{aligned}$$

When we set $(x, \eta, \zeta) = (x, 0, \zeta)$ in this equation, it follows from the condition III′ presupposed above that $2\Omega$ is non-negative and hence that the same is true of the last quadratic form on the right. With the help of the remark about quadratic forms made in the last paragraph, it follows that if $\sigma$ is sufficiently large and negative the integral (91·9) is positive definite.

The same remark about quadratic forms justifies the statement that there is a negative constant $c$ so large that

$$\begin{aligned} J_2(\eta, \sigma) &> c(\eta_{i1}\,\eta_{i1} + \eta_{i2}\,\eta_{i2}) + \int_{x_1}^{x_2} (2\Omega - \sigma\eta_i\eta_i)\,dx \\ &> \int_{x_1}^{x_2} \left[\frac{d(ch\eta_i\eta_i)}{dx} + 2\Omega - \sigma\eta_i\eta_i\right] dx\,, \end{aligned}$$

where $h(x)$ is a function having a continuous derivative on $x_1x_2$ and having the end-values $h(x_1) = -1$, $h(x_2) = 1$. The introduction of the function $h$ is a device due to Morse [23, p. 534]. The integral on the right in the last inequality has the form of (91·9) and hence is positive definite if $\sigma$ is sufficiently large and negative. It follows at once that $J_2(\eta, \sigma)$ is also positive definite for such values $\sigma$.

LEMMA 91·3. *The least upper bound $\sigma_1$ of the values $\sigma$ for which* $J_2(\eta, \sigma)$ *is positive definite is the smallest characteristic number of the boundary-value problem (91·3) or (91·4).*

One can see, without difficulty, that the sum $J_2(\eta, \sigma_1)$ must be non-negative when $\sigma_1$ is the least upper bound described in the lemma. Otherwise there would be a set $\eta_i$ making $J_2(\eta, \sigma_1) < 0$, and this set would also make $J_2(\eta, \sigma) < 0$ for values $\sigma < \sigma_1$ and near $\sigma_1$. The sum $J_2(\eta, \sigma_1)$ cannot be positive definite, since the criterion $IV_2'$ for positive definiteness of $J_2(\eta, \sigma)$, in Section 90, holds for $\sigma$ slightly greater than $\sigma_1$ when it holds for $\sigma_1$. Hence there must be an admissible set $\eta_i$ satisfying the conditions $\Phi_\beta = \Psi_\mu = 0$ and giving $J_2(\eta, \sigma_1)$ the value zero. This set $\eta_i$ is, then, a minimizing set for $J_2(\eta, \sigma_1)$ and, consequently, satisfies the conditions (91·3) with the value $\sigma_1$. Thus $\sigma_1$ is a characteristic number. For every other characteristic number $\sigma_2$ the corresponding characteristic set $\eta_i$ satisfies the conditions $\Phi_\beta = \Psi_\mu = 0$ and is such that $J_2(\eta, \sigma_2) = 0$. Hence $J_2(\eta, \sigma_2)$ is not positive definite, and $\sigma_2$ is necessarily greater than $\sigma_1$.

The preceding lemmas now justify, without difficulty, the following theorem:

THEOREM 91·1. *A necessary and sufficient condition that the second variation* $J_2(\eta, 0)$ *from formula (91·2) be non-negative on the class of admissible sets* $\eta_i(x)$ *satisfying the conditions* $\Phi_\beta = \Psi_\mu = 0$ *in (91·1) is that the smallest characteristic number* $\sigma_1$ *of the boundary-value problem (91·3) of the second variation be non-negative. A necessary and sufficient condition for* $J_2(\eta, 0)$ *to be positive definite is* $\sigma_1 > 0$. These conditions equivalent to IV may be designated by $IV_3$.

In the preceding paragraphs the case was excluded when the second variation $J_2$ and the functions $\Psi_\mu$ depend upon the constants $\xi_1$ and $\xi_2$. Results for this case, analogous to the preceding ones, can, however, be proved without difficulty. We define $J_2$ by the equation

$$(91\cdot10)\qquad \begin{aligned} J_2(\xi, \eta, \sigma) &= 2\gamma[\xi_1, \eta(x_1), \xi_2, \eta(x_2)] \\ &\quad + \int_{x_1}^{x_2} [2\omega - \sigma(\eta_i\eta_i + \xi_1^2 + \xi_2^2)]\, dx \end{aligned}$$

and regard it as a function on the class of admissible sets $\xi_1$, $\xi_2$, $\eta_i(x)$ satisfying conditions in the usual forms

$$(91\cdot11)\qquad \begin{gathered} \Phi_\beta(x, \eta, \eta') = 0, \qquad \Psi_\mu[\xi_1, \eta(x_1), \xi_2, \eta(x_2)] = 0, \\ x_1 = \text{const.}, x_2 = \text{const.} \end{gathered}$$

To reduce the problem of minimizing $J_2(\xi, \eta, \sigma)$ in the class of sets just defined to one of the type studied above, we re-write $J_2$ and the conditions (91·11) in the forms

$$\begin{aligned} J_2 &= 2\gamma[\eta_{n+1}(x_1), \eta_i(x_1), \eta_{n+2}(x_2), \eta_i(x_2)] \\ &\quad + \int_{x_1}^{x_2} [2\omega - \sigma(\eta_i\eta_i + \eta_{n+1}^2 + \eta_{n+2}^2)]\, dx, \end{aligned}$$

$$(91\cdot12)\qquad \begin{gathered} \Phi_\beta(x, \eta, \eta') = \eta_{n+1}' = \eta_{n+2}' = 0 \\ \Psi_\mu[\eta_{n+1}(x_1), \eta_i(x_1), \eta_{n+2}(x_1), \eta_i(x_2)] = 0, \\ x_1 = \text{const.}, x_2 = \text{const.} \end{gathered}$$

The minimum problem is, then, that of finding, in the class of admissible sets $\eta_j(x)$ $(j = 1, \ldots, n+2)$ satisfying the conditions (91·12), one which minimizes $J_2$. This is a problem of the type specified by (91·1) and (91·2). It has associated with it a sequence of three lemmas and a theorem which are quite analogous to those stated above and which give a criterion for the non-negativeness or positive definiteness of the second variation $J_2(\xi, \eta, 0)$ in its usual form.

**92. A sufficiency theorem applicable to some important abnormal cases.** In his paper [38] on sufficient conditions for the problem of Bolza a theorem [p. 815, Theor. 9·2] analogous to the following one was proved by Hestenes:

THEOREM 92·1. *Let* E *be an arc without corners belonging to the class* $\mathfrak{M}$ *which, by definition, consists of all admissible arcs satisfying the conditions* $\phi_\beta = \psi_\mu = 0$. *If* E *has a set of multipliers of the form* $l_0 = 1$, $l_\beta(x)$ *with which it satisfies the conditions I,* $II'_N$, *III′, IV′, then it is a non-singular extremal, and there exists in* (x, y)*-space a neighborhood* F *of the arc* E *such that* J(C) > J(E) *for every arc* C *of the class* $\mathfrak{M}$ *in* F *not identical with* E *and having its end-points sufficiently near to those of* E.

This statement differs from that of the basic sufficiency theorem, Theorem 82·1, only in the absence of the assumption that the arc $E$ is normal. The proof of Theorem 92·1 given here is effected by making it depend upon the normal case of Theorem 82·1.[7]

If the order of abnormality of $E$ is $q$, there must be $q$ linearly independent abnormal sets of multipliers and constants $l_{0\sigma} = 0$, $l_{\beta\sigma}(x)$, $e_{\mu\sigma}$ $(\sigma = 1, \ldots, q)$ with which $E$ satisfies the multiplier rule of Theorem 74·1. The equation

$$(92{\cdot}1) \qquad [F_{\sigma y'_i}\,\eta_i]_1^2 + e_{\mu\sigma}\Psi_\mu = 0$$

with $F_\sigma = l_{\beta\sigma}\phi_\beta$ is for each $\sigma$ an identity in the variables $\xi_1, \xi_2, \eta_{i1}, \eta_{i2}$, since this is what the identity in (74·9) becomes for the multipliers $l_{0\sigma} = 0$, $l_{\beta\sigma}(x)$, $e_{\mu\sigma}$ when the end-values of $dx, dy_i$ are replaced by those of $\xi$, $y'_i\,\xi + \eta_i$. The usual integration by parts applied to the integral of the sum

$$l_{\beta\sigma}\,\Phi_\beta = F_{\sigma y_i}\,\eta_i + F_{\sigma y'_i}\,\eta'_i$$

gives the equation

$$(92{\cdot}2) \qquad \int_{x_1}^{x_2} l_{\beta\sigma}\,\Phi_\beta\,dx = [F_{\sigma y'_i}\,\eta_i]_1^2 ,$$

so that for every admissible set of variations satisfying the equations $\Phi_\beta = 0$ we find, with the help of equations (92·1) and (92·2),

$$(92{\cdot}3) \qquad [F_{\sigma y'_i}\,\eta_i]_1^2 = 0 , \qquad e_{\mu\sigma}\Psi_\mu = 0 .$$

The matrix of $q$ sets of values $e_{\mu\sigma}$ $(\sigma = 1, \ldots, q)$ is necessarily of rank $q$. Otherwise there would be a linear combination of these sets vanishing identically; and the same linear combination of the sets $l_{0\sigma}$, $l_{\beta\sigma}(x)$, $e_{\mu\sigma}$ would then also

[7] See Bliss [56], pp. 373–74.

vanish identically, according to the remark in the paragraph preceding Corollary 74·1. This is, however, impossible, since these sets are, by hypothesis, linearly independent.

In the following paragraphs the variable $\rho$ is understood to have as its range a subset of $q$ of the numbers $\mu = 1, \ldots, p$ such that the determinant $|e_{\rho\sigma}|$ is different from zero, and the variable $\nu$ will have the range complementary to that of $\rho$. The second equation (92·3) then shows that for an admissible set $\xi_1$, $\xi_2$, $\eta_i(x)$ the equations $\Psi_\rho = 0$ are consequences of the equations $\Phi_\beta = \Psi_\nu = 0$.

THEOREM 92·2. *Let* E *be an arc satisfying the hypotheses of Theorem 92·1, and let* $\rho$ *and* $\nu$ *be variables whose ranges are the subsets of the numbers* $\mu = 1, \ldots, \mathrm{p}$ *determined in the last paragraph. Then the arc* E *is normal for the modified problem of minimizing the functional* $\mathrm{J(C)} + \mathrm{e}_\rho\, \psi_\rho(\mathrm{C})$ *in the class of admissible arcs* C *satisfying the reduced system of equations* $\phi_\beta = \psi_\nu = 0$, *and the arc* E *with the multipliers* $l_0 = 1$, $l_\beta(\mathrm{x})$, $\mathrm{e}_\nu$ *satisfies the hypotheses of Theorem 92·1 for the modified problem. Furthermore, if* $\mathrm{J(E)} + \mathrm{e}_\rho\, \psi_\rho\, \mathrm{(E)}$ *is a strong relative minimum for the modified problem, then* J(E) *is a similar minimum for the original problem.*

It is easy to see that the arc $E$ is normal for the modified problem. For if $E$ had for that problem a set of non-vanishing multipliers of the form $l_0 = 0, l_\beta(x)$, $e_\nu$, the set $l_0 = 0$, $l_\beta(x)$, $e_\rho = 0$, $e_\nu$ would be multipliers for $E$ and the original problem, necessarily linearly expressible in terms of the $q$ sets $l_{0\sigma} = 0$, $l_{\beta\sigma}(x)$, $e_{\mu\sigma}$ $(\sigma = 1, \ldots, q)$. This is, however, impossible on account of the fact that the determinant $|e_{\rho\sigma}|$ is not zero.

The arc $E$ satisfies the hypotheses of Theorem 92·1 for the modified problem with the multipliers $l_0 = 0$, $l_\beta(x)$, $e_\nu$, as may be seen by an examination of the conditions I, $\mathrm{II}'_N$, III′, IV′. For the condition IV′ one needs to note that, on account of the second equation (92·3), the restricted system of equations of variation $\Phi_\beta = \Psi_\nu = 0$ implies the complete original system $\Phi_\beta = \Psi_\mu = 0$.

Since the class of arcs in which a minimizing one is sought for the modified problem includes as a subclass those among which a minimizing arc is sought for the original problem, and since on the subclass the values of the functionals $J(C) + e_\rho\, \psi_\rho(C)$ and $J(C)$ are equal, the last statement of the theorem is evidently true.

Thus we see that the proof of the sufficiency theorem for the abnormal arcs studied by Hestenes can be reduced to a proof of the minimizing property for an arc which is normal. The abnormal cases covered in Theorem 92·1 are the most interesting ones for which sufficient conditions have so far been established. Further interesting results concerning abnormality are found in the papers 59, 60, and 61 by McShane.

# APPENDIX

# APPENDIX

## EXISTENCE THEOREMS FOR IMPLICIT FUNCTIONS AND DIFFERENTIAL EQUATIONS

The development of the theory of the calculus of variations depends intimately upon existence theorems for implicit functions and differential equations. References to such theorems are frequent and of fundamental importance in the theory. As a result of their use in the calculus of variations the theorems themselves have undergone extensions and improvements which have not always found their way into the textbooks on the theory of functions of a real variable. Notable among such extensions are the theorems of Section 2, below, concerning implicit functions, and the imbedding theorem for differential equations in Section 5. On account of their great usefulness these existence theorems are presented here in a form which it is hoped will be especially convenient for students of the calculus of variations. The presentation is based upon mimeographed notes which the author has used in recent years in his classes at the University of Chicago.

### I. EXISTENCE THEOREMS FOR IMPLICIT FUNCTIONS[1]

**1. The fundamental existence theorem for implicit functions.** The equations whose solutions are to be studied have the form

$$f_i(x_1, \ldots, x_m; y_1, \ldots, y_n) = 0 \quad (i = 1, \ldots, n).$$

When convenient, the sets $(x_1, \ldots, x_m; y_1, \ldots, y_n)$, $(x_1, \ldots, x_m)$, $(y_1, \ldots, y_n)$ may be denoted more simply by $(x, y)$, $x$, $y$, respectively; and the notations $(a, b)$, $a$, $b$ in the following theorems will indicate sets of similar types. By $D(x, y)$ is meant the functional determinant

$$D(x, y) = \frac{\partial(f_1, \ldots, f_n)}{\partial(y_1, \ldots, y_n)} = \left| \frac{\partial f_i}{\partial y_k} \right| .$$

The neighborhood $(a, b)_\epsilon$ is the totality of points $(x, y)$ satisfying the inequalities

$$|x_r - a_r| \leqq \epsilon, \quad |y_i - b_i| \leqq \epsilon \quad (r = 1, \ldots, m;\ i = 1, \ldots, n),$$

and $a_\epsilon$, $b_\epsilon$ have similar meanings. With these understandings as to notations the fundamental theorem is now the following:

[1] See Bliss, *Fundamental Existence Theorems* (Princeton Colloquium of the American Mathematical Society) (1909); Bolza, *Vorlesungen über Variationsrechnung* (2d ed.; 1933), chap. iv, pp. 154–88.

THEOREM 1·1. *Let* p = (a, b) *be a point with the following properties:*

(1) *the functions* $f_i(x, y)$ *are continuous and have continuous derivatives* $\partial f_i/\partial y_k$ *in a neighborhood* N *of* p;

(2) $f_i(a, b) = 0$ $(i = 1, \ldots, n)$;

(3) $D(a, b) \neq 0$.

*Then there exists a set of functions* $y_i(x_1, \ldots, x_m)$ *single valued and continuous in a neighborhood* $a_\delta$ *and having the following properties:*

(1) *The points* $[x, y(x_1, \ldots, x_m)]$ *which they define are in* N *and satisfy the equations* $f_i = 0$;

(2) *There exists a constant* $\epsilon$ *such that for each* x *in* $a_\delta$ *the set* $[x, y(x_1, \ldots, x_m)]$ *is the only solution* (x, y) *of the equations* $f_i = 0$ *satisfying the inequalities*

$$y_i(x_1, \ldots, x_m) - \epsilon < y_i < y_i(x_1, \ldots, x_m) + \epsilon;$$

(3) $y_i(a_1, \ldots, a_m) = b_i$ $(i = 1, \ldots, n)$;

(4) *In a sufficiently small neighborhood* $a_\delta$ *the functions* $y_i(x_1, \ldots, x_m)$ *have continuous partial derivatives of as many orders as are possessed by the functions* $f_i$ *in the neighborhood* N.

To prove the theorem it can first be shown that in a sufficiently small neighborhood $(a, b)_\epsilon$ the equations $f_i = 0$ can have no pair of distinct solutions $(x, y)$, $(x, y')$ with the same projection $x$. By Taylor's formula with integral form of remainder

$$(1 \cdot 1) \qquad f_i(x, y') - f_i(x, y) = B_{i1}(y_1' - y_1) + \ldots + B_{in}(y_n' - y_n),$$

where

$$B_{ik}(x, y, y') = \int_0^1 f_{iy_k}[x, y + \theta(y' - y)]\, d\theta .$$

The determinant $B(x, y, y') = |B_{ik}|$ has the initial value $B(a, b, b) = D(a, b) \neq 0$, and hence a neighborhood $(a, b)_\epsilon$ can be chosen within the neighborhood $N$ of the theorem and so small that in it the determinant $B(x, y, y')$ remains different from zero. The expression (1·1) can then vanish for a pair of points $(x, y)$, $(x, y')$ in $(a, b)_\epsilon$ only if $y$ and $y'$ are identical. For the purposes of later paragraphs it should be noted that $D(x, y) = B(x, y, y)$ is necessarily different from zero in the neighborhood $(a, b)_\epsilon$ where $B(x, y, y')$ does not vanish.

There exists a neighborhood $a_\delta$ in which every $x$ belongs to a solution $(x, y)$ in $(a, b)_\epsilon$. To prove this, one may make use of the auxiliary function

$$\varphi(x, y) = f_1^2 + \ldots + f_n^2 .$$

On the closed set of points $(x, y) = (a, \eta)$ for which $\eta$ ranges on the boundary of $b_\epsilon$ the inequality

$$\varphi(a, \eta) = \varphi(a, \eta) - \varphi(a, b) > 0$$

is satisfied, since by the results of the preceding paragraph $\varphi(a, y)$ vanishes only at $y = b$ in the neighborhood $b_\epsilon$. Hence the inequality

$$\varphi(x, \eta) - \varphi(x, b) > 0$$

holds true when $x$ lies in a sufficiently small neighborhood $a_\delta$ and $\eta$ has the same range as before. This implies, however, that for each fixed $x$ in $a_\delta$ the continuous function $\varphi(x, y)$ has its minimum at a point $y$ interior to $b_\epsilon$, and not at a point $y = \eta$ on the boundary of $b_\epsilon$. At such a minimizing interior point for $\varphi$ the derivatives

$$\frac{1}{2}\frac{\partial \varphi}{\partial y_i} = f_1 \frac{\partial f_1}{\partial y_i} + \dots f_n \frac{\partial f_n}{\partial y_i}$$

must vanish; and since $D(x, y) \neq 0$ in $(a, b)_\epsilon$, it follows that the functions $f_i$ all vanish. To each $x$ in $a_\delta$ there corresponds, therefore, a solution $(x, y)$ of the equations $f_i = 0$ in $(a, b)_\epsilon$.

The single-valued functions $y_i(x_1, \dots, x_m)$ thus defined in the neighborhood $a_\delta$ are continuous. For if their values at $x$ and $x + \Delta x$ are denoted, respectively, by $y$ and $y + \Delta y$ the equations

$$\begin{aligned} 0 = f_i(x+\Delta x, y+\Delta y) &= f_i(x+\Delta x, y+\Delta y) \\ &\quad - f_i(x+\Delta x, y) + f_i(x+\Delta x, y) \\ &= \sum_k B_{ik}\Delta y_k + f_i(x+\Delta x, y), \end{aligned} \tag{1·2}$$

where the arguments of $B_{ik}$ are $(x, y, y') = (x + \Delta x, y, y + \Delta y)$, show that the increments $\Delta y_k$ approach zero with $\Delta x$. The conclusions of the theorem, with the exception of (2) and (4), are now evident.

Conclusion (2) can be readily established. The set of points $[x, y(x_1, \dots, x_m)]$ defined by the functions $y_i(x_1, \dots, x_m)$ on the neighborhood $a_\delta$ is in $(a, b)_\epsilon$, and hence the determinant $D(x, y) = B(x, y, y)$ is different from zero on it. The determinant $B(x, y, y')$ will remain different from zero for every pair $(x, y)$, $(x, y')$ in a sufficiently small neighborhood of the type defined by the inequalities in conclusion (2) of the theorem. In such a neighborhood the expressions (1·1) show, as before, that there can be no pair of distinct solutions $(x, y)$, $(x, y')$.

To prove conclusion (4) let $\Delta x_2 = \dots = \Delta x_m = 0$ in equations (1·2). These equations can then be written in the form

$$\sum_k B_{ik}\frac{\Delta y_k}{\Delta x_1} + C_i = 0,$$

where

$$C_i = \int_0^1 f_{ix_1}(x_1 + \theta\Delta x_1, x_2, \dots, x_m, v)\, d\theta .$$

It is evident that as $\Delta x_1$ approaches zero the quotients $\Delta y_k/\Delta x_1$ approach definite limits, and the existence of the derivatives of the functions $y_i(x_1, \dots, x_m)$

with respect to the variables $x_2, \ldots, x_m$ can be similarly proved. Furthermore, the derivatives with respect to $x_r$ satisfy the equations

$$\sum_k \frac{\partial f_i}{\partial y_k}\frac{\partial y_k}{\partial x_r} + \frac{\partial f_i}{\partial x_r} = 0 \qquad (i = 1, \ldots, n),$$

and these equations can be solved for $\partial y_k/\partial x_r$ $(k = 1, \ldots, n)$. The expressions so found are continuous in $x_1, \ldots, x_m$. Since the functions $y_i(x_1, \ldots, x_m)$ have continuous first derivatives, it follows from the same expressions that when the functions $f_i$ have continuous second derivatives the functions $y_i(x_1, \ldots, x_m)$ will have the same property. By an easy induction one obtains then the conclusion (4) of the theorem.

**2. An extension of the theorem of the preceding section.** The theorem which has just been established shows that, if a single initial solution $(a, b)$ of a system of equations $f_i(x, y) = 0$ is known, there will, in general, be a continuous set of solutions $[x, y(x_1, \ldots, x_m)]$ containing the initial one. In the following paragraphs it is to be proved that every continuous set of solutions $[x, y(x_1, \ldots, x_m)]$ with suitable properties is itself a part of a larger set. If $A$ is a set of points $x$, the notation $A_\delta$ indicates the set of points $x$ each of which satisfies the inequalities $|x_r - a_r| \leq \delta$ $(r = 1, \ldots, m)$ with at least one point $a$ of $A$.

THEOREM 2·1. *Let* P *be a set of points* $[x, y(x_1, \ldots, x_m)]$ *defined by a set of functions* $y_i(x_1, \ldots, x_m)$ *which are single valued and continuous in a bounded closed region* A *of* x*-space and with the further properties:*

(1) *The functions* $f_i(x, y)$ *are continuous and have continuous derivatives in a neighborhood* N *of* P;

(2) $f_i(x, y) = 0$ *in* P $\qquad (i = 1, \ldots, n)$;

(3) $D(x, y) \neq 0$ *in* P.

*Then there exists a set of functions* $Y_i(x_1, \ldots, x_m)$ *single valued and continuous in a neighborhood* $A_\delta$ *and having the properties:*

(1) *The points* $[x, Y(x_1, \ldots, x_m)]$ *which they define are in* N *and satisfy the equations* $f_i = 0$;

(2) *There exists a constant* $\epsilon$ *such that for each* x *in* $A_\delta$ *the set* $[x, Y(x_1, \ldots, x_m)]$ *is the only solution* (x, y) *of the equalities* $f_i = 0$ *satisfying the inequalities*

$$Y_i(x_1, \ldots, x_m) - \epsilon < y_i < Y_i(x_1, \ldots, x_m) + \epsilon \qquad (i = 1, \ldots, n);$$

(3) $Y_i(x_1, \ldots, x_m) = y_i(x_1, \ldots, x_m)$ *in* A;

(4) *In a sufficiently small neighborhood* $A_\delta$ *the functions* $Y_i(x_1, \ldots, x_m)$ *have continuous partial derivatives of as many orders as are possessed by the functions* $f_i$ *in the neighborhood* N.

To prove this, one should note first that the set of points $P$ is bounded and closed because $A$ is bounded and closed and that the functions $y_i(x)$ are continuous in $A$.

There exists a neighborhood $P_\epsilon$ in which no two distinct solutions $(x, y)$ of the equations $f_i = 0$ have the same projection $x$. Otherwise, for every positive integer $k$ there would be a set $(x, y, y')_k$ for which $(x, y)_k$ and $(x, y')_k$ are distinct solutions of the equations $f_i = 0$ in the neighborhood $P_{1/k}$. The sequence of points $(x, y, y')_k$ would be bounded and hence would have an accumulation point $(\xi, \eta, \eta')$. The point $(\xi, \eta)$ would necessarily be in $P$. Otherwise, since $P$ is closed, there would be neighborhoods $(\xi, \eta)_\epsilon$, $P_\epsilon$ having no point in common. The former would contain an infinity of the points $(x, y)_k$, and therefore surely some of those for which $1/k < \epsilon$ and which are in $P_\epsilon$. But this is impossible. Similarly, $(\xi, \eta')$ would be in $P$, and $(\xi, \eta')$ would coincide with $(\xi, \eta)$, since no two distinct points in $P$ have the same projection $\xi$. In every neighborhood of $(\xi, \eta)$ there would then be an infinity of the distinct solutions $(x, y)_k$, $(x, y')_k$ of the equations $f_i = 0$, which is impossible, according to the first paragraph of the proof of the preceding theorem. The existence of a neighborhood $P_\epsilon$ containing no two distinct solutions $(x, y)$, $(x, y')$ of the equations $f_i = 0$ is therefore proved.

There exists a neighborhood $A_\delta$ with $\delta \leqq \epsilon$ in which every $x$ is the projection of a solution $(x, y)$ of the equations $f_i = 0$ in $P_\epsilon$. Otherwise, for each positive integer $k$ there would be a point $(x)_k$ in the neighborhood $A_{1/k}$ which would not be the projection of any solution of the equations $f_i = 0$ in $P_\epsilon$. The sequence $(x)_k$ would be bounded and would have an accumulation point $\xi$ which, by an argument similar to that of the last paragraph, would be in $A$. It would therefore belong to a point $(\xi, \eta)$ of $P$. According to the proof of the fundamental theorem of the preceding section, however, there would then be a neighborhood $\xi_\delta$ in which every point $x$ would belong to a solution $(x, y)$ of the equations $f_i = 0$ in the neighborhood $(\xi, \eta)_\epsilon$. Thus the assumption made above would be contradicted; and it is evident that there must be a neighborhood $A_\delta$ in which every point $x$ belongs to a solution of the equations $f_i = 0$ in $P_\epsilon$, which may be denoted by $[x, Y(x_1, \ldots, x_m)]$.

The single-valued functions $Y_i(x_1, \ldots, x_m)$ defining the solutions of the equations $f_i = 0$ in $P_\epsilon$ for the points $x$ in $A_\delta$ are continuous and have continuous derivatives of as many orders as are possessed by the functions $f_i$ in the neighborhood $N$. This follows from conclusion (4) of the theorem of the preceding section applied at the point $(a, b) = [x, Y(x_1, \ldots, x_m)]$, at which all the hypotheses of that theorem are satisfied, provided only that the neighborhood $P_\epsilon$ is taken so small that the determinant $D(x, y)$ is everywhere different from zero in it. Thus conclusions (1) and (4) of the theorem of this section are proved. Conclusion (3) is an immediate consequence of the fact that in the neighborhood $P_\epsilon$ no two distinct solutions of the equations $f_i = 0$ can have the same projection $x$. Conclusion (2) follows from the second paragraph of the proof of the theorem applied to the set of points $[x, Y(x_1, \ldots, x_m)]$ corresponding to the points $x$ in $A_\delta$.

## II. EXISTENCE THEOREMS FOR DIFFERENTIAL EQUATIONS[2]

In the following paragraphs the existence and imbedding theorems for differential equations which are useful in the calculus of variations will be deduced. The notations of the preceding pages on implicit functions will again be useful, with the additional agreement that the modulus of $y$ is defined by the equation

$$\text{mod}\, y = (y_1^2 + \ldots + y_n^2)^{1/2}.$$

**3. The existence of a solution through an initial point.** The system of equations to be considered has the form

$$\frac{dy_i}{dx} = f_i(x, y_1, \ldots, y_n) \qquad (i = 1, \ldots, n), \tag{3·1}$$

and the initial point through which a solution is sought is $(\xi, \eta) = (\xi, \eta_1, \ldots, \eta_n)$. The functions $f_i(x, y)$ are supposed to have the following properties:

(*a*) They are single valued and continuous in a neighborhood $(\xi, \eta)_\epsilon$;

(*b*) There exists a constant $k$ such that for every pair of points $(x, y)$ and $(x, Y)$ in $(\xi, \eta)_\epsilon$

$$|f_i(x, y) - f_i(x, Y)| < \frac{k}{n^{1/2}} \text{mod}(y - Y) \qquad (i = 1, \ldots, n).$$

The factor $1/n^{1/2}$ is introduced for convenience. The maximum of the absolute values $|f_i|$ in the neighborhood $(\xi, \eta)_\epsilon$ will be denoted by $M$. By a solution of the equations (3·1) is meant always a set of functions $y_i(x)$ which, with their derivatives $y_i'(x)$, are continuous on an interval $x_1x_2$ and satisfy the equations. Such a solution is said to be interior to $(\xi, \eta)_\epsilon$ if all the points $[x, y(x)]$ which it defines on $x_1x_2$ are in this neighborhood. The first theorem to be proved is then the following:

THEOREM 3·1. *If the functions* $f_i(x, y)$ *have the properties described above in a neighborhood* $(\xi, \eta)_\epsilon$, *then there exists in* $(\xi, \eta)_\epsilon$ *one and but one solution* $y_i(x)$ *of equations (3·1) through the initial point* $(\xi, \eta)$. *The solution* $y_i(x)$ *is defined and interior to* $(\xi, \eta)_\epsilon$ *at least on the interval* $|x - \xi| \leqq l$, *where* $l$ *is the smaller of* $\epsilon$ *and* $\epsilon/M$.

To prove the theorem consider the sequence of functions starting with $y_{i0} = \eta_i$ and defined successively by the equations

$$\begin{aligned} y_{i1} &= \eta_i + \int_\xi^x f_i(x, y_0)\,dx, \\ y_{i2} &= \eta_i + \int_\xi^x f_i(x, y_1)\,dx, \\ &\cdots\cdots\cdots\cdots \\ y_{i,m+1} &= \eta_i + \int_\xi^x f_i(x, y_m)\,dx, \\ &\cdots\cdots\cdots\cdots, \end{aligned} \tag{3·2}$$

where in the integrands only the second subscripts of the $y_{im}$ are indicated.

[2] For earlier presentations and further references see Bliss, *op. cit.*, and "The Solutions of Differential Equations of the First Order as Functions of Their Initial Values," *Annals of Mathematics*, 2d ser., VI (1905), 49–68; also Bolza, *op. cit.*

The functions of the sequence are all well defined on the interval $|x - \xi| \leqq l$, since the set $y_{i1}$ evidently has this property; and since when the set $y_{im}$ defines points $(x, y_m)$ in $(\xi, \eta)_\epsilon$, then also

$$|y_{i,m+1} - \eta_i| = \left| \int_\xi^x f_i(x, y_m)\, dx \right| \leqq M|x - \xi| < \epsilon .$$

Consequently, the points $(x, y_{m+1})$ are also in $(\xi, \eta)_\epsilon$ and can be used to define the next functions of the sequence.

It can now be shown that the series

$$(3\cdot 3) \qquad y_{i1} + (y_{i2} - y_{i1}) + \ldots + (y_{im} - y_{i,m-1}) + \ldots$$

converge uniformly on the interval $|x - \xi| \leqq l$, so that the same is true of the sequence of functions $y_{im}$. If $P$ is a constant such that $|y_{i1} - y_{i0}| \leqq P$ on the interval $|x - \xi| \leqq l$, then one can easily see, by an inductive proof with the help of the property $(b)$, that

$$|y_{i2} - y_{i1}| \leqq \left| \int_\xi^x \frac{k}{n^{1/2}} \operatorname{mod}(y_1 - y_0)\, dx \right| \leqq P \frac{k|x - \xi|}{1!},$$

$$\cdots\cdots\cdots\cdots\cdots\cdots\cdots\cdots$$

$$|y_{i,m+1} - y_{im}| \leqq P \frac{(k|x - \xi|)^m}{m!} \leqq P \frac{(kl)^m}{m!}.$$

Hence the terms of the series (3·3) after the first are dominated by the terms of the convergent series of constants $P(e^{kl} - 1)$. Since the terms of the series (3·3) are all continuous functions of $x$ on the interval $|x - \xi| \leqq l$, the same is true of its limit $y_i(x)$.

The limit functions $y_i(x)$ satisfy the integral equations

$$(3\cdot 4) \qquad y_i(x) = \eta_i + \int_\xi^x f_i[x, y(x)]\, dx ,$$

since the two members of this equation are the limits of the corresponding sequences in equations (3·2). It follows at once, by differentiating the last equation, that the system $y_i(x)$ is a solution of (3·1).

There cannot be two distinct solutions $y_i(x)$, $z_i(x)$ through the initial point $(\xi, \eta)$. Such a pair of solutions would, in fact, satisfy the relations

$$y_i = \eta_i + \int_\xi^x f_i(x, y)\, dx ,$$

$$z_i = \eta_i + \int_\xi^x f_i(x, z)\, dx ,$$

$$|y_i - z_i| \leqq \left| \int_\xi^x \frac{k}{n^{1/2}} \operatorname{mod}(y - z)\, dx \right| .$$

If $Q$ is the maximum of the expressions $|y_i(x) - z_i(x)|$ on $|x - \xi| \leqq l$, the last inequality shows successively that

$$|y_i - z_i| \leqq Qk|x - \xi|$$
$$\cdot \quad \cdot \quad \cdot \quad \cdot \quad \cdot \quad \cdot$$
$$\leqq Q\frac{(k|x-\xi|)^m}{m!} \leqq Q\frac{(kl)^m}{m!}.$$

Since this expression approaches zero as $m$ increases indefinitely, it follows that $y_i(x) \equiv z_i(x)$, and the two solutions must be identical.

**4. Existence theorem for linear equations.** For a system of equations linear in the variables $y_i$, of the form

$$(4\cdot 1) \qquad \frac{dy_i}{dx} = A_{ik}(x, b_1, \ldots, b_s)y_k + B_i(x, b_1, \ldots, b_s) \qquad (i = 1, \ldots, n),$$

the methods of the preceding section give further results of importance. It is presupposed that the functions $A_{ik}(x, b)$, $B_i(x, b)$ are continuous for all sets $(x, b)$ satisfying the conditions

$$x_1 \leqq x \leqq x_2, \qquad (b_1, \ldots, b_s) \text{ in a region } B,$$

where $B$ is a bounded closed region in the space of points $(b_1, \ldots, b_s)$. Then one can prove:

THEOREM 4·1. *Through each initial point* $(\xi, \eta)$ *with* $x_1 \leqq \xi \leqq x_2$, *and for each set* b *in* B, *equations (4·1) have one and but one solution. The functions* $y_i(x, \xi, \eta, b)$ *defining this solution and their derivatives* $y_{ix}$ *are continuous for all sets* $(x, \xi, \eta, b)$ *satisfying the conditions*

$$(4\cdot 2) \qquad x_1 \leqq x, \ \xi \leqq x_2, \qquad b \text{ in } B.$$

If in the sequence (3·2) the functions $f_i$ are the second members of equations (4·1), it is easy to see that the functions $y_{im}(x, \xi, \eta, b)$ of the sequence are defined and continuous for all sets $(x, \xi, \eta, b)$ satisfying the conditions

$$(4\cdot 3) \qquad x_1 \leqq x \leqq x_2, \qquad x_1 \leqq \xi \leqq x_2, \qquad |\eta_i| \leqq C, \qquad b \text{ in } B,$$

where $C$ is an arbitrary constant. The constants $k$, $P$ of the convergence proof can be selected so that they are effective simultaneously for all $x, \xi, \eta, b$ satisfying the conditions (4·3). Hence the sequence $y_{im}(x, \xi, \eta, b)$ converges uniformly for all sets $(x, \xi, \eta, b)$ satisfying (4·3), and the limit functions $y_i(x, \xi, \eta, b)$ are continuous for all sets $(x, \xi, \eta, b)$ satisfying (4·2), since the constant $C$ is arbitrary. The equations (4·1), satisfied by these functions, show that the derivatives $y_{ix}$ have the same continuity property. The proof of the uniqueness of the solution when $\xi, \eta, b$ are fixed is identical with the uniqueness proof of the last section.

**5. The imbedding theorem.** In Section 3, above, it was shown that through each initial point $(\xi, \eta)$ there exists one and but one solution of the differential equations (3·1) defined on a properly chosen interval $|x - \xi| \leqq l$. In the present section it is proposed to prove that a solution $E$, already known, is always a member of a family of such solutions determined by neighboring initial points. The theorem to be established is the following one:

THEOREM 5·1. THE IMBEDDING THEOREM. *If in a neighborhood* R *of the points* (x, y) *on an arc* E *having equations of the form*

$$y_i = y_i(x) \qquad (x_1 \leqq x \leqq x_2) \tag{5·1}$$

*the functions* $f_i(x, y)$ *have the continuity properties* (a) *and* (b) *of Section 3, and if* E *is a solution of the differential equations (3·1), then through every point* $(\xi, \eta)$ *sufficiently near to* E *there passes one and but one solution*

$$y_i = y_i(x, \xi, \eta)$$

*of the differential equations. The functions* $y_i(x, \xi, \eta)$ *and their derivatives* $y_{ix}(x, \xi, \eta)$ *are continuous and satisfy the differential equations (3·1) identically for all sets* $(x, \xi, \eta)$ *in a neighborhood* N *of those belonging to* E.

In order to prove the theorem it should first be noted that the curve (5·1) satisfies the equations

$$y_i(x) = y_i(\xi) + \int_\xi^x f_i[x, y(x)]\, dx\,, \tag{5·2}$$

since it is a solution of equations (3·1). The notation $E_\epsilon$ will be used to denote the totality of points $(x, y)$ satisfying the conditions

$$x_1 \leqq x \leqq x_2\,, \qquad |y_i - y_i(x)| \leqq \epsilon\,;$$

and $E_\delta$ will represent a similar neighborhood for which

$$\delta < \epsilon e^{-kl}\,, \qquad l = x_2 - x_1\,.$$

It is always understood that the constant $\epsilon$ is taken so small that the whole of $E_\epsilon$ is contained in the neighborhood $R$ of $E$ where the functions $f_i$ have the continuity properties of the theorem.

The proof is made by means of the sequence of approximation functions $y_{im}(x, \xi, \eta)$ defined by the equations (3·2), in which, however,

$$y_{i0}(x, \xi, \eta) = \eta_i + y_i(x) - y_i(\xi)\,. \tag{5·3}$$

The elements $y_{im}(x, \xi, \eta)$ of the sequence are well-defined and continuous for all sets $(x, \xi, \eta)$ satisfying the conditions

$$x_1 \leqq x \leqq x_2\,, \qquad (\xi, \eta) \text{ in } E_\delta\,, \tag{5·4}$$

since with the help of equations (5·3), (3·2), (5·2), and the property (*b*) it follows successively that

$$|y_{i0} - y_i(x)| = |\eta_i - y_i(\xi)| \leqq \delta\,,$$

$$|y_{i1} - y_i(x)| \leqq \left|\eta_i - y_i(\xi) + \int_\xi^x \{f_i(x, y_0) - f_i[x, y(x)]\}\, dx\right|$$

$$\leqq \delta\left\{1 + \frac{k|x-\xi|}{1!}\right\},$$

. . . . . . . . . . . . . . . . . . . . . . . . . . . . . . . . .

$$|y_{im} - y_i(x)| < \delta\left\{1 + \frac{k|x-\xi|}{1!} + \ldots + \frac{(k|x-\xi|)^m}{m!}\right\};$$

and the last expression is less than $\delta e^{kl}$, which is, in turn, less than $\epsilon$. Hence, every approximation curve lies in the neighborhood $E_\epsilon$ and can be used to define the succeeding one.

The convergence proof for the sequence $y_{im}(x, \xi, \eta)$ is identical with that of Section 3. It should be noticed, however, that a constant $P$ exists such that

$$|y_{i1}(x, \xi, \eta) - y_{i0}(x, \xi, \eta)| \leqq P$$

for all sets $(x, \xi, \eta)$ satisfying the conditions (5·4), on account of the continuity of $y_{i1}$ and $y_{i0}$. Hence the convergence of the sequence $y_{im}(x, \xi, \eta)$ is uniform in the region of points $(x, \xi, \eta)$ defined by (5·4), and the limit-function $y_i(x, \xi, \eta)$ is also continuous in that region.

The proof that $y_i(x, \xi, \eta)$ satisfies equations (3·1) and is the only solution of these equations through the initial point $(\xi, \eta)$ is the same as that of Section 3. The continuity of $y_{ix}(x, \xi, \eta)$ in the region defined by (5·4) follows from equations (3·1) and the continuity of $y_i(x, \xi, \eta)$.

If the existence theorem of Section 3 is applied at the end-points of $E$, an extended solution $E'$ is found on an interval $x_1'x_2'$ containing $x_1x_2$ in its interior. The arguments of the preceding paragraphs applied to $E'$ justify the continuity properties of $y_i(x, \xi, \eta)$ and $y_{ix}(x, \xi, \eta)$, not only for points $(x, \xi, \eta)$ with $x_1 \leqq x \leqq x_2$, but also for a neighborhood $N$ of the kind described in Theorem 5·1.

**6. Derivatives with respect to constants of integration.** In order to describe the circumstances under which the solution $y_i(x, \xi, \eta)$ of the last section has partial derivatives with respect to the constants $\xi, \eta$, let us consider first a family of solutions

$$y_i = Y_i(x, b) \tag{6·1}$$

of equations (3·1), including the original solution $E$ for the parameter values

$$x_1 \leqq x \leqq x_2, \quad b_h = b_h^0 \quad (h = 1, \dots, r) \tag{6·2}$$

and having functions $y_i(x, b)$ and their derivatives $y_{ix}(x, b)$ continuous in a neighborhood of the values $(x, b)$ satisfying the conditions (6·2). Then we can prove:

THEOREM 6·1. *If the functions* $f_i(x, y)$ *are continuous and have continuous partial derivatives of orders* $\leqq q$ *with respect to the variables* $y$ *in a neighborhood* $R$ *of the points* $(x, y)$ *on the arc* $E$, *and if at one particular value* $x = \xi$ *the functions* $Y_i(\xi, b)$ *have their partial derivatives of orders* $\leqq q$ *with respect to the variables* $b$ *continuous near* $b = b^0$, *then the solutions* $Y_i(x, b)$ *of equations (3·1) and their derivatives* $Y_{ix}(x, b)$ *have continuous partial derivatives of orders* $\leqq q$ *with respect to the variables* $b$ *at every point* $(x, b)$ *in a neighborhood of the sets* $(x, b)$ *belonging to* $E$ *specified in (6·2).*

*If the functions* $f_i$ *have continuous partial derivatives of orders* $\leqq q$ *with respect to all of the variables* $x, y$ *in the neighborhood* $R$, *then the functions* $Y_i(x, b)$ *and* $Y_{ix}(x, b)$ *have continuous partial derivatives of orders* $\leqq q$ *with respect to all of the variables* $x, b$ *in a neighborhood of the values* $(x, b)$ *belonging to* $E$ *specified in (6·2).*

The theorem will be proved for the case when there is only one parameter $b$. The extension for several parameters is simple.

To prove the existence of the first derivatives $\partial Y_i/\partial b$ for values $x \neq \xi$, it should first be noted that for values $b$, $b + \Delta b$ near $b^0$ the quotients

$$z_i = \frac{Y_i(x,\ b+\Delta b) - Y_i(x,\ b)}{\Delta b} = \frac{\Delta Y_i}{\Delta b}$$

are solutions of the linear equations

$$\frac{dz_i}{dx} = A_{ik}(x,\ b,\ \Delta b)\, z_k\ , \tag{6·3}$$

where

$$A_{ik} = \int_0^1 f_{ik}(x,\ Y + \theta \Delta Y)\, d\theta\ .$$

The notation $f_{ik}$ is used for the derivative $\partial f_i/\partial y_k$. The functions $A_{ik}$ are continuous in a neighborhood of the values $(x, b, \Delta b)$ satisfying the conditions

$$x_1 \leqq x \leqq x_2\ , \qquad b = b^0\ , \qquad \Delta b = 0\ .$$

Hence, according to Theorem 4·1, there exists through the initial point $(\xi, \zeta)$ one and but one solution $z_i(x, \xi, \zeta, b, \Delta b)$ $(i = 1, \ldots, n)$ of the linear equations (6·3). For this solution the functions $z_i$ and their derivatives $z_{ix}$ are continuous at sets $(x, \xi, \zeta, b, \Delta b)$ with $\zeta$ arbitrarily chosen and with values $(x, \xi, b, \Delta b)$ in a neighborhood of those defined by the conditions

$$x_1 \leqq x\ , \qquad \xi \leqq x_2\ , \qquad b = b^0\ , \qquad \Delta b = 0\ .$$

The solutions $z_i = \Delta Y_i/\Delta b$ of equations (6·3) are expressible in the form

$$\frac{\Delta Y_i}{\Delta b} = z_i \left[ x,\ \xi,\ \left(\frac{\Delta Y}{\Delta b}\right)_\xi,\ b,\ \Delta b \right],$$

where the notation $(\Delta Y/\Delta b)_\xi$ stands for the set of initial values of the quotients $\Delta Y_i/\Delta b$ at $x = \xi$. If these quotients approach limits as $\Delta b$ approaches zero, as supposed in the theorem, it follows from the last equation that the same is true for $\Delta Y/\Delta b$ at every value of $x$. Thus it is clear that the derivatives $\partial Y_i/\partial b$ exist, have the values

$$\frac{\partial Y_i}{\partial b} = z_i \left[ x,\ \xi,\ \left(\frac{\partial Y}{\partial b}\right)_\xi,\ b,\ 0 \right],$$

and are continuous for all sets $(x, b)$ in a neighborhood of those specified by the conditions (6·2).

The preceding paragraph is a proof of the first part of Theorem 6·1 for $q = 1$. We now assume the theorem true for integers $\leqq q$ and prove that it holds for $q + 1$. We start with the assumptions that the functions $f_i$ have continuous derivatives of orders $\leqq q + 1$ in the variables $y$ and that at a fixed value $x = \xi$ the family of solutions (6·1) has continuous partial derivatives of orders $\leqq q+1$ with respect to $b$. The equations

$$\frac{db}{dx} = 0\ , \qquad \frac{dz_i}{dx} = f_{ik}[x,\ Y(x,\ b)]\, z_k \tag{6·4}$$

are of the type (3·1) in the variables $x, b, z$. They have a family of solutions

$$b, \quad z_i(x, b) = Y_i(x, b) \tag{6·5}$$

analogous to (6·1) for equations (3·1). It contains an initial solution analogous to $E$ for the values (6·2). The functions $z_i(\xi, b)$ have continuous derivatives of orders $\leqq q$ with respect to $b$, since $Y_i(\xi, b)$ is now assumed to have derivatives of orders $\leqq q + 1$. The second members of equations (6·4) have continuous derivatives of orders $\leqq q$ with respect to $b$ and $z_k$ in a neighborhood of the values $x, b, z$ belonging to the initial solution of (6·4) defined by the values (6·2). Hence the family (6·5) has continuous derivatives of orders $\leqq q$ with respect to $b$ in a neighborhood of the values $(x, b)$ specified by the conditions (6·2), since the theorem is now supposed to hold for the integer $q$. The functions $Y_i(x, b)$ have, therefore, continuous derivatives of orders $\leqq q + 1$ with respect to $b$ in the same neighborhood, which was to be proved. That the same is true of the functions $Y_{ix}(x, b)$ is seen by substituting $Y_i(x, b)$ in equations (3·1).

The second paragraph of Theorem 6·1 can easily be justified for $q = 1$ by establishing first, as above, the existence of continuous derivatives $Y_{ix}(x, b)$ and $Y_{ib}(x, b)$. Then it follows from equations (3·1) with $Y_i(x, b)$ substituted that $Y_{ix}$ has continuous first derivatives.

The induction needed for the second part of the theorem is much like the one above. We start with the assumptions that the functions $f_i$ have continuous derivatives of orders $\leqq q + 1$ with respect to all of the variables $x, y$ and that $y_i(\xi, b)$ has continuous derivatives of orders $\leqq q + 1$ with respect to $b$. The second members of equations (6·4) now have continuous derivatives of orders $\leqq q$ with respect to all of the variables $x, b, z_i$; and their solutions (6·5) have, therefore, continuous derivatives of orders $\leqq q$ with respect to all of the variables $x, b$ in a neighborhood of the values $(x, b)$ specified by (6·2). It follows readily, by an argument like that of the next to the last paragraph, that $Y_i$ and $Y_{ix}$ have derivatives of orders $\leqq q + 1$ in all of the variables $x, b$. Thus Theorem 6·1 is completely proved.

If the family (6·1) contains $n$ parameters $b_k$ $(k = 1, \ldots, n)$ and is such that the functional determinant $|\partial Y_i/\partial b_k|$ is everywhere different from zero, then the equations

$$Y_i(\xi, b) = \eta_i \tag{6·6}$$

will, in general, have solutions $b_k(\xi, \eta)$ which define a solution

$$Y_i[x, b(\xi, \eta)]$$

of the differential equations (3·1) through the point $(\xi, \eta)$. On account of the uniqueness of the solution through $(\xi, \eta)$ we must then have

$$Y_i[x, b(\xi, \eta)] \equiv y_i(x, \xi \ \eta), \tag{6·7}$$

where the functions on the right are the ones whose existence was stated in Theorem 5·1. We shall use this remark to advantage in the proof of the following theorem:

THEOREM 6·2. *If the functions* $f_i(x, y)$ *are continuous and have continuous partial derivatives of orders* $\leqq q$ *with respect to the variables* $y$ *in a neighborhood* $R$ *of the points* $(x, y)$ *on the arc* $E$, *then there is a neighborhood* $N$ *of the points* $(x, \xi, \eta)$ *on* $E$ *in which the functions* $y_i(x, \xi, \eta)$ *of Theorem 5·1 and their derivatives* $y_{ix}(x, \xi, \eta)$ *have continuous partial derivatives of orders* $\leqq q$ *with respect to the parameters* $\eta_k$ *for each fixed* $\xi$.

*If the functions* $f_i$ *have continuous partial derivatives of orders* $\leqq q$ *with respec to all the variables* $x, y$ *in a neighborhood* $R$, *then there is a neighborhood* $N$ *in which the functions* $y_i$ *and their derivatives* $y_{ix}$ *have continuous partial derivatives of orders* $\leqq q$ *with respect to all of the variables* $x, \xi, \eta$.

There is always a family (6·1) containing $E$ and having $n$ parameters $b$ such that the functional determinant $|\partial Y_i/\partial b_k|$ is everywhere different from zero. Such a family is the one defined by $y_i(x, \xi, \eta)$ for a fixed value $\xi$. The functional determinant $|\partial y_i/\partial \eta_k|$ has the value unity at $x = \xi$ and is different from zero everywhere, since its columns form a fundamental system of solutions of the linear equations

$$z_i' = f_{ik}[x, y(x, \xi, \eta)] z_k .$$

The proof of this well-known property is like that of Section 12 of Part I above for the case when there are four variables $z$.

The equations (6·6) have initial solutions $\xi, \eta, b$ defined by the conditions

$$(\xi, \eta) \text{ on the arc } E, \qquad b = b^0 .$$

Hence, according to Theorem 2·1, they have a solution $b_i(\xi, \eta)$ defined and continuous in a neighborhood of the values $(\xi, \eta)$ belonging to the arc $E$ and having the values $b_i^0$ whenever $(\xi, \eta)$ is on $E$. As a consequence of the hypotheses of the first part of Theorem 6·2, the functions $b_i(\xi, \eta)$ have continuous derivatives of orders $\leqq q$ with respect to the variables $\eta_k$ when $\xi$ is fixed. According to the hypotheses of the second part of the theorem, the functions $b_i(\xi, \eta)$ have continuous derivatives of orders $\leqq q$ with respect to all of the variables $\xi, \eta$. On account of the identity (6·7) these properties justify the conclusions of the theorem.

It is perhaps interesting to note that, as a result of the hypotheses of the first part of the theorem, the functions $y_i(x, \xi, \eta)$ have more continuous derivatives than are there specified. The solution $b_k(\xi, \eta)$ has, in fact, in that case, a part of its derivatives of orders $\leqq q$ with respect to all of the variables $\xi, \eta$ continuous. The continuous ones are those which do not involve more than one differentiation with respect to $\xi$. Evidently, the same will then be true of the derivatives of $y_i(x, \xi, \eta)$ and $y_{ix}(x, \xi, \eta)$ with respect to the variables $\xi, \eta$.

COROLLARY 6·3. *Suppose that the equations*

$$\frac{dy_i}{dx} = f_i(x, y_1, \ldots, y_n, b_1, \ldots, b_s) \qquad (i = 1, \ldots, n) \tag{6.8}$$

*have a particular solution* E *for special values* $b_{r0}$ $(r = 1, \ldots, s)$ *of the parameters* b *and that the functions* $f_i(x, y, b)$ *are continuous and have continuous partial derivatives with respect to the variables* $y_k$, $b_r$ *in a neighborhood of the values* $(x, y, b)$ *belonging to* E. *Then for parametric values* $b_r$ *sufficiently near to the* $b_{r0}$ *there exists one and but one solution of equations* (6·8) *through a point* $(\xi, \eta)$ *sufficiently near to* E. *The functions*

$$y_i = y_i(x, \xi, \eta, b)$$

*defining this solution, and their derivatives* $y_{ix}$, *are continuous in a neighborhood* N *of the values* $(x, \xi, \eta, b)$ *belonging to* E. *If the functions* $f_i(x, y, b)$ *have continuous derivatives of orders* $\leqq q$ *with respect to the variables* $y_k$, $b_r$, *then for each fixed* $\xi = x_0$ *the functions* $y_i$, $y_{ix}$ *have partial derivatives of orders* $\leqq q$ *with respect to* $\eta_k$, $b_r$ *continuous at each* $(x, \eta, b)$ *such that* $(x, x_0, \eta, b)$ *is in* N. *If the functions* $f_i(x, y, b)$ *have all partial derivatives of orders* $\leqq q$ *continuous, then the functions* $y_i$, $y_{ix}$ *have all partial derivatives of orders* $\leqq q$ *with respect to the variables* $x, \xi, \eta, b$ *continuous in* N.

These results are immediate consequences of the preceding corollaries applied to the system of equations

$$\frac{dy_i}{dx} = f_i(x, y, b), \qquad \frac{db_r}{dx} = 0 \qquad (i = 1, \ldots, n; \; r = 1, \ldots, s).$$

In conclusion, attention may be called to a formula which is sometimes useful. The matrix $\|y_{i\eta_k}(x, \xi, \eta)\|$ reduces to the identity matrix at $x = \xi$, and its columns form a fundamental system of solutions of the linear equations

$$z_i' = f_{ik}[x, y(x, \xi, \eta)] \, z_k. \tag{6·9}$$

Every solution $z_i$ of these equations is expressible in the form

$$z_i = \zeta_k \, y_{i\eta_k}, \tag{6·10}$$

where the $\zeta_k$ are the initial values of the functions $z_k$ at $x = \xi$. This is evident since the second members of equations (6·10) are solutions of the equations (6·9) and have at $x = \xi$ the initial values $\zeta_i$ which characterize uniquely the solutions $z_i$.

On account of the identities

$$y_i(\xi, \xi, \eta) = \eta_i,$$

we have the equation

$$y_{ix}(\xi, \xi, \eta) + y_{i\xi}(\xi, \xi, \eta) = 0;$$

and we see that the solution $y_{i\xi}(x, \xi, \eta)$ of equations (6·9) has at $x = \xi$ the initial values

$$y_{i\xi}(\xi, \xi, \eta) = -y_{ix}(\xi, \xi, \eta) = -f_i(\xi, \eta).$$

Hence, by means of (6·10), the solution $y_{i\xi}$ is expressible in the form

$$y_{i\xi}(x, \xi, \eta) = -f_k(\xi, \eta)\, y_{i\eta_k}(x, \xi, \eta). \tag{6·11}$$

These equations show that for a fixed value $x$ the functions $y_i(x, \xi, \eta)$ are $n$ independent solutions $g(\xi, \eta)$ of the partial differential equations

$$\frac{\partial g}{\partial \xi} + f_k(\xi, \eta)\frac{\partial g}{\partial \eta_k} = 0\,.$$

They also express the fact that for a fixed $x$, $y$ the equations

$$y_i = y_i(x, \xi, \eta) \tag{6·12}$$

define a curve with running coordinates $\xi$, $\eta$ which satisfies equations (3·1). On account of the uniqueness of the solution of equations (3·1) through the point $(\xi, \eta)$ or through the point $(x, y)$, it follows readily that equations (6·12) have the solutions

$$\eta_i = y_i(\xi, x, y)\,,$$

and conversely. This property is closely related to those above.

# BIBLIOGRAPHY

## A BIBLIOGRAPHY FOR THE PROBLEM OF BOLZA

In the following list, references are frequently made to *Contributions to the Calculus of Variations, Department of Mathematics of the University of Chicago.* These books will be designated simply as *Contributions.*


1. A. MAYER, "Zur Aufstellung der Kriterien des Maximums und Minimums der einfachen Integrale bei variabeln Grenzwerten," *Leipziger Berichte*, XXXVI (1884), 99–128.
2. SCHEEFFER, "Die Maxima und Minima der einfachen Integrale zwischen festen Grenzen," *Mathematische Annalen*, XXV (1885), 522–93.
3. A. MAYER, "Zur Aufstellung der Kriterien des Maximums und Minimums der einfachen Integrale bei variabeln Grenzwerten," *Leipziger Berichte*, XLVIII (1896), 436–65.
4. MASON, "Randwertaufgaben bei gewöhnlichen Differentialgleichungen." Dissertation, Göttingen, 1903. See also *Mathematische Annalen*, LVIII (1904), 528–44.
5. CAIRNS, "Die Anwendung der Integralgleichungen auf die zweite Variation bei isoperimetrischen Problemen." Dissertation, Göttingen, 1907.
6. RICHARDSON, "Das Jacobische Kriterium der Variationsrechnung und die Oszillationseigenschaften linearer Differentialgleichungen 2. Ordnung," *Mathematische Annalen*, LXVIII (1910), 279–304, and LXXI (1911), 214–32.


The ideas of Hilbert concerning the relationship between boundary-value problems and the calculus of variations have become accessible, for the most part, through the papers of his students, such as references 4, 5, and 6 above. For simpler cases see reference 14 below.


7. HAHN, "Über Variationsprobleme mit variabeln Endpunkten," *Monatshefte für Mathematik und Physik*, XXII (1911), 127–36.
8. BOLZA, "Über den anormalen Fall beim Lagrangeschen und Mayerschen Problem mit gemischten Bedingungen und variabeln Endpunkten," *Mathematische Annalen*, LXXIV (1913), 430–46.
9. LECAT, "Calcul des variations," *Encyclopêdie des sciences mathêmatiques*, II 31 (1913), pp. 156–58.
10. HANCOCK, *Theory of Maxima and Minima.* 1917. Pp. iv+193.
11. BLISS, "The Problem of Mayer with Variable End-Points," *Transactions of the American Mathematical Society*, XIX (1918), 305–14.
12. LAREW, "Necessary Conditions in the Problem of Mayer in the Calculus of Variations," *Transactions of the American Mathematical Society*, XX (1919), 1–22.
13. LAREW, "The Hilbert Integral and Mayer Fields for the Problem of Mayer in the Calculus of Variations," *Transactions of the American Mathematical Society*, XXVI (1924), 61–67.
14. LOVITT, *Linear Integral Equations.* 1924. Pp. xiii+253.
15. BLISS, "A Boundary Value Problem of the Calculus of Variations," *Bulletin of the American Mathematical Society*, XXXII (1926), 317–31.

16. COPE, "An Analogue of Jacobi's Condition for the Problem of Mayer with Variable End-Points." Dissertation, University of Chicago, 1927. See also *American Journal of Mathematics*, LIX (1937), 655–72.
17. BLISS, "The Problem of Lagrange in the Calculus of Variations," *American Journal of Mathematics*, LII (1930), 673–744.
18. BOYCE, "An Envelope Theorem and Necessary Conditions for a Problem of Mayer with Variable End-Points." Dissertation, University of Chicago, 1930. See also *Contributions 1930*, pp. (5)–(43).
19. MORSE, "The Problems of Lagrange and Mayer under General End Conditions," *Proceedings of the National Academy of Sciences*, XVI (1930), 229–33.
20. GRAVES, "On the Problem of Lagrange," *American Journal of Mathematics*, LIII (1931), 547–54.
21. HEFNER, "The Condition of Mayer for Discontinuous Solutions of the Lagrange Problem." Dissertation, University of Chicago, 1931. See also *Contributions 1931–1932*, pp. (95)–(130).
22. MORSE, "Sufficient Conditions in the Problem of Lagrange with Fixed End-Points," *Annals of Mathematics*, XXXII (1931), 567–77.
23. MORSE, "Sufficient Conditions in the Problem of Lagrange with Variable End Conditions," *American Journal of Mathematics*, LIII (1931), 517–46.
24. MORSE and MYERS, "The Problems of Lagrange and Mayer with Variable End-Points," *Proceedings of the American Academy of Arts and Sciences*, LXVI (1931), 235–53.
25. BLISS, "The Problem of Bolza in the Calculus of Variations," *Annals of Mathematics*, XXXIII (1932), 261–74.
26. BLISS and SCHOENBERG, "On the Derivation of Necessary Conditions for the Problem of Bolza," *Bulletin of the American Mathematical Society*, XXXVIII (1932), 858–64.
27. CARATHÉODORY, "Die Theorie der zweiten Variation beim Problem von Lagrange," *Sitzungsberichte der Bayerischen Akademie der Wissenschaften*, 1932, pp. 99–114.
28. CURRIER, "The Variable End-Point Problem of the Calculus of Variations Including a Generalization of the Classical Jacobi Conditions," *Transactions of the American Mathematical Society*, XXXIV (1932), 689–704.
29. GRAVES, "On the Weierstrass Condition for the Problem of Bolza in the Calculus of Variations," *Annals of Mathematics*, XXXIII (1932), 747–52.
30. HESTENES, "Sufficient Conditions for the General Problem of Mayer with Variable End-Points." Dissertation, University of Chicago, 1932. See also *Transactions of the American Mathematical Society*, XXXV (1933), 479–90; and *Contributions 1931–1932*, pp. (339)–(359).
31. HU, "The Problem of Bolza and Its Accessory Boundary Value Problem." Dissertation, University of Chicago, 1932. See also *Contributions 1931–1932*, pp. (361)–(443).
32. MYERS, S. B., "Adjoint Systems in the Problem of Mayer under General End Conditions," *Bulletin of the American Mathematical Society*, XXXVIII (1932), 303–12.
33. REID, "A Boundary Value Problem Associated with the Calculus of Variations," *American Journal of Mathematics*, LIV (1932), 769–90.

34. Bliss and Hestenes, "Sufficient Conditions for a Problem of Mayer in the Calculus of Variations," *Transactions of the American Mathematical Society*, XXXV (1933), 305–26. See also *Contributions 1931–1932*, pp. (295)–(337).

35. Bower, "The Problem of Lagrange with Finite Side Conditions." Dissertation, University of Chicago, 1933. See also *Contributions 1933–1937*, pp. (1)–(51).

36. Carathéodory, "Über die Einteilung der Lagrangeschen Variationsprobleme nach Klassen," *Commentarii mathematici Helvitici*, V (1933), 1–10.

37. Graves, "A Transformation of the Problem of Lagrange in the Calculus of Variations," *Transactions of the American Mathematical Society*, XXXV (1933), 675–82.

38. Hestenes, "Sufficient Conditions for the Problem of Bolza in the Calculus of Variations," *Transactions of the American Mathematical Society*, XXXVI (1934), 793–818.

39. Reid, "Analogues of the Jacobi Condition for the Problem of Mayer in the Calculus of Variations," *Annals of Mathematics*, XXXV (1934), 836–48.

40. Carathéodory, *Variationsrechnung und partielle Differentialgleichungen erster Ordnung*, 1935. Pp. xi+407.

41. Morse, "Sufficient Conditions in the Problem of Lagrange without Assumptions of Normality," *Transactions of the American Mathematical Society*, XXXVII (1935), 147–60.

42. Perlin, "Sufficient Conditions for a Minimum in the Problem of Lagrange with Isoperimetric Conditions," Dissertation, University of Chicago, 1937. See also *Contributions 1933–1937*, pp. (207)–(241).

43. Reid, "Discontinuous Solutions in the Non-parametric Problem of Mayer in the Calculus of Variations," *American Journal of Mathematics*, LVII (1935), 69–93.

44. Reid, "The Theory of the Second Variation for the Non-parametric Problem of Bolza," *American Journal of Mathematics*, LVII (1935), 573–86.

45. Bliss, "The Evolution of Problems of the Calculus of Variations," *American Mathematical Monthly*, XLIII (1936), 598–609.

46. Hestenes, "The Problem of Bolza in the Calculus of Variations in Parametric Form," *American Journal of Mathematics*, LVIII (1936), 391–406.

47. Hestenes, "On Sufficient Conditions in the Problems of Lagrange and Bolza," *Annals of Mathematics*, XXXVII (1936), 543–51.

48. Wiggin, "A Boundary Value Problem of the Calculus of Variations." Dissertation, University of Chicago, 1936. See also *Contributions 1933–1937*, pp. (243)–(275).

49. Denbow, "A Generalized Form of the Problem of Bolza." Dissertation, University of Chicago, 1937. See also *Contributions 1933–1937*, pp. (449)–(484).

50. Hestenes, "A Direct Sufficiency Proof for the Problem of Bolza in the Calculus of Variations," *Transactions of the American Mathematical Society*, XLII (1937), 141–54.

51. Reid, "A Direct Expansion Proof of Sufficient Conditions for the Non-parametric Problem of Bolza," *Transactions of the American Mathematical Society*, XLII (1937), 183–90.

52. Reid, "Sufficient Conditions by Expansion Methods for the Problem of Bolza in the Calculus of Variations," *Annals of Mathematics*, XXXVIII (1937), 662–78.

53. SMILEY, "Discontinuous Solutions for the Problem of Bolza in Parametric Form." Dissertation, University of Chicago, 1937. See also *Contributions 1933–1937*, pp. (527)–(566).

54. TEACH, "The Hamilton-Jacobi Theory for the Problem of Lagrange in Parametric Form." Dissertation, University of Chicago, 1937. See also *Contributions 1933–1937*, pp. (165)–(206).

55. VALENTINE, "The Problem of Lagrange with Differential Inequalities as Added Side Conditions." Dissertation, University of Chicago, 1937. See also *Contributions 1933–1937*, pp. (403)–(447).

56. BLISS, "Normality and Abnormality in the Calculus of Variations," *Transactions of the American Mathematical Society*, XLIII (1938), 365–76.

57. BLISS, "Definitely Self-adjoint Boundary Value Problems," *Transactions of the American Mathematical Society*, XLIV (1938), 413–28.

58. BRADY, "The Minimum of a Function of Integrals in the Calculus of Variations." Dissertation, University of Chicago, 1938. See also *Contributions 1938–1941*, pp. (1)–(52).

59. HESTENES, "A Sufficiency Proof for Isoperimetric Problems in the Calculus of Variations," *Bulletin of the American Mathematical Society*, XLIV (1938), 662–67.

60. BOBONIS, "Differential Systems with Boundary Conditions Involving the Characteristic Parameter." Dissertation, University of Chicago, 1939. See also *Contributions 1938–1941*, pp. (99)–(138).

61. HESTENES, "Generalized Problem of Bolza in the Calculus of Variations," *Duke Mathematical Journal*, V (1939), 309–24.

62. HESTENES and REID, "A Note on the Weierstrass Condition in the Calculus of Variations," *Bulletin of the American Mathematical Society*, XLV (1939), 471–73.

63. LANDERS, MARY K., "The Hamilton-Jacobi Theory for the Problems of Bolza and Mayer." Dissertation, University of Chicago, 1939. See also *Contributions 1938–1941*, pp. (209)–(291).

64. MCSHANE, "On Multipliers for Lagrange Problems," *American Journal of Mathematics*, LXI (1939), 809–19.

65. NORDHAUS, "The Problem of Bolza for Double Integrals in the Calculus of Variations." Dissertation, University of Chicago, 1939. See also *Contributions 1938–1941*, pp. (53)–(97).

66. REID, "Isoperimetric Problems of Bolza in Non-parametric Form," *Duke Mathematical Journal*, V (1939), 675–91.

67. HAZARD, "Index Theorems for the Problem of Bolza in the Calculus of Variations." Dissertation, University of Chicago, 1940. See also *Contributions 1938–1941*, pp. (293)–(356).

68. MCSHANE, "An Estimate of the Weierstrass $E$-Function, "*Annals of Mathematics*, XLI (1940), 314–20.

69. MCSHANE, "A Remark concerning Sufficiency Theorems for the Problem of Bolza," *Bulletin of the American Mathematical Society*, XLVI (1940), 698–701.

70. MCSHANE, "Existence Theorems for Bolza Problems in the Calculus of Variations," *Duke Mathematical Journal*, VII (1940), 28–61.

71. MCSHANE, "On the Second Variation in Certain Anormal Problems of the Calculus of Variations," *American Journal of Mathematics*, LXIII (1941), 516–30.

72. Hestenes, "The Problem of Bolza in the Calculus of Variations," *Bulletin of the American Mathematical Society*, XLVIII (1942), 57–75.
73. Karush, "Isoperimetric Problems and Index Theorems in the Calculus of Variations." Dissertation, University of Chicago, 1942.
74. McShane, "Sufficient Conditions for a Weak Relative Minimum in the Problem of Bolza," *Transactions of the American Mathematical Society*, LII (1942), 344–79.
75. Lewis, "Sufficiency Proofs for the Problem of Bolza in the Calculus of Variations." Dissertation, University of Chicago, 1943.
76. McShane, "On the Theory of Relative Extrema," *Mathematical Reviews*, IV (1943), 48.
77. Myers, F. G., "Sufficiency Theorems for the Problem of Lagrange," *Duke Mathematical Journal*, X (1943), 73–97.

# INDEX

# INDEX

PRINTED IN U.S.A.